Birgit Rogalla

A First Course in
Computational Physics

Second Edition

Paul L. DeVries • Javier E. Hasbun

JONES & BARTLETT
LEARNING

D0939782

World Headquarters
Jones and Bartlett Learning
5 Wall Street
Burlington, MA 01803
978-443-5000
info@jblearning.com
www.jblearning.com

Jones and Bartlett Learning
Canada
6339 Ormindale Way
Mississauga, Ontario L5V 1J2
CANADA

Jones and Bartlett
Learning International
Barb House, Barb Mews
London W6 7PA
UK

First Indian Edition 2011
Reprinted 2014

Jones and Bartlett India Pvt. Ltd.
B-1, 4262/3, Ansari Road, Daryaganj
New Delhi – 110 002
Tel. 011–4361 3900
info@jbpubindia.net
www.jblearning.com

ISBN : 978-93-80108-94-0

Printed in India by Raj Press, New Delhi.

To Judi, Brandon, and Janna.
— PLD

To Laura M. Roth and Vijay A. Singh, who inspired
my appreciation for computational physics.
— JEH

Contents

Preface

Computers have changed the way physics is done, but those changes are only slowly making their way into the typical physics curriculum. This textbook is designed to help speed that transition.

Computational physics is now widely accepted as a third, equally valid complement to the traditional experimental and theoretical approaches to physics. It clearly relies upon areas that lie some distance from the traditional physics curriculum, however. In this text, we attempt to provide a reasonably thorough, numerically sound foundation for its development. However, we have not attempted to be rigorous; this is not meant to be a text on numerical analysis. Likewise, this is not a programming manual: We assume that the student is already familiar with the elements of the computer language and is ready to apply it to the task of scientific computing.

The MATLAB programming environment is used throughout this text. It is widely available, continually updated, and its popularity is rapidly growing, particularly in the areas of Engineering and Mathematics. Its seamless integration of visualization tools into the programming environment renders it particularly attractive and greatly enhances the value of computation.

The various chapters of the text discuss different types of computational problems, with exercises developed around problems of physical interest. Topics such as root finding, Newton-Cotes integration, and ordinary differential equations are included and presented in the context of physics problems. These are supplemented by discussions of topics such as orthogonal polynomials and Monte Carlo integration, and by a chapter on partial differential equations. A few topics rarely seen at this level, such as computerized tomography, are also included. Within each chapter, the student is led from relatively elementary problems and simple numerical approaches through derivations of more complex and sophisticated methods, often culminating in the solution to problems of significant difficulty. The goal is to demonstrate how numerical methods are used to solve the problems that physicists face. The text introduces the student to the *process* of approaching problems from a computational point of view: understanding the physics and describing it in mathematical terms, manipulating the mathematics to the point where a numerical method can be applied, obtaining a numerical solution, and understanding the physical problem in terms of the numerical solution that has been generated.

The material is presented at the level of a student who has successfully completed a typical year-long course in university physics. Many of our topics would normally be considered to be more advanced than this, but the computational approach enables the student to apply more than his or her own analytic tools to the problem. It is unlikely, however, that any but the most serious of students will complete the text in one semester. There is an abundance of material so that the instructor can choose topics so as to best meet the needs of the students.

A First Course in Computational Physics, Second Edition is the product of several years of classroom experience. As a result, some passages of the original text have been rewritten and many sections reordered. It has been substantially enhanced with additional sections on chaos, classical mechanics, and quantum mechanics. Correspondingly, the number of figures and code fragments, as well as exercises, has increased, leading to (we hope) a better book. We are indebted to all the students and colleagues who have partcipated in its development, and look forward to hearing further ideas for its continued improvement.

Paul L. De Vries
Volunteer Bay, Ohio

Javier E. Hasbun
Carrollton, Georgia

Introduction

This is a book about Physics. Or at least, about how to do physics. The simple truth is that the computer now permeates our society and has changed the way we think about many things, including science in general and physics in particular. It used to be that there was theoretical physics, which dealt with developing and applying theories, often with an emphasis on mathematics and "rigor." There was experimental physics, which was also concerned with theories, and testing their validity in the laboratory; but was primarily concerned with making observations and quantitative measurements. Now there is computational physics, in which numerical experiments are performed in the computer laboratory—an interesting marriage of the traditional approaches to physics. However, just as the traditional theoretician needs a working knowledge of analytic mathematics, and the traditional experimentalist needs a working knowledge of electronics, vacuum pumps, and data acquisition, the computational physicist needs a working knowledge of numerical analysis and computer programming. Beyond these basic tools, a physicist must know how to use them to achieve the ultimate goal: to understand the physical universe.

In this text, we'll discuss the tools of the computational physicist, from integrating functions and solving differential equations to using the Fast Fourier Transform to follow the time evolution of a quantum mechanical wavepacket. Our goal is not to turn every student into a computational physicist, but to make you aware of what is involved in computational physics. Even if you, personally, never do any serious computing, it's necessary for you to have some idea of what is done, so that you have at least a vague idea of what is reasonably possible, and what is not. Most of you, though, will find yourselves doing some computing, and are likely to use some aspects of what's presented here—canned programs rarely exist for novel, interesting physics, and so we have to write them ourselves! We hope to provide you with some useful tools and enough experience so that you develop some intuition and insight into how physics in your generation will be conducted.

In this chapter we'll introduce you to programming, and to a philosophy of programming that we've found to be useful. We'll also discuss some of the details of editing files, and creating and running MATLAB programs. And most importantly, we'll present a brief description of some of the elements of good programming. This discussion is not intended to transform you into a computer wizard—simply to help you write clear, reliable programs in a timely manner. And finally, we will use computer graphics to help us with our physics problems. The capability of *visualizing* a numerical solution as it's being generated is a tremendous tool in understanding both the solution as well as the numerical methods. The integration of such graphics capabilities into the computing environment is one of the many strengths of MATLAB.

1.1 MATLAB®—The Language of Technical Computing

There's a large variety of computer languages out there that could be (and are!) used in computational physics: BASIC, C, FORTRAN, and JAVA, each has its ardent supporters. These languages have supporters because they all have their particular merits, which should not be lightly dismissed. Indeed, many (if not most) computing professionals know and use more than one programming language, choosing the best language for the job at hand. Generally speaking, physicists are usually not "computing professionals." We're not interested in the mechanics of computing except when it directly relates to a problem we're trying to solve. With this in mind, there's much to be said for a language, or a language environment, which allows us to get to the meat of the issue—solving physics problems—as quickly and easily as possible.

MATLAB, originally developed as a MATrix LABoratory, fills that need. (As do many other excellent tools.) What sets MATLAB apart is its widespread use and acceptance in the Mathematics and particularly Engineering curriculum. Thus, in the spirit of "not re-inventing the wheel," we adopt MATLAB in this text.

This text assumes knowledge of MATLAB throughout; a Tutorial is included in the Appendix to help get you started. One of MATLAB's most useful features is an extensive help facility that can quickly provide assistance when needed. We do not assume that you are fluent in the language or knowledgeable in scientific programming. As far as computer programming is concerned, this text is primarily concerned with how to perform scientific calculations, not in how to code a particular statement. To that extent, any language would be suitable.

1.2 Getting Started

Before we're through, you'll learn many things about computing, and a few things about computers. While most of what we have to say will be pertinent to any computer or computing system, our specific comments and examples in this text are directed toward microcomputers. Unfortunately, you need to know quite a bit to even begin. There are operating systems, prompts, commands, macros, batch files, and other technical details *ad nauseam*. We assume that you already know some MATLAB, are reasonably intelligent and motivated, and have access to an appropriate personal computer with MATLAB installed. (A student version for use with this text is available through The MathWorks website.) We will then introduce you to the technicalities a little at a time, as it is needed. A consequence of this approach is that you may never learn all the details, which is just fine for most of you; we adopt the attitude that you should be required to know as few of these technical details as possible, *but no fewer*! A brief introduction to getting started with MATLAB is contained in the Appendix, but this text is by no means a MATLAB manual. If you want to know more, the online tools available at www.mathworks.com are the definitive reference, along with any number of well-written manuals, and your local computer wizard (and there is *always* a local wizard) can help you over the rough spots.

It has been said that a journey of a thousand miles begins with a single step, and so it is that we must *start*, someplace. Traditionally, the first program that anyone writes is one that says "hello":

```
fprintf('Hello World \n')
```

Now, admittedly this program doesn't do much—but at least it doesn't take long to do it! There are many different ways of writing output, but the `fprintf` statement used here is probably the easiest. The computer simply writes to the *standard input/output* device, which is just the screen, and writes according to its default formatting rules, which is O.K. for right now. Later, we will specify a particular manner in which the information is to be displayed, and what we want displayed is just the message contained between the two single quote marks. (The \n is an "end of line" indicator, so that the message will be printed and the cursor moved to the next line.) Numerical data can also be displayed with this construction, by simply providing the name of the variable to be printed.

There are two modes in which statements are executed in MATLAB. The first is an "interactive mode" in which the statement is executed immediately. That is, once the MATLAB environment has been entered, you are presented with a prompt, typically (using a student edition)

```
EDU>>
```

Simply typing in the statement, followed by the Enter key, instructs the computer to execute the statement. For our example, your screen would look something like

```
EDU>>fprintf('Hello World \n')
Hello World
EDU>>
```

The prompt indicates that MATLAB is ready for another statement to be entered. This interactive mode is well-suited for quick and simple calculations, and perhaps a little debugging (error removal) of simple code, but is obviously NOT appropriate for long programs that are to be used repeatedly.

For that purpose, we'll want to collect the statements together into a file, and execute the entire contents of that file. In MATLAB, these files are often called *scripts*, are stored in files given a .m extension, and are referred to as "M-files." (Aficionados recognize scripts, functions, and subfunctions, but we'll leave those distinctions for later, and for the Appendix.) That is, a program editor could be used to write a file named Hello.m, who's entire contents were the single line

```
fprintf('Hello World, using a separate file. \n')
```

To execute this program from within the MATLAB environment, we'd simply enter the name of the file (without the .m extension), and the contents of the file would be executed, resulting in the screen looking like

```
EDU>>Hello
Hello World, using a separate file.
EDU>>
```

However, MATLAB has it's own editor for which you need merely to click on File > New > M-file to open a new empty file. (File > Open would be used to open an existing file.) It's a good idea, and the standard convention, to include some extra lines of comments at the beginning of the file, so that it becomes

```
% Hello.m
% This is a little script that gets us started
fprintf('Hello World, using a separate file. \n')
```

The first character is %, which identifies the line as a comment, not to be executed. The first line is just the name of the file, and the second (and possibly succeeding lines, each begun with a %) provide a brief description of the script; the purpose of the program.

We are primarily concerned with the process of solving problems using the computer. However, we need to say a little about the computer code itself. Over time "the code," e.g., a collection of specific statements, tends to take on a life of its own. Certainly, it's to no one's advantage to "reinvent the wheel." A particular program (or even a portion of a program) that is of proven value tends to be used over and over again, often modified or "enhanced" to cover a slightly different circumstance. Often these enhancements are written by different people over an extended period of time. In order to control the growth of the code in orderly channels, in order to understand the code after we've been away from it for awhile, and in order to understand someone else's code, it is *absolutely essential* that we know and exercise good programming practices. A first step in that direction is to take responsibility for your work. Add a few more comment statements to the top of the program, with your name and contact information, and perhaps a revision history as well. For example, I might actually write

```
% Hello.m
% This program simply writes a greeting to the screen.
%
% Prof. Paul DeVries, (paul.devries@muohio.edu)
% Last revised: June 2009
fprintf('Hello World, using a separate file. \n')
```

This might be a bit much for this script, since it's strictly an example. But the idea is important—if we develop good habits now, we'll have them when we really need them! Since your instructor might require different information, or want it in a different form, we will forego this header information in the remainder of this text, but it's still a good idea.

> The first lines of every MATLAB file should contain the name of the file and a brief description of the purpose of the code.

1.3 A Numerical Example

While Hello has given us a good start, most of the work we want to do is of a numerical nature, so let's write a simple program that *computes* something. Let's see, how about computing the average between two numbers that you type into the keyboard? Sounds good. You'll read in one number, then another, and then compute and display the average. The MATLAB script might look something like this:

```
% average.m
% Computes the average of two numbers typed in
% at the keyboard, and writes the answer
clear;                    % It's good practice to clear the
                          % memory when running scripts.
first    = input(' first = ');
second   = input('second = ');
Average  = (first+second)/2;
fprintf('Average = %3.2f\n',Average)
```

Clearly, there are several things going on here that we have yet to discuss. The statement clear clears the memory, so we start with a clean slate of variables. The next line declares a variable, by its mere appearance on the left side of an equals sign. (This is very different from many languages, which require an explicit declaration of the variable.) Internally, this is a place in memory where a numerical value can be stored. The input statement first prints a prompting message, which is enclosed between the single quote marks, and then instructs the computer to read a value from the standard input. The equality says to actually replace the contents of the memory location associated with the variable `first` with this value. After "inputting" the second value, the "calculation" is performed with the next statement, in which `Average` is defined as the average of the two numbers. We've seen the `fprintf` statement before, but this time an actual format in which to print the number has been supplied, `%3.2f`, and the name of the variable to be printed is specified. We're also printing some information that identifies the output, so that we can easily understand what has been calculated.

> Output should always be self-descriptive.

EXERCISE 1.1
Modify `average.m` so that the number of addends is arbitrary and is obtained when you run the program.

1.4 Code Fragments

Examples of code and fragments of programs, which are intended to help you develop your computational physics skills, are listed throughout this text. To save you the drudgery of entering these fragments, and to avoid the probable errors associated with their entry, many of these fragments are included with this text. Rarely are these fragments complete or ready-to-run—they're only guides, but will (hopefully) propel you in a constructive direction. Exercises having a code fragment on the CD are indicated by 💿 in the margin. For example, there's a fragment associated with the next exercise, stored in the file `Fragment1_2.m`. (Note that you'll want to rename this file as you develop your program.) Most of the exercises *do not* have code fragments, simply because they can be successfully completed by modifying the programs written for previous exercises. `Fragment1_2.m` is something of a rarity, in that the entire code is included.

With reference to the previous exercise, let's briefly discuss how computers work internally. For each variable such as `first`, some amount of memory is set aside. The *value* of the variable is then stored in this space. Some computer languages distinguish between *single precision* numbers, for which they allocate 4 bytes, and *double precision* numbers, for which they allocate 8 bytes. A single precision number has approximately 8 significant digits. When two such numbers are multiplied, the result has 16 significant digits. But there's no room to store them—there's only room for 8! As calculations are performed, the results are rounded in order to fit into the space allotted, introducing an error. After many calculations, the accuracy of the result can be severely degraded, as will be demonstrated in Exercise 1.2.

This is called *round-off error*, and can be diminished by allocating more space for each variable.

Scientific computing often involves *real numbers*. MATLAB provides two **floating point** approximations to real numbers, with the data types `single` and `double`. Their internal representation in computer memory is similar to scientific notation, with the `double` allocating more bits for both the significand and the exponent than does `single`. Due to the amount of space set aside to store these variables, a `single` variable can represent 7 significant (decimal) digits, often termed "single precision," while a `double` can represent 15 digits, "double precision."

The difference between the real numbers of mathematics and the floating point numbers of computers can be significant. While there are an infinite number of real numbers, there are only a finite number of floating point numbers, so in general, the value of *any* `single` or `double` variable is only an approximation to its "real" value. Furthermore, the *distribution* of numbers isn't the same. That is, there are an infinite number of real numbers between, say 1 and 10. But because of the finite storage available, there is a specific number of values between 1 and 10 that can be expressed by a `single` variable, for example. And exactly the same number can be expressed between 10 and 100, so the density of expressible numbers is 10 times less! Of course, a `double` variable can express more numbers, and the density of expressible numbers is larger, but it's still finite.

In scientific programming, single precision is almost never enough. While it might suffice for the final result, there may be thousands or even millions of intermediate calculations, with the rounding error from each one of them contributing to the accumulated error. The developers of MATLAB are well aware of this, so they chose double precision to be the default type for all variables. Consequently, we need to go to a little extra effort to demonstrate that this can affect our results. Consider the following little program

```
%  FloatingPoint.m
%  This program demonstrates the value of DOUBLE PRECISION
%  variables.
%
%  If we start with one, and add one-millionth a million
%  times, what do we get?
clear;
doublePrecisionResult = 1.0;              % double precision is the default
singlePrecisionResult = single(1.0);      %  for floating point numbers
fprintf ('This may take a while...\n')
for i =1:1000000
   % "sum" must be used to add single precision numbers
       singlePrecisionResult = sum([singlePrecisionResult, single(0.000001)]);
       doublePrecisionResult = doublePrecisionResult  + 0.000001;
end
fprintf('Which is closer to two, %8.6f or %8.6f?\n', ...
        singlePrecisionResult, doublePrecisionResult )
```

Note that the "+" sign *cannot* be used for addition of single precision numbers, so that the sum function must be employed. The *for loop* executes each addition a million times, so that any errors that might exist have ample opportunity to accumulate. Finally, the values of the variables are written to the screen.

EXERCISE 1.2
One might think that the two results would be the same in this program. Execute the program and find out for yourself. Are you convinced that double precision is important?

It's rather obvious that the results from this program are not what would naively be expected. What is perhaps a little surprising is how much they differ. This is, of course, why MATLAB uses double precision variables throughout. (NOTE: This is exactly the opposite of what you might learn in a "computer science" class, reflecting the very different directions of our two disciplines.) We should emphasize that we have not actually *eliminated* the error by using double precision variables, we have simply made it smaller by several orders of magnitude. There are other sources of error, due to the approximations being made and the numerical methods being used, that have nothing to do with round-off error, and are not affected by the type declaration. For example, if we were to use x as an approximation for $\sin x$, we would introduce a substantial *truncation error* into the solution. Errors can also be introduced (or existing errors magnified) by the particular algorithm being used, so that the *stability* of the algorithm is crucial. The consistent use of double precision variables effectively reduces the round-off error to a level that can usually be ignored, allowing us to focus our attention on other sources of error in the problem.

1.5 A Brief Guide to Good Programming

When asked what are the most important characteristics of a good computer program, many people—particularly novices—will say speed and efficiency, or maybe reliability or accuracy. Certainly these are desirable characteristics—reliability, in particular, is an extremely desirable virtue. A program that sometimes works, and sometimes doesn't, isn't of much value. But a program that is not as fast or as efficient or as accurate can still be of use, if we understand the limits of the program. Don't be concerned with *efficiency*—it's infinitely preferable to have a slow, fat code that works to a fast, lean code that doesn't! And as for *speed*—the only "time" that really matters is how long it takes you to solve the problem, not how long it takes the program to execute. The reason the computer program was written in the first place was to solve a particular problem, and if it solves that problem—within known and understood limitations—then the program must be deemed a success. How best can we achieve that success?

We have come to the conclusion that the single most important characteristic of any computer program in computational physics is *clarity*. If it is not clear what the program is attempting to do, then it probably won't do it. If it is not clear what methods and algorithms are being used, then it's virtually impossible to know if it's working correctly. If it is not clear what the variables represent, we can't determine that the assignments and operations are valid. If the program is not clear, its value is essentially zero.

On the other hand, if a program is written to be as clear as possible, then we are more likely to understand what it's intended to do. If (and when) errors of logic are made, those errors are more easily recognized because we have a firm understanding of what the code was designed to do. Simple errors, such as mistaking one variable for another, entry errors, and so on, become much less likely to be made and much easier to detect. Modifying the code or substituting a new subroutine for an old one is made simpler if we clearly understand how each subroutine works and how it relates to the rest of the program. Our goal is to "solve" the given problem, but the path to that goal is made much easier when we strive to write our programs with clarity.

Begin by considering the process of writing a program as a whole. In the early days of computing there was generally a rush to enter the code and execute it, often before the problem was totally understood. Not surprisingly, this resulted in much wasted effort—as the problem became better understood, the program had to be modified or even totally rewritten. Today, the entire discipline of "software engineering" has arisen to provide mechanisms by which programs can be reliably written in an efficient manner. The programs we will develop are generally not so long or involved that all the formal rules of software development need be imposed—but that doesn't mean we should proceed haphazardly, either.

> Think about the problem, not the program.

A standard problem-solving approach to any new and difficult problem is to break the original problem into more manageable sized pieces, or "chunks." This gives us a better understanding of the total problem, since we now see it as a sequence of smaller steps, and also provides a clue as to how to proceed—"chunk" it again! Ultimately, the pieces become small enough that we can solve them individually, and from the pieces, build a solution to the original problem.

When applied to computational problems, this problem-solving strategy is called *top-down design* and *structured programming*, as depicted in Figure 1.1. These strategies enhance our understanding of the problem while simultaneously clari-

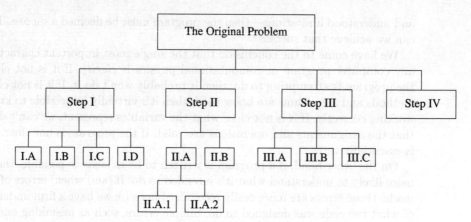

Figure 1.1 An example of the hierarchy resulting from top-down program design.

fying the steps necessary for a computational solution to the problem. In practice, top-down design and structured programming are accomplished by creating a hierarchy of steps leading to the solution. At the highest level, the problem is broken into a few logical pieces. Then each of these pieces is broken into its logical pieces, and so on. At each level of the hierarchy, the steps become smaller, more clearly defined, and more detailed. At some point, the individual steps are the appropriate size for a *function*. There are no hard and fast rules on how small these units should be—the logical connectedness of the unit is far more important than the physical length—but functions exceeding a hundred lines or so of code are probably rare, and are often quite smaller. Top-down design doesn't stop at this level, however. Functions themselves can be logically broken into separate steps, so that top-down design extends all the way down to logical steps within a single program unit.

Clearly, a lot of effort is expended in this design phase. The payoff, at least partially, is that the programming is now very easy—the individual steps at the lowest, most detailed level of the design are implemented in computer code, and we can work our way up through the design hierarchy. Since the purpose of each piece is clearly defined, the actual programming should be very straightforward. With the top-down programming design, a hierarchy was developed with each level of refinement at a lower, more detailed level than the previous one. As we actually write the code, the process is reversed—that is, each discrete unit of code is written separately, and then combined with other units as the next higher level is written.

Alternatively, one can commence the programming in conjunction with the top-down design phase. That is, as the top levels of the program are being designed, the associated code can be written, calling as-yet unwritten functions from the lower levels. Since the specific requirements of the lower level functions will not be known initially, this code will normally be incomplete—these *stubs*, however, clearly reflect the design of the program and the specific areas where further development is required. The most important factor in either case is that the coding is secondary to the design of the program itself, which is accomplished by approaching the total problem one step at a time, and successively refining those steps.

> Design down.

As we write the computer code for these discrete steps, we are naturally led to *structured programming*. Functions at the lower levels of the hierarchy, for example, contain logical blocks of code corresponding to the lowest steps of the design hierarchy. Functions at the higher levels consist of calls to functions that lie below them in the hierarchy. We can further enhance the structure of the program by insisting on linear program flow, so that control within a function (or within a block of code) proceeds from the top to the bottom in a clear and predictable fashion. Various constructs, such as `if-else-end` blocks, `for` and `while` loops, are major assets in establishing such control. To assist in readability, we frequently use indentation to provide a visual clue to the "level" of the code and to separate different blocks of code.

As you develop the actual code, constantly be aware of the need for clarity. Rarely is there only a single approach that works—usually, there are many different ways a specific task can be implemented. When confronted with a choice, choose the one that leads to the clearest, most readable code. Avoid *cleverness* in your coding—what looks clever today, might look incomprehensible tomorrow. And don't worry about *efficiency*—your attempts to optimize the code might actually thwart MATLAB's efforts to achieve the same goal. The primary technique for improving efficiency is changing algorithms, not rewriting the code. (Unless you know *what* needs to be rewritten, and *how* to improve it, your efforts will likely be wasted, anyway.)

Overall program clarity is further promoted by appropriate documentation, beginning with a clear statement of what the program, or function, is *supposed* to be doing. It may happen that the code doesn't actually perform as intended, but if the intention isn't clearly stated, this discrepancy is difficult to recognize. The in-line documentation should then describe the method or algorithm being used to carry out that intention, at the level of detail appropriate for that subprogram in the design hierarchy. That is, a function at the highest level should describe the sequence of major steps that it accomplishes; a description of how each of these steps is accomplished is contained within the functions that accomplish them. This description need not be—and in fact, should not be—a highly detailed narrative. Rather, the requirement is that the description be *clear* and *precise*. If the Newton-Raphson method is being used, then the documentation should say so! And if a particular reference was used to develop the implementation of the Newton-Raphson method, then the reference should be cited!

We've already argued that each function should contain information describing its intended purpose, the author, and a revision history. We've now added to that list a statement of the algorithm used and references to it. Furthermore, the input and output of the program unit should be described, as well as the meaning of all variables. All this information should reside at the beginning of the program unit. Then within the unit, corresponding to each block of structured code, there should be a brief statement explaining the function of that block of code. Always, of course, the purpose of this documentation is clarity—obvious remarks don't contribute to that goal. As an example, there are many instances in which we might want to calculate the value of a function at different points in space. A fragment of code to do that might look like

```
% Loop over "i" from 1 to 10
    for i=1:10
    ...
    end
```

The comment statement in this fragment does not contribute to clarity. To the extent that it interferes with reading the code, it actually *detracts* from clarity. A better comment might be

```
% Loop over all points on the grid
```

But, it still doesn't tell us *what* is being done! A truly useful comment should *add* something to our understanding of the program, and not simply be a rewording of the code. An appropriate comment for this case might be

```
% Calculate the electrostatic potential at
% all points on the spatial grid.
```

This comment succinctly describes what the block of code will be doing, and significantly contributes to the clarity of the program. Good documentation is not glamorous, but it's not difficult, either.

Another way to enhance the clarity of a program is through the choice of variable names. Imagine trying to read and understand a computer code calculating thermodynamic quantities in which the variable x34 appears. The name x34 simply does not convey much information, except perhaps that it's the 34th variable. It would be far better to call it pressure, if that's what it is. (MATLAB has no limitation on the length of a name, although the first 64 characters must be unique.) Using well-named variables not only helps with keeping track of the variables themselves, it helps make clear the relations between them. For example, the line

```
x19=x37*y12
```

doesn't say much. Even a comment might not really help:

```
% Calculation of force from Newton's Second Law
    x19=x37*y12
```

But using well-chosen names, the meaning of the variables and the relation between them become much clearer:

```
Force = Mass * Acceleration
```

Because the meaning of the statement is now obvious, we don't need the comment statement at all! This is an example of *self-documenting code*, so clear in what is being done that no further documentation is needed. It's also an example of the extreme clarity that we should strive for in all our programming efforts. When good names are combined with good documentation, the results are programs that are easy to read and to understand, and to test and debug—programs that work better, are written in a shorter amount of total time, and provide the solution to your problems in a timely manner.

A result of top-down design and structured programming is that functions can easily be made self-contained. Such modularity is a definite advantage to testing and debugging the program, and makes it easier to maintain and modify at a later time. During the process of refinement, the purpose of each function has been well-defined. Comments should be included in the function to record this purpose, reference algorithms, to specify clearly the required input and output, and to describe precisely how the routine performs. Note that this has the effect of *hiding* much detailed information from the rest of the program. That is, this function was designed to perform some particular task. The rest of the program doesn't need to know how it's done, but only the function's required input and expected output. If, for some reason, *we* want to know, then the information is there, and the program as a whole is not overburdened by a lot of unnecessary detail. Furthermore, if at some later time we want to replace this function, we will then have all the information to know exactly what must be replaced.

1.6 Debugging and Testing

When the programming guidelines we've discussed are utilized, the resulting programs are often nearly error free. Still, producing a totally error-free program on the first attempt is relatively rare. The process of finding and removing errors is called *debugging*. To some, debugging is nearly an art form—perhaps even a black art—yet it's a task that's amenable to a systematic approach.

The entire debugging process is greatly facilitated by our top-down, structured programming style that produces discrete, well-defined units of code. The first step is to develop these units individually. Common errors, such as misspelling variable names and having unmatched parentheses, are easily detected and corrected. Each "stand alone" function should be stored in its own M-file, along with any subfunctions that are unique to it.

Each function should be tested before being integrated into the larger project. These tests will typically include several specific examples, and comparing the results to those obtained by hand or from some other source. It's tempting to keep these tests as simple as possible, but that rarely exercises the code sufficiently. For example, a code that works perfectly with an input parameter of $x = 1.0$, 2.0, or 3.0 might fail for $x = 1.23$. Remember, you are trying to see if it will *fail*, not if it will succeed. Another item that should always be tested is the behavior of the code at the ends—the first time through a loop, or the last, are often where errors occur.

Another common problem that is easily addressed at this level is one of data validity. Perhaps you've written a function to evaluate one of the special functions that often arise in physics, such as the Legendre polynomial, a function defined on the interval $-1 \leq x \leq 1$. What does the code do if the argument $x = 1.7$ is passed to it? Obviously, there is an error somewhere for this to have happened. But that error is *compounded* if this function doesn't recognize the error. All functions should check that the input variables are reasonable, and if they're not, they should write an "error message" stating the nature of the problem and then terminate the execution of the program.

This is a good point at which to *rethink* what's been done. As the program was designed, an understanding of the problem, and of its solution, was developed. Now, a step in that solution has been successfully implemented, and your understanding is even deeper. This is the time to ask, *Is there a better way of doing the same thing?* With your more complete understanding of the problem, perhaps a clearer, more concise approach will present itself. In particular, complex, nested, and convoluted control structures should be reexamined—Is it *really* doing what you want? Is there a more direct way of doing it?

You should also think about *generalizing* the function. Yes, it was designed to perform a specific task, and you've determined that it does it. But could it be made more general, so that it could be used in other situations? If you needed to do a task *once*, you'll probably need to do it *again*! Invest the extra effort now, to be rewarded later when you don't have to duplicate your work. A little additional effort here, while the workings of the code are fresh in your mind, can make subsequent programming projects much easier.

Once we have ascertained that the code produces correct results for typical input, thoroughly documented the intended purpose of the code and the methods and algorithms used, included input verification, reexamined its workings and perhaps generalized it, the code can be marked "provisionally acceptable" and we can move on to the next program unit. After all the functions within one logical phase of the project are complete, we can test that phase. We note that the acceptance of a program is *never* more than provisional. The more we use a particular piece of code, the more confident of it we become. However, there is always the chance that within it there lurks a bug, just waiting for an inopportune time to crawl out.

1.7 A Cautionary Note

From time to time, we all make near catastrophic mistakes. For example, it's entirely possible—even *easy*—to tell the computer to delete all your work. Clearly, you wouldn't do this intentionally, but such accidents happen more often than you might think. Some program editors can help—they maintain copies of your work so that you can UnDo your mistakes or Restore your work in case of accidents. Find out if your editor does this, and if so, learn how to use it! There are also "programmer's tools" that allow you to recover a "deleted" file. As a final resort, make frequent backups of your work so that you never loose more than the work since the last backup. For example, when entering a lot of program code, or doing a lot of debugging, make a backup every half hour or so. Then, if the unspeakable happens, you've only lost a few minutes of work. Plan now to use one or more of these "safety nets." A little time invested now can save you an immense amount of time and frustration later on.

1.8 Elementary Computer Graphics

It's often the case that a sketch of a problem helps to solve and understand the problem. In fact, *visualization* is an important topic in computational physics today—computers can perform calculations much faster than we can sift through a printout to understand them, and so we are asking the computer to present those results in a form more appropriate for human consumption, e.g., graphically. Our present interest is very simple—instead of using graph paper and pencil to produce our sketches by hand, let's have the computer do it for us.

Fortunately, MATLAB has built-in graphics support, and is one of its greatest attributes. In fact, MATLAB is capable of producing much more sophisticated plots that we're likely to need. Our emphasis will be in producing relatively simple graphs, for our own use, rather than in creating plots to be included in textbooks, for example. With this in mind, we have chosen to use only a few of the graphics commands available to us.

As often happens, there are many ways to accomplish essentially the same thing. We'll begin with a simple task: to draw a "plus" sign on the screen. We'll accomplish this by using the line(x,y) command. Recall that x and y are vectors, containing the x- and y-coordinates of the points to be connected by a series of lines. The command

```
line([-10 10], [0.5 0.5])
```

can be typed at the MATLAB prompt and is sufficient to have a new window open and a horizontal line to be drawn. However, if we then type

```
line([0 0], [0 1])
```

to draw a vertical line, the scaling on the graph changes. MATLAB makes an effort to choose "nice" coordinates, but those are subject to change as more lines are drawn, and may not produce the figure we would prefer. The axis command allows us to control this. For example,

```
axis([-20 20 -1 2])
```

rescales the graph, putting the "plus" sign in the middle of the figure. Of course, while the interactive mode is ideal for experimenting, we prefer to place commands in an M-file, such as

```
% PlusSign.m
% This little program demonstrates the use of
%   some of the elementary graphics commands available.
clear;                  % It is good practice to clear the
                        % memory when running scripts
%  The data range is -10 < x < 10,
%                      0 < y < 1
axis( [-20 20 -1 2] )
line( [-10.0, 10.0], [0.5, 0.5] ) % comma used as "delimiter"
line( [  0.0   0.0], [0.0 1.0] ) % space used as "delimiter"
```

(Note that the elements of a row vector can be separated by a comma, as in the first line statement, or by a simple space, as in the second.) This program should produce a "+" on your computer screen.

EXERCISE 1.3
Verify that PlusSign works as advertised.

Let's work through something a little more interesting: plotting a sine curve on the domain $0 \le x \le 10$. To approximate the continuous curve, we'll draw several straight line segments—as the number of line segments increases, the graph will look more and more like a continuous curve. Let's use 50 line segments, just to see what it looks like. These, of course, will be supplied in the arrays x and y. Rather than line, we'll use the more general plot command. And we can make the display area a little larger than that actually occupied by the curve, just for aesthetic reasons. The appropriate code might then look like the following:

```
% sine.for
% A quick example:  drawing a sine curve
%
% calculate the sine at x starting at zero in steps of 0.2,
%     store it in y
clear;
for i=1:50
    x(i)=(i-1)*0.2;
    y(i)=sin(x(i));
end
hold on;
axis([-1 11 -1.1 1.1])
plot( x, y)
```

This code should produce the line drawing in Figure 1.2. For us, graphics are an aid to our understanding, a tool in our quest of problem solving, so that simple

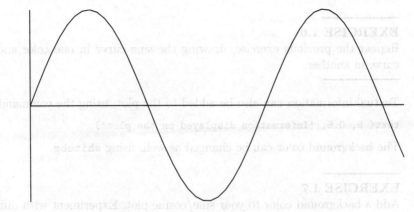

Figure 1.2   Plot of a sine curve, $0 \leq x \leq 10$.

drawings such as this are entirely adequate. We could, however, add some labeling
to the figure and a title, using something like

```
xlabel('This is the x axis')
ylabel('This is the y axis')
title('This is the title of the plot')
```

to make it more useful.

 EXERCISE 1.4
Reproduce Figure 1.2, with appropriate legends and title added.

Of course, there's no restriction to plotting only one curve on a figure! Note, however, that a second **plot** command would have the effect of erasing data already
displayed. To avoid this, the command **hold on** should be included.

EXERCISE 1.5
Plot both the sine and cosine curves in a single figure.

● **1.9 And in Living Color!**

The addition of color greatly enhances the quality of graphic presentations. This is
easily done, using some of the capabilities of the **plot** command. In particular,

```
plot( x, y, 'r')
```

plots the data in the color red. In general, we'll find color very useful. Various options
with the plot command are explained by the **help plot** command in MATLAB.

EXERCISE 1.6
Repeat the previous exercise, drawing the sine curve in one color and the cosine curve in another.

Textual information can also be added to the plot, using the command `text`.

`text( 5, 0.5, 'Information displayed on the plot')`

The background color can be changed as well, using `whitebg`.

EXERCISE 1.7
Add a background color to your sine/cosine plot. Experiment with different colors to find combinations that appeal to you.

1.10 Classic Curves

We feel compelled to comment that while graphics are extraordinarily useful, they're also a lot of fun. And that's great—learning should be an enjoyable process, or else it's unlikely to be successful! The ease with which we can generate curves and figures also inspires us to *explore* the various possibilities. Of course, we're not the first to tread this path ....

One of the "virtues" we've heard espoused for the computer generation is that students do not now have the background in classic mathematics that they once did. We fail to see how this is much of a virtue. Those old guys did a lot of very nice work. We would rather take a constructionist attitude: that we should build upon what they accomplished, rather than denying them their rightful place in the history and logical development of science and mathematics.

To that end, we suggest you apply the modern capabilities of computers, and graphing, to some of the classic analytic work, for the sole purpose of enjoying and appreciating its elegance. Table 1.1 presents some of the possibilities.

EXERCISE 1.8
Plot one (or more) of these classic figures. Many of these curves are of physical and/or historic interest—do a little reference work, and see what you can find about the curve you chose.

The availability of computer graphics has encouraged the exploration of functions that otherwise would never have been considered. For example, Professor Fey of the University of Southern Mississippi suggests the function

$$r = e^{\cos\theta} - 2\cos 4\theta + \sin^5\left(\theta/12\right), \tag{1.1}$$

an eminently humane method of butterfly collecting.

Table 1.1 Classic Curves in the Plane

Bifolium	$(x^2 + y^2)^2 = ax^2 y$ $r = a \sin \theta \cos \theta^2$
Cissoid of Diocles	$y^2(a - x) = x^3$ $r = a \sin \theta \tan \theta$
Conchoid of Nicomedes	$(y - a)^2(x^2 + y^2) = b^2 y^2$ $r = a \csc \theta \pm b$
Deltoid	$x = 2a \cos \phi + a \cos 2\phi$ $y = 2a \sin \phi - a \sin 2\phi$
Folium of Descartes	$x^3 + y^3 - 3axy = 0$ $r = \dfrac{3a \sin \theta \cos \theta}{\sin \theta^3 + \cos \theta^3}$
Hypocycloid with Four Cusps	$x^{2/3} + y^{2/3} = a^{2/3}$ $x = a \cos \phi^3, y = a \sin \phi^3$
Involute of a Circle	$x = a \cos \phi + a\phi \sin \phi$ $y = a \sin \phi - a\phi \cos \phi$
Lemniscate of Bernouli	$(x^2 + y^2)^2 = a^2(x^2 - y^2)$ $r^2 = a^2 \cos 2\theta$
Limacon of Pascal	$(x^2 + y^2 - ax)^2 = b^2(x^2 + y^2)$ $r = b + a \cos \theta$
Nephroid	$x = \frac{1}{2}a(3 \cos \phi - \cos 3\phi)$ $y = \frac{1}{2}a(3 \sin \phi - \sin 3\phi)$
Ovals of Cassini	$(x^2 + y^2 + b^2)^2 - 4b^2 x^2 = k^4$ $r^4 + b^4 - 2r^2 b^2 \cos 2\theta = k^4$
Logarithmic Spiral	$r = e^{a\theta}$
Parabolic Spiral	$(r - a)^2 = 4ak\theta$
Spiral of Archimedes	$r = a\theta$

(continued)

Table 1.1   Classic Curves in the Plane (continued)

Spiral of Galileo	$r = a\theta^2$
Strophoid	$y^2 = x^2 \dfrac{a - x}{a + x}$
	$r = a \cos 2\theta \sec \theta$
Three-Leaved Rose	$r = a \sin 3\theta$
Tractrix	$x = a \operatorname{sech}^{-1} y/x - \sqrt{a^2 - y^2}$
Witch of Agnesi	$y = \dfrac{8a^3}{x^2 + 4a^2}$
	$x = 2a \cot \phi,\, y = a(1 - \cos 2\phi)$

Note that some of these curves are more easily described in one coordinate system than another. (Other curves are most easily expressed parametrically: both x and y are given in terms of the parameter ϕ.) MATLAB's `polar(theta,r)` function behaves for polar coordinates much the same as `plot(x,y)` behaves for Cartesian coordinates.

EXERCISE 1.9

Plot Fey's function on the domain $0 \le \theta \le 24\pi$. The artistic aspect of the curve is enhanced if it's rotated 90° by using the transformation

$$x = r \cos(\theta + \pi/2),$$
$$y = r \sin(\theta + \pi/2).$$

1.11 Monster Curves

The figures we've been discussing are familiar to all those with a background in real analysis, and other "ordinary" types of mathematics. But mathematicians are a funny group—around the turn of the century, they began exploring some very unusual "curves." Imagine, if you will, a curve that is everywhere continuous, but nowhere differentiable! A real *monster*, wouldn't you say? Yet the likes of Hilbert, Peano, and Sierpinski investigated these monsters—not a lightweight group, to say the least.

One particularly curious figure was due to Helge von Koch in 1904. As with many of these figures, the easiest way to specify the curve is to describe how to construct it. And perhaps the easiest way to describe it is with *production rules*. (This is the "modern" way of doing things—Helge didn't know about these.)

Figure 1.3   The first three steps of the von Koch construction.

Let's imagine that you're instructing an incredibly stupid machine to draw the figure, so we want to keep the instructions as simple as possible. To describe the von Koch curve, we need only four instructions: F, to go forward one step; $+$, to turn to the right by 60°; $-$, to turn to the left by 60°; and T, to reduce the size of the step by a factor of one third. To construct the von Koch curve, we begin with an equilateral triangle with sides of unit length. The instructions to draw this triangle are simply

$$F + +F + +F + +. \tag{1.2}$$

To produce a new figure, we follow two rules: first, add a T to the beginning of the instruction list; and second, replace F by a new set of instructions:

$$F \rightarrow F - F + +F - F. \tag{1.3}$$

That is, every time an F appears in the original set of instructions, it is replaced by $F - F + +F - F$. If we follow these rules, beginning with the original description of the figure, we produce a new list of instructions:

$$TF - F + +F - F + +F - F + +F - F + +F - F + +F - F + +. \tag{1.4}$$

The first steps in this process are illustrated in Figure 1.3. To obtain the ultimate result, simply repeat this process an infinite number of times! Well, not quite, because that would require an infinite amount of time and computer resources. But a nice approximation to that result can be generated using five levels of iteration, as in Figure 1.4.

How long is the curve obtained? A "classical" shape, like a circle, has a length that can be approached by taking smaller and smaller chords, larger and larger n-polygon approximations to the circle. It's an "ordinary," finite length line on a two dimensional surface. But the von Koch curve is not so ordinary. The length of the original curve was three units, but then each side was replaced by four line segments of one third the original length, so that its length was increased by four thirds. In fact, *at every iteration*, the length of the curve is increased by four thirds. So, the length of the curve after an infinite number of iterations is infinite! Actually, the length of the curve between any two points on it is infinite, as well. And yet

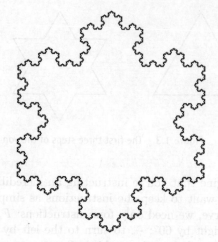

Figure 1.4   The von Koch curve, a.k.a. the Snowflake.

it's all contained within a circle drawn around the original equilateral triangle! Not a typical figure.

We can invent other curves as well, with the addition of some new instructions. Let's add R, to turn right 90°, L to turn left 90°, and Q to reduce the step length by a factor of a quarter. A square can then be drawn with the instructions

$$FRFRFRFR. \qquad (1.5)$$

An interesting figure can then be produced by first appending Q to the front of the list, and making the replacement

$$F \rightarrow FLFRFRFFLFLFRF. \qquad (1.6)$$

EXERCISE 1.10
Draw the figure resulting from three iterations of these production rules, which we might call a variegated square. Note that while the length of the perimeter continues to increase, the area bounded by the perimeter is limited.

Should we care about such monsters? Do they describe anything in Nature? The definitive answer to that question is not yet available, but some interesting observations can be made about them, and their relation to the physical world.

For example, exactly how long is the coastline of Lake Erie? If you use a meter stick, you can measure a certain length, but you clearly have not measured the *entire* length because there are features smaller than a meter that were overlooked. So you measure again, this time with a half-meter stick, and get a new "length."

This second length is larger than the first, and so you might try again with a shorter stick, and so on. Now the question is: Do the lengths converge to some number. The answer is: Not always—the von Koch curve, for example.

Benoit Mandelbrot spent the better part of the period between 1960 and 1990 looking at these questions. He coined the word *fractal* to describe such geometries, because the curve is something more than a line, yet less than an area—its dimension is *fractional*.

We're all aware that a point has zero dimension, a line has one dimension, a surface two, and so on. We'll refer to this as its *Euclidean dimension*. But as we've seen, some geometrical objects—such as the von Koch curve—seem to have a "different" dimension.

Consider a simple line segment of unit length. If we use a ruler of 1 unit in length, we obviously would find that the length of the line is 1. Of course, if our ruler were actually smaller by a scale factor s, we would find that it's length would be s. (That is, if the new unit were 1/3 the length of the original, we would find the line segment to be 3 units long.) Now consider an area, such as a unit square. With the original ruler, we would find the area to be 1, but with the shortened ruler, we would find it to be s^2. And for a cube, the volume as measured with the new ruler would be s^3. In other words, we find that $\mathcal{N}$ scales as

$$\mathcal{N} = \left(\frac{1}{s}\right)^D = s^{-D}, \tag{1.7}$$

where $\mathcal{N}$ is the number of "new units" and D is the dimension. For "ordinary" objects, this is entirely consistent with our usual perception of dimension. Taking logarithms of both sides, we find

$$D = \frac{\log \mathcal{N}}{\log 1/s}. \tag{1.8}$$

The German mathematician Felix Hausdorff suggested that this definition could be generalized to arbitrary objects. That is, we can simply *define* the dimension of an object by Equation 1.8, and not require it to be an integer. Back to the von Koch curve: in the construction, each line segment is divided into 4 pieces ($\mathcal{N} = 4$), scaled down by a factor of 3 ($s = 1/3$). Thus

$$D = \frac{\log 4}{\log 3} \approx 1.2618\ldots \tag{1.9}$$

This says that somehow the curve is more than a simple line, but less than an area.

EXERCISE 1.11

What is the fractal dimension of the variegated square?

To account for the possibility that the Hausdorff dimension might be an integer, a more precise definition is that a *fractal* is a geometric object whose Hausdorff dimension is greater than its Euclidean dimension.

1.12 Box Counting

If the fractal is sufficiently "simple," then the analytic method described previously can be applied to find its dimension. But in other cases, a computational approach is required.

The method we use is called "box counting," and we'll demonstrate it with the von Koch curve. We assume that the geometrical object is confined to a plane and is of finite extent. We'll cover this limited region of the plane with a uniform distribution of squares, with edge length s, and simply count how many squares contain a portion of the von Koch curve. In the limit that the scale factor

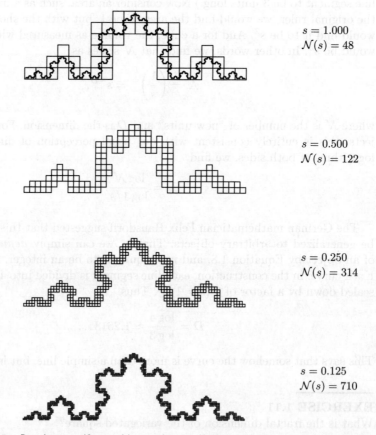

$$s = 1.000$$
$$\mathcal{N}(s) = 48$$

$$s = 0.500$$
$$\mathcal{N}(s) = 122$$

$$s = 0.250$$
$$\mathcal{N}(s) = 314$$

$$s = 0.125$$
$$\mathcal{N}(s) = 710$$

Figure 1.5 Drawing a uniform grid over the von Koch curve, and counting the number of boxes required to cover the figure. For clarity, the curve has only been drawn with the largest scale grid.

becomes very small, this should approximate the Hausdorff dimensionality. Let's write Equation 1.7 as

$$\mathcal{N}(s^{-1}) = \lim_{s \to 0} k s^{-D_F}, \tag{1.10}$$

where k is a proportionality constant, so that

$$D_F = \lim_{s \to 0} \left[\frac{\log \mathcal{N}(s^{-1})}{\log s^{-1}} - \frac{\log k}{\log s^{-1}} \right]. \tag{1.11}$$

Thus D_F is simply the slope of the line of $\log \mathcal{N}(s^{-1})$ *versus* $\log s^{-1}$.

Figure 1.5 demonstrates this box counting process. Various scale factors s are used to draw boxes that contain (or you might say *cover*) the von Koch curve. As expected, the smaller the scale factor, the more boxes are necessary to cover the curve.

EXERCISE 1.12

From the data provided in Figure 1.5, make a plot of $\log \mathcal{N}(s^{-1})$ *versus* $\log s^{-1}$. Estimate D_F as the slope of the straight line drawn through the plotted data points.

● **1.13 The Mandelbrot Set**

Mandelbrot has done more than coin a word, of course. Scarcely a person this side of Katmandu has not heard of and seen an image of the Mandelbrot set. It has become the signature of an entirely new area of scientific investigation: chaotic dynamics. And yet it's "created" by an extraordinarily simple procedure—for some complex number c, we start with $z = 0$ and evaluate subsequent z's by the iteration

$$z = z^2 + c. \tag{1.12}$$

If z remains finite, even after an infinite number of iterations, then the point c is a member of the Mandelbrot set. (It was a simple matter to construct the von Koch curve, too!)

We want to use our new-found graphics tools to help us visualize the Mandelbrot set. We will use the most basic, simpleminded, and incredibly slow method known to calculate the set: straightforward application of Equation 1.12. And even then, we'll only *approximate* the set—an infinite number of iterations can take a long time.

It turns out that if $|z|$ ever gets larger than 2, it will eventually become infinite. So we'll only iterate the equation a few times, say 30; if $|z|$ is still less than 2, then there's a good chance that c is a member of the set. The *computing* involved is rather obvious, and shouldn't be much trouble.

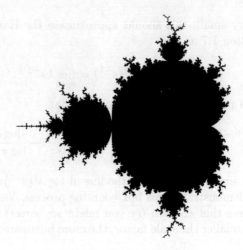

Figure 1.6   The Mandelbrot set.

To construct the image of Figure 1.6, we let $c = x + iy$ and considered the domain $-1.8 \leq x \leq 0.9$ and $-1.0 \leq y \leq 1.0$. Clearly, the number of points we consider will affect the resolution of the image generated. Let's be somewhat conservative, and consider only a 200 by 160 size grid. (As we'll see, even this limited array will be rather time consuming.) That is, we'll consider the points

$$x = -1.9 + i\frac{2.7}{200} \tag{1.13}$$

and

$$y = -1.0 + j\frac{2.0}{160}. \tag{1.14}$$

As we cycle through the grid, we are considering different specific values of c. And for each c, we test to determine if it's a member of the Mandelbrot set by iterating Equation 1.12. The appropriate computer code to display the Mandelbrot set might then look like the following:

```
% Mandelbrot.m
%
% This program computes and plots the Mandelbrot set,
% using a simple minded and incredibly slow procedure.
%
clear;
im = complex(0.0,1.0); % im, z, and z0 are complex numbers
z0 = complex(0,0);     % initial value of z
Max_Iteration = 30;

% Image to be computed in the region -1.8 < x < 0.9,
%                                    -1.0 < y < 1.0.
```

```
xMin = -1.8;
xMax =  0.9;
yMin = -1.0;
yMax =  1.0;
axis([xMin xMax yMin yMax]);

dx = (xMax-xMin)/200;
dy = (yMax-yMin)/160;
fprintf(' Please wait ...\n');

% Cycle over all the pixels on the screen to be included
% in the plot. Each pixel represents a particular complex
% number, c. Then determine, for this particular c, if
% |z| -> infinity as the iteration proceeds.

hold on
for x = xMin:dx:xMax
    for y = yMin:dy:yMax
        c = x + im*y;
        % Initialize z, and begin the iteration
        z = z0;
        counter = 0;
        while (abs(z) < 2.0 & counter <= Max_Iteration)
            if(counter <= Max_Iteration)
                z = z*z + c;
                counter=counter+1;
            end
        end
        % If  |z|  is still < 2, and if counter = Max_Iteration,
        % call the point "c" a member of the Mandelbrot set and plot it
        if(counter >= Max_Iteration)
            plot(x,y,'k.')
        end
    end
end
```

Note that a marker is being plotted, rather than a single pixel on the display screen, consistent with the coarseness of the image.

EXERCISE 1.13

Produce a nice picture of the Mandelbrot set, following the suggestions presented here. (Be prepared to wait a bit.)

One of the really interesting things about fractals is their *self-similarity*—that is, as you look at the image closer and closer, you see similar shapes emerge. With the von Koch Snowflake, this self-similarity was virtually exact. With the Mandelbrot set, the images are not exact duplicates of one another, but are certainly familiar.

EXERCISE 1.14

Modify the program to accept xMin, xMax, yMin, and yMax from the user. Then pick a small section of the complex plane, where *something* is happening, and generate an image with enlarged magnification. For example, you might investigate the region $-0.7 \leq x \leq -0.4$, $0.5 \leq y \leq 0.7$. By mapping these coordinates onto the same region of the screen used previously, you are effectively magnifying the image.

As you investigate the boundary of the Mandelbrot set at a finer scale, you should also increase the number of iterations used to determine membership in the set. Determining membership is an example of a fundamental limitation in computation— since we cannot in practice iterate an infinite number of times, we are always including a few points in our rendering that do not really belong there.

What sets fractals apart from other unusual mathematical objects is their visual presentation, as seen in numerous books and even television shows. There is even some debate as to whether "fractals" belong to mathematics, or to computer graphics. In either case, the images can certainly be striking. Their aesthetic appeal is particularly evident when they are rendered in color. In the current instance, we'll use color to indicate the number of iterations a particular point c survived before it exceeded 2. That is, rather than denoting points *in* the Mandelbrot set, we'll denote points *outside* the Mandelbrot set, with the color of the point indicating *how far* outside the set the point is. The "membership" loop will be replaced by

```
% Initialize z, and begin the iteration
z = z0;
counter = 0;
while (abs(z) < 2.0 && counter <= Max_Iteration)
    if(counter <= Max_Iteration)
        z = z*z + c;
        counter = counter + 1;
    end
end
% If |z| > 2, denote how far OUTSIDE
%   the set the point "c" is:
if(counter < Max_Iteration)  % |z| has exceeded 2...
    % The darker the color, the closer it is
    %   to the Mandelbrot set.
    c1 = 1.0 - counter / Max_Iteration;
    plot(i,j,'.','Color',[c1 0 0]);
end
```

Setting the color in this way has the effect of cycling through all the colors available on your particular computer. (Actually, the above code cycles through the various reds.)

EXERCISE 1.15

Try this code to explore the Mandelbrot set, and see if you can find some particularly pleasing venues. Remember that as you "magnify" the image, you should also increase the iteration maximum beyond the 30 present in the listing of the code.

These images can be almost addictive. Certainly, the images are very interesting. As you attempt greater magnification, and hence increase the iteration maximum, you will find that the calculation can be painfully slow, if it isn't already. The problem is in fact in the iteration, particularly as it involves complex arithmetic. In general, we're not particularly interested in efficiency. But in this case we can clearly identify where the code is inefficient, so that effort spent here to enhance its speed is well spent. In particular, a less simpleminded algorithm should be used.

1.14 Logistic Maps, Bifurcation, and Lyapunov Exponents

Often associated with the study of fractals, the topic of *chaos* has become an area of intense interest. Simply put, chaos is the seemingly random behavior of certain systems, even though those systems are clearly deterministic in nature. A common thread is that only nonlinear systems exhibit chaos. Since nonlinear systems are actually much more common than the easily-studied linear ones, chaos should be expected to be common, and indeed that's exactly what we've found.

A full treatment of chaotic systems is far beyond the scope of this text, but we can at least demonstrate some of their characteristics by investigating a disarmingly simple system with surprisingly complex behavior: a simple model of population growth. Let's suppose that for every year that goes by, the population increases by a factor of α. That is,

$$x_{n+1} = \alpha x_n, \tag{1.15}$$

where x_n is the population in the n-th year. For $\alpha > 1$, this model clearly describes an exponential growth in the population, something that's not sustainable over the long term. (For $\alpha < 1$, it leads to an exponential *decay* in the population.) Eventually, overpopulation will occur, which will diminish this growth. This effect can be included in the model by including a limiting factor, such that

$$x_{n+1} = \alpha x_n(1 - x_n). \tag{1.16}$$

(This definition of x_n describes a *relative* population that can range from 0 to 1.) So, this model has the property that if x is small, the population may grow rapidly

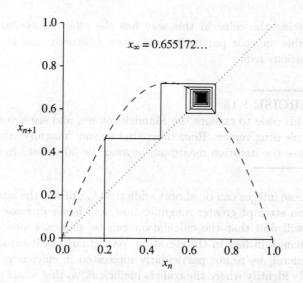

Figure 1.7 The logistic map, with $f(x)$ and $y(x)$ also displayed.

early on because of plenty of available resources. However, as the population grows, the available resources are depleted and the population decays. The parameter α models environmental effects such as drought, disease, and limited resources that affect the population. This simple model, described by Equation 1.16, is the *logistic map*. What makes it of interest to us is its unexpected behavior for certain values of α.

To demonstrate, consider how the population changes with the choice of $\alpha = 2.9$, starting with $x_0 = 0.2$. Initially, the population changes from year to year, as would be expected. But as n gets large, the population converges to a single value, $x_\infty = 0.655172$, as illustrated in Figure 1.7. Now, what might be surprising is that this is the limiting value of the population *independent of the initial population*. While the details of the map will differ, the fixed point x_∞ will be the only final solution, the so-called one-cycle solution. This is a *stable fixed point* of the map, and is also known as an *attractor*.

EXERCISE 1.16
Write a code that will reproduce the logistic map of Figure 1.7 for $\alpha = 2.9$ and $x_0 = 0.2$. Try other values of x_0 to verify the claim that the population always converges to the same fixed point.

You might ask yourself *why* the map approaches a fixed point. One way of thinking about it is to consider the two functions,

$$y(x) = x$$

and

$$f(x) = \alpha x(1 - x).$$

Clearly, the functions are equal where they cross and at that point

$$x_\infty = \alpha x_\infty (1 - x_\infty), \tag{1.17}$$

which is nothing more than the large n limit of Equation 1.16. For a different α the two curves will cross at a different value of x, and indeed that's what we find. In fact, solving for x_∞, we find that

$$x_\infty = 1 - \frac{1}{\alpha}. \tag{1.18}$$

EXERCISE 1.17

Try $\alpha = 2.7$ and 2.8 to see how the logistic map is affected. Verify that the fixed point is correctly given by Equation 1.18.

So, the two functions cross at the fixed point. As a practical matter we can see that it's stable, in the sense that the x_n get closer and closer to x_∞ as n increases. But can we prove this stability? Let's define the difference between the current x_n and the fixed point to be

$$\epsilon_n = x_n - x_\infty. \tag{1.19}$$

We'll assume that n is sufficiently large that ϵ_n is "small." Then

$$\epsilon_{n+1} + x_\infty = \alpha(\epsilon_n + x_\infty)(1 - \epsilon_n - x_\infty) \tag{1.20}$$

or

$$\epsilon_{n+1} = \alpha(1 - 2x_\infty - \epsilon_n)\epsilon_n, \tag{1.21}$$

where we've used the fact that

$$x_\infty = \alpha x_\infty (1 - x_\infty). \tag{1.22}$$

Since ϵ_n is small we can ignore the smaller term ϵ_n^2 and find

$$\epsilon_{n+1} \approx \alpha(1 - 2x_\infty)\epsilon_n$$
$$= (2 - \alpha)\epsilon_n \tag{1.23}$$

That is, Equation 1.23 tells us that the difference will become smaller and smaller if

$$|2 - \alpha| < 1, \tag{1.24}$$

or

$$1 < \alpha < 3. \tag{1.25}$$

Conversely, if α doesn't satisfy this condition, the $|\epsilon_{n+1}|$ will increase in magnitude, and the fixed point is *unstable*. This stability issue is quite similar to stable and unstable equilibria in classical mechanics.

We might also note that, even for α for which the fixed point is stable, as α increases toward 3 (or decreases toward 1), $|\epsilon_{n+1}|$ is only slightly less than $|\epsilon_n|$ so that the convergence is slower and more iterations of the logistic map are necessary to reach the attractor.

EXERCISE 1.18

Write a program converge to plot x_n versus n, up to $n_{max} = 100$, and run it for $\alpha = 2.7$, 2.8, and 2.9. This will display the same information as the logistic map of the previous exercises, but in a manner that clearly indicates how rapidly the iteration converges.

The value $\alpha = 3$ is clearly "special" in some way. For $\alpha > 3$, the stability analysis we've just developed tells us that $|\epsilon_n|$ is growing, so that the fixed point given by Equation 1.23 is *unstable*. But what happens? Here, of course, is the beauty of the computational approach: rather than delving into the mathematics, we can simply execute the program and see what happens. In particular, for $\alpha = 3.1$, we obtain the results of Figure 1.8.

Clearly, we do not reach a converged result. On the other hand, we do reach a point where the population periodically bounces back and forth between two fixed values, $x_a = 0.558014$ and $x_b = 0.764567$. This is said to be a two-cycle solution, with two period-2 fixed points.

EXERCISE 1.19

Use converge to verify this result. How do x_a and x_b change as α is increased? Decreased?

It's interesting to consider this result in terms of the logistic map. Writing 1.16 as

$$x_{n+1} = f(x_n), \tag{1.26}$$

we have found that

$$x_a = f(x_b)$$
$$x_b = f(x_a). \tag{1.27}$$

But this observation leads to the relation

$$x_a = f\left(f(x_a)\right), \tag{1.28}$$

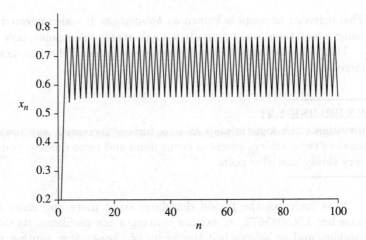

Figure 1.8   For $\alpha = 3.1$, the x_n do not converge to a single value.

a *double mapping*. Of course, we can define a new function, $f^{[2]}(x)$, such that

$$f^{[2]}(x) = f(f(x))$$
$$= \alpha(\alpha x(1 - x))(1 - \alpha x(1 - x)) \qquad (1.29)$$

Investigating where this function intersects with $y(x) = x$ leads to a cubic equation for the fixed points,

$$x^3 - 2x^2 + \frac{1 + \alpha}{\alpha}x + \frac{1 - \alpha^2}{\alpha^3} = 0. \qquad (1.30)$$

This equation has a root at

$$x = 1 - \frac{1}{\alpha}, \qquad (1.31)$$

as expected. (This is the root we had found earlier.) However, from the earlier discussion, this root is unstable for $\alpha > 3$. The other two roots are at

$$x_\pm = \frac{1 + \alpha}{2\alpha}\left(1 \pm \sqrt{\frac{\alpha - 3}{1 + \alpha}}\right). \qquad (1.32)$$

These roots are imaginary for $\alpha < 3$, while for $\alpha > 3$ they are real. Furthermore, they can be shown to be stable points of the double mapping.

EXERCISE 1.20
Show that the remaining roots of Equation 1.32 are stable.

So, what we have is one stable root for $\alpha < 3$. It remains stable until it reaches 3, at which time it becomes unstable while two new (real) stable roots appear.

This behavior of roots is known as *bifurcation*. It's also referred to as *period doubling*: where there was originally a single stable fixed point, now there are two.

This behavior begs to be further investigated: What happens as α is further increased?

EXERCISE 1.21

Investigate the logistic map as α is further increased, say toward 3.5. Since the onset of the doubling seems to occur more and more quickly, you should increase α very slowly past this point.

As α increases the period doublings come more and more rapidly. As α approaches 3.569945672, x_n neither converges nor oscillates, its value appears to be random, and we've reached the realm of *chaos*. (Put another way, chaos theory has been described as the "study of unstable aperiodic behavior in deterministic nonlinear dynamic systems.") For larger values of α the behavior is largely chaotic, although there are islands of periodicity, which again exhibit period doublings leading to chaos.

A useful way of visualizing these results is a bifurcation diagram, as in Figure 1.9, which simply plots x_n versus α. As a practical matter, n will always be less than infinity, but should be made a relatively large number (say, 1000 or more) to ensure that the ultimate result has been obtained.

As with the Koch snowflake and the Mandelbrot set, the bifurcation diagram exhibits the interesting characteristic of self-similarity. As you examine the diagram at a finer scale, the same general image repeats itself. The maps associated with examples of chaotic behavior are fractal.

EXERCISE 1.22

Explore the bifurcation diagram at a finer scale. For example, consider the region $3.53 < \alpha < 3.59$ and $0.4 < x_n < 0.6$. Note that you should increase the number of iterations, to ensure that any transients have passed.

Another hallmark of chaos is its sensitivity to initial conditions. In the realm of a stable fixed point, we found that x_∞ was the ultimate consequence of the iteration, no matter the initial x_o. In the chaotic regime, quite the opposite is the case: If one iteration begins with x_o and another with $x_o + \delta$, the difference between the two iterations grows exponentially. The Russian mathematician A. M. Lyapunov (1857–1918) studied a way to identify chaotic conditions for certain parameters of a problem. He proposed that the difference between two values of x_n for large n can be approximated by

$$d_n = \delta e^{n\lambda}. \tag{1.33}$$

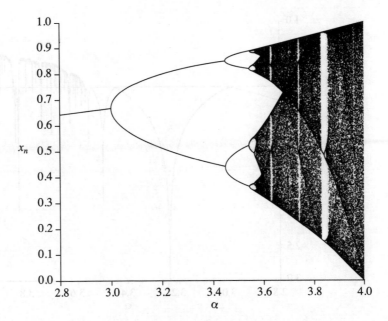

Figure 1.9   A bifurcation diagram.

If $\lambda < 0$, the difference between the two solutions becomes exponentially smaller and the two solutions converge to the same result, indicating that the solution is insensitive to the initial conditions. However, if $\lambda > 0$ the difference will diverge and chaos results.

The initial difference between the two solutions is

$$d_o = x_o + \delta - x_o = \delta. \tag{1.34}$$

After one iteration the difference is

$$d_1 = f(x_o + \delta) - f(x_o) \approx \delta \frac{df}{dx}\Big|_{x_o}, \tag{1.35}$$

for small δ. The next iteration would involve the second iteration of the map, $f(f(x))$, which we denote as $f^{[2]}(x)$. After the n-th iteration the difference will then be

$$d_n = f^{[n]}(x_o + \delta) - f^{[n]}(x_o), \tag{1.36}$$

but by Equation 1.33, this is just $\delta e^{n\lambda}$. Dividing by δ and taking the logarithm, we find

$$\ln\left(\frac{f^{[n]}(x_o + \delta) - f^{[n]}(x_o)}{\delta}\right) = n\lambda, \tag{1.37}$$

or

$$\lambda = \frac{1}{n}\ln\left(\frac{f^{[n]}(x_o + \delta) - f^{[n]}(x_o)}{\delta}\right) \approx \frac{1}{n}\left|\frac{df^{[n]}(x)}{dx}\right|_{x=x_o}. \tag{1.38}$$

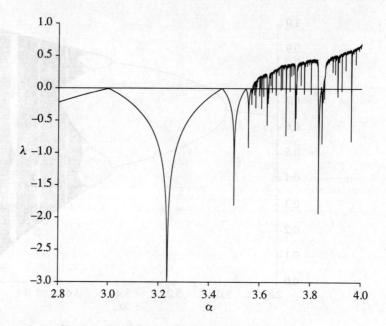

Figure 1.10 The Lyapunov exponent as a function of α.

Using the chain rule to evaluate the derivative, we find

$$\left.\frac{df^{[n]}(x)}{dx}\right|_{x=x_o} = \left.\frac{df(x)}{dx}\right|_{x=x_{n-1}} \left.\frac{df(x)}{dx}\right|_{x=x_{n-2}} \cdots \left.\frac{df(x)}{dx}\right|_{x=x_o}. \tag{1.39}$$

Finally, taking the limit as $n \to \infty$ we obtain

$$\lambda = \lim_{n \to \infty} \frac{1}{n} \sum_{i=0}^{n-1} \ln\left|\frac{df(x_i)}{dx}\right|, \tag{1.40}$$

an expression for the *Lyapunov exponent*. A plot of λ versus α for the logistic map is shown in Figure 1.10. We see that even after the onset of chaos, there are regions of α where λ becomes less than zero and stable periodic orbits occur amongst the generally chaotic behavior.

An outline of a program to calculate and plot λ as a function of α might look like the following:

```
fprime = inline(...)   % Use an inline function to evaluate
                       % the derivative.
N = . . .              % Number of iterations

%  Create a loop for the various alpha
alpha(j) = . . .
```

```
x(1) = . . .            % Initialize the iteration
for i = 1:N             % Do the iteration for this value of alpha
    x(i+1) = . . .
end
lambda(j) = sum( log( abs( alpha(j)*fprime(x) ) ) )/(N+1);
%  End of loop

plot < lambda versus alpha >
```

EXERCISE 1.23

Flesh out the outline and write a program to reproduce the Lyapunov exponent versus α plot for the logistic function.

1.15 References

The ultimate reference for MATLAB is the The MathWorks website,

> www.mathworks.com.

Here you can find examples and tutorials, as well as the definitive reference for the language. A list of references they recommend can be found at

> www.mathworks.com/support/books/.

The Mandelbrot set and the topic of fractals have captured the imagination of many of us. For the serious enthusiast, there's

> Benoit B. Mandelbrot, *The Fractal Geometry of Nature,* W. H. Freeman, New York, 1983.

Two of the finest books, both including many marvelous color photographs, are

> H. O. Peitgen and P. H. Richter, *The Beauty of Fractals,* Springer-Verlag, Berlin, 1986.

> *The Science of Fractal Images,* edited by Heinz-Otto Peitgen and Dietmar Saupe, Springer-Verlag, Berlin, 1988.

There are many fine books on chaos, but for a readable introduction there are sections in two mechanics texts,

> S. T. Thornton and J. B. Marion, *Classical Dynamics, 5th Edition,* Thomson-Brooks/Cole, Belmont CA, 2004.

V. Barger and M. Olsson, *Classical Mechanics: A Modern Perspective, Second Edition,* McGraw-Hill, New York, 1995.

And of course, for a popular discourse,

J. Gleick, *Chaos: Making a New Science.* Viking, New York, 1987.

chapter

2

Functions and Roots

A natural place for us to begin our discussion of computational physics is with a discussion of functions. After all, the formal theory of functions underlies virtually all of scientific theory, and their use is fundamental to any practical method of solving problems. We'll discuss some general properties, but always with an eye toward what is computationally applicable.

In particular, we'll discuss the problem of finding the roots of a function in one dimension. This is a relatively simple problem that arises quite frequently. Important in its own right, the problem provides us an opportunity to explore and illustrate the interplay among formal mathematics, numerical analysis, and computational physics. And we'll apply it to an interesting problem: the determination of quantum energy levels in a simple system.

By the way, MATLAB has several built-in functions for determining the roots of functions. Our primary purpose, however, is not in teaching you the workings of MATLAB, but how to approach problem solving from a computational point of view. Root finding is a topic of sufficient complexity to be of interest, yet elementary enough for us to consider without a great deal of foundation being developed. Thus it is a nearly ideal vehicle for us to begin our study of computational physics.

2.1 Finding the Roots of a Function

We'll begin our exploration of computational physics by discussing one of the oldest of numerical problems: finding the x value for which a given function $f(x)$ is zero. This problem often appears as an intermediate step in the study of a larger problem, but is sometimes *the* problem of interest, as we'll find later in this chapter when we investigate a certain problem of quantum mechanics.

For low-order polynomials, finding the zero of a function is a trivial problem: If the function is $f(x) = x - 3$, for example, the equation $x - 3 = 0$ is simply rearranged to read $x = 3$, which is the solution. Closed-form solutions for the roots

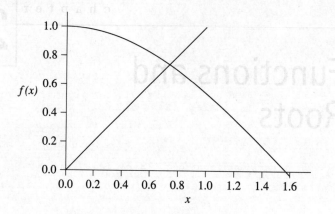

Figure 2.1   The functions x and $\cos x$.

exist for quadratic, cubic, and quartic equations as well, although they become rather cumbersome to use. But no general solution exists for polynomials of fifth-order and higher! Many equations involving functions other than polynomials have no analytic solution at all.

So what we're really seeking is a method for solving for the root of a nonlinear equation. When expressed in this way, the problem seems anything *but* trivial. To help focus our attention on the problem, let's consider a specific example: Let's try to find the value of x for which $x = \cos x$. This problem is cast into a "zero of a function" problem simply by defining the function of interest to be

$$f(x) = \cos x - x. \tag{2.1}$$

Such transcendental equations are not (generally) solvable analytically.

The first thing we might try is to draw a figure, such as Figure 2.1, in which $\cos x$ and x are plotted. The root is simply the horizontal coordinate at which the two curves cross. The eye has no trouble finding this intersection, and the graph can easily be read to determine that the root lies near $x = 0.75$. But greater accuracy than this is hard to achieve by graphical methods. Furthermore, if there are a large number of roots to find, or if the function is not an easy one to plot, the effectiveness of this graphical method rapidly decreases—we have no choice but to attempt a solution by numerical means. What we would like to have is a reliable numerical method that will provide accurate results with a minimum of human intervention.

From the figure, it's clear that a root lies between zero and $\pi/2$; that is, the root is *bracketed* between these two limits. We can improve our brackets by dividing the interval in half, and retaining the interval that contains the root. We can then check to see how small the bracket has become: If it is still too large, we halve the interval again! By doing this repeatedly, the upper and lower limits of the interval approach the root. Sounds like this just might work! Since the interval is halved at each step, the method is called *bisection*. The general construction of the computer code might be something like

```
< Main Program identification   >
< initialize limits of bracket >
< call Root Finding algorithm   >
< print result, and end         >
```

```
%-----------------------------------------------------------

< function identification>
< prepare for looping: set initial values, etc.>
< TOP of the loop -- loop through the body as long as
                     the bracket is too large>
< Body of the loop: divide the interval in half,
                    determine which half contains the root,
                    redefine the limits of the bracket >
< Once the bracket has been sufficiently narrowed,
  cease looping >
< put on finishing touches (if needed), and end >
```

These lines are referred to as *pseudocode* since they convey the intended content of the program but don't contain the actual executable statements. Let's first determine what the program should do, then worry about how to do it.

> Think first, then code.

As indicated in the pseudocode, it's extremely important to use functions to break the code into manageable pieces. This modularity aids immensely in the clarity and readability of the code—the main program simply becomes a list of calls to the various functions, so that the overall logic of the program is nearly transparent. Modularity also isolates one aspect of a problem from all the others: All the details of finding the root will be contained in the root-finding routine, in effect *hidden* from the rest of the program! This structure generally helps in developing and maintaining a program as well, in that a different approach to one aspect of the problem can be investigated by replacing a function, rather than totally rewriting the program.

After having a general outline of the entire program in pseudocode, we can now go back and expand upon its various components. In a large, complicated project, this refinement step will be performed several times, each time resulting in a more detailed description of the functioning of the code than the previous one. In this process, the program practically "writes itself." For this project, we might begin the refinement process by determining what needs to be passed to the function, and naming those variables appropriately. For example, the function should be given the limits of the bracketed interval: let's name these variables Left and Right, for example, in the function. (Note, however, that different names, such as x_initial and x_final, might be more appropriate in the calling routine.) In one sense, providing reasonable names for variables is simple stuff, easy to implement, and not very important. Not important, that is, until you try to remember (six months from now) what a poorly-named variable, like x34b, was supposed to mean!

Give your variables meaningful names.

(MATLAB assists in the writing of good programs by providing intelligent choices of the types of variables. As discussed in Chapter 1, it's extremely important to use double precision variables in scientific computing. To this end, the default for *all* numerical variables is that they are double precision. Defaults for other variable types are similarly well-chosen. For example, if we write code like

```
n = 3.0;
m = single(3.0);
p = 2+3i;
s = 'abc';
```

then n will be a double precision variable. Of course, in MATLAB the basic entity is an array, so it is also an array of one double precision variable. There may be times when a single precision variable is more appropriate, and so a function is provided to create one. Hence m is a single precision variable, or an array of one. The variable i is actually a *function* in MATLAB, given the value $\sqrt{-1}$, so that p is a complex number—or array—whose real and imaginary components are both double precision. Note that j is similarly defined, and either can be overwritten with an assignment statement so that, for example, either can be used as an index in a for loop. And finally, s is a string variable, and a 3-element array of characters. You can query MATLAB about the variable types with the whos command.)

Of course, we need to provide the function whose root we're seeking. For the moment, we'll simply define it in a subfunction, FofX. Oh, and we want the root passed back to the calling program! Our first refinement of the code might then look like

```
% bisection.m
% Finds the root of the equation
%        f(x) = cos(x)-x = 0
% using the bisection method.

function bisection
% Initialize variables:
```

```
clear;
x_initial = 0;
x_final   = pi/2;      % MATLAB knows the value of pi
% call the root-finding algorithm, store value in "root"

root = Bisect( x_initial, x_final);

        < print result, and end>

%----------------------------------------------------
function [y] = FofX(x)
% This is an example of a nonlinear function whose
% root cannot be found analytically.

y = cos(x) - x;
%----------------------------------------------------
function [Middle] = Bisect(Left, Right)
    < prepare for looping: set initial values, etc.>
    < TOP of the loop -- loop through the body as long as
                    the bracket is too large>
    < Body of the loop: divide the interval in half,
                    determine which half contains the root,
                    redefine the limits of the bracket >
    < Once the bracket has been sufficiently narrowed,
      cease looping >
    < put on finishing touches (if needed), and end >
```

The program is almost complete, although we've yet to begin the root-finding function itself! This is a general characteristic of the "top–down" programing we've described—first, write an outline for the overall design of the program, and then refine it successively until all the details have been worked out. In passing, we note that MATLAB knows the cosine function, as well as sine, logarithm, etc.

Now, let's concentrate on the root-finding function. The beginning of the code might look something like the following:

```
function [Middle] = Bisect(Left, Right)
% Finding the root of f(x), known to be bracketed between
% Left and Right, by the Bisection method.  The root is
% stored in the variable Middle, and is returned to the
% calling routine as the value of Bisect.

% Initialization of variables

        fLeft   = f(Left);
        fRight  = f(Right);
        Middle  = (Left+Right)/2.0;
        fMiddle = f(Middle);
                ...
```

In addition to using reasonable names for variables, we've also tried to use selective capitalization to aid in the readability of the code. The single most important characteristic of your computer programs should be their clarity, and the readability of the code contributes significantly to that goal. Note that MATLAB is case sensitive, so that `Left` and `left` are *not* the same variable.

How do we determine which subinterval contains the root? As in most puzzles, there are many ways we can find the answer. And the idea that occurs first is not necessarily the best. It's important to try various ideas, knowing that some will work and some won't. This particular puzzle has a well-known solution, however. If the root is in the left side, then `fLeft` and `fMiddle` will be of opposite sign and their product will be either zero or negative. So, if the expression `fLeft * fMiddle <= 0` is true, the root is in the left side; if the expression is false, the root must be in the right side. *Voila!* Having determined which subinterval contains the root, we then redefine `Middle` to be `Right` if the root is in the left subinterval, or `Middle` to be `Left` if the root is in the right subinterval. This part of the code then looks like

```
% Determine which half of the interval contains the root
   if( fLeft*fMiddle <= 0.0)
       Right  = Middle;     % The root is in left subinterval:
       fRight = fMiddle;
   else
       Left  = Middle;      % The root is in right subinterval:
       fLeft = fMiddle;
   end
% The root is now bracketed between Left and Right !
```

The `if-else-end` construct is ideally suited to the task at hand. In general, the `if` statement provides a logical condition to be evaluated. If it's "true," then the statements immediately following it (until the `else` statement) are executed. If "false," the statements between the `else` and `end` statements are executed. In the present case, the condition will be evaluated as "true" if the root lies in the left subinterval.

Our pseudocode is quickly being replaced by actual code, but a critical part yet remains: How to terminate the process. Exactly what is the appropriate criterion for having found a root? Or to put it another way, what is the acceptable error in finding the root, and how is that expressed as an error condition?

Basically, there are two ways to quantify an error: in absolute terms, or in relative terms. The *absolute error* is simply the magnitude of the difference between the true value and the approximate value,

$$\text{Absolute error} = |\text{true value} - \text{approximate value}|. \qquad (2.2)$$

Unfortunately, this measure of the error isn't as useful as you might think. Imagine two situations: In the first, the approximation is 1178.3 while the true value is 1178.4, and in the second situation the approximation is 0.15 while the true value is 0.25. In both cases the absolute error is 0.1, but clearly the approximation in the first case is better than in the second case. To gauge the *accuracy* of the approximation, we need to know more than merely the absolute error.

A better sense of the accuracy of an approximation is (usually) conveyed using a statement of *relative error*, comparing the difference between the approximation and the true value to the true value. That is,

$$\text{Relative Error} = \left| \frac{\text{True Value} - \text{Approximate Value}}{\text{True Value}} \right|. \qquad (2.3)$$

The relative error in the first situation is $\left| \frac{0.1}{1178.4} \right| = 0.00008$, while in the second case it is $\left| \frac{0.1}{0.25} \right| = 0.4$. The higher accuracy of the first case is clearly associated with the much smaller relative error. Note, of course, that relative error is not defined if the true value is zero. And as a practical matter, the only quantity we can actually compute is an approximation to the relative error,

$$\text{Approximate Relative Error}$$
$$= \left| \frac{\text{Best Approximation} - \text{Previous Approximation}}{\text{Best Approximation}} \right|. \qquad (2.4)$$

Thus, while there may be times when absolute accuracy is appropriate, most of the time we will want relative accuracy. For example, wanting to know x to within 1% is usually a more reasonable goal than simply wanting to know x to within 1, although this is not always true. (For example, in planning a trip to the Moon you might well want to know the distance to within 1 meter, not to within 1%!) Let's assume that in the present case our goal is to obtain results with relative error less than 5×10^{-8}. In this context, the "error" is simply our uncertainty in locating the root, which in the bisection method is just the width of the interval. (By the way, this accuracy in a trip to the Moon gives an absolute error of about 20 meters. Imagine being 20 meters above the surface, the descent rate of your lunar lander brought to zero, and out of gas. How hard would you hit the surface?) Defining these additional variables, adding some output statements, and cleaning up a few loose ends, the total code might look something like

```
% bisection.m
% The purpose of this function is to find the root of the equation
%          f(x) = cos(x)-x = 0
% using the bisection method.
function bisection
clear;
% Initialize variables
x_initial = 0.0;
x_final   = pi/2;
% call the root-finding function
Root = Bisect(x_initial,x_final);
```

```
% < print result >

function [y] = FofX(x)
% This is an example of a nonlinear function
% whose root cannot be found analytically.
y = cos(x) - x;


function [Middle] = Bisect(Left,Right)
% Finding the root of the function by BISECTION. The
% root is known(?) to be bracketed between LEFT and RIGHT.
TOL   = 5e-3;                 % will eventually be decreased to 5e-8
error = 10*TOL;
% Initialization of variables
fLeft  = FofX(Left);
fRight = FofX(Right);
% Top of the Bisection loop
iterations = 0;
while (error > TOL)
    Middle  = (Left+Right)/2.0;
    fMiddle = FofX(Middle);
    iterations = iterations + 1;
    % Determine which half of the interval contains the root
    if( fLeft*fMiddle <= 0.0)
        Right  = Middle;        % The root is in left subinterval:
        fRight = fMiddle;
    else
        Left  = Middle;         % The root is in right subinterval:
        fLeft = fMiddle;
    end
    % The root is now bracketed between (new) Left and Right !
    % Check for the relative error condition: If too big,
    % bisect again; if small enough, print result and end.
    error = abs((Right-Left)/Middle);
end
% Remove after routine has been debugged.
fprintf(' Root found at %10.6f\n',Middle)
fprintf(' %4.0f iterations\n',iterations)
```

We've introduced the parameter TOL to describe the desired tolerance. In the initial stages of writing and testing the program, TOL can be made relatively large and any lurking errors found quickly. Only after the code is known to be functioning properly should the tolerance be decreased to achieve the desired level of accuracy. Alternatively, we could pass the tolerance to the function as a parameter. We have also coded an fprintf statement in the function. This is appropriate during the initial development phase, but should be removed—or "commented out" by inserting % at the beginning of the line—after we're satisfied that the function is working properly. The purpose of this routine is to *find* the root—if displaying it is desired, it should be done in a routine that calls `Bisect`, not in `Bisect` itself.

At the bottom of the loop, the relative error is computed, although the test is executed at the top of the `while` loop. (The location of the test forces us to define an initial value for `error` before entering the `while` loop.) If the error is greater than the declared tolerance, a bisection step is performed; if not, the result is printed. The program certainly looks like it's ready to run. In fact, it's foolproof!

Well, maybe not *fool* proof. It might happen that six months from now you need to find a root, and so you adopt this code. But what if you misjudge, or simply are incorrect, in your bracketing? As developed, the code *assumes* that there is a root between the initial `Left` and `Right`. In practice, finding such brackets might be rather difficult, and certainly calls for a different strategy than is being implemented here. Modify the code to include an explicit check that *verifies* that the root is bracketed. This verification should be performed after all the initialization has been accomplished but prior to the beginning of the main loop. In large, complex computer codes such *data validation* can become of preeminent importance to the overall success of the computation.

EXERCISE 2.1

Using the code we've developed, with your data validation, find the root of the equation $f(x) = \cos x - x = 0$ by the method of bisection. How many iterates are necessary to determine the root to 8 significant digits?

2.2 A Recursive Algorithm

Occasionally we'll find that a function will be defined in terms of itself. The prime example is the factorial: mathematically, the factorial can be *defined* as

$$n! = n(n-1)!, \quad 0! = 1. \tag{2.5}$$

That is, to calculate $n!$, we just multiply $(n-1)!$ by n. And we can evaluate $(n-1)!$ by multiplying $(n-2)!$ by. . . you get the idea. The process is terminated when we get to $0!$, which is defined as being 1.

We've seen that MATLAB allows a function to call other functions. This permits us to break a large programming task into a sequence of smaller and smaller ones, until we get to the point that we have a task that "deserves" to be implemented as its own method. Furthermore, a MATLAB function can call itself, just as in the mathematical definition of the factorial. Implementing this mathematical function in computer code is quite straightforward remembering, of course, to terminate the recursion appropriately:

```
% fact.m
% This function demonstrates the use of recursion to evaluate
```

```
%    the FACTORIAL function.
%
%  Note that MATLAB already has a built-in "factorial" function, which
%  should be used in actual applications.
%
function f = fact(n)

if (n==1)          % The termination step.
    f=1.;
    return;
end;

f = n*fact(n-1);
```

(It is essential that a termination step be provided in a recursive algorithm, and it should always appear at the beginning of the code.) In terms of a clear correlation between the mathematics and the computer code, it doesn't get much better than this!

EXERCISE 2.2

Write a program that prompts the user for an integer n, and then evaluates and displays $n!$. (You should verify that the number is a non-negative integer—data validation, remember. To see how this might be done, enter **type factorial** at the MATLAB prompt, which will display MATLAB's factorial script.)

Clearly, the factorial function is ideally suited for recursive evaluation. There are other problems that naturally lend themselves to recursive solutions, and root finding is one of them. Consider: An interval containing a root is identified, it's divided in half, the interval containing a root is identified, it's divided in half, the interval containing a root is identified,.... As with any recursion, we must be certain to halt the process at some point, but the basic structure of the solution cries out for recursion.

In essence, the `while` loop is removed, the "data shuffling" (e.g., assigning `Middle` to either `Left` or `Right`) is replaced by recursive calls with appropriate interval limits, and a way to halt the recursion (based on the specified error criterion) is crafted. The calling routine needs only to be changed to the new name of the function; the major change is in the *body* of the bisection method:

```
function [Middle] = RecursiveBisect(Left,Right)
% Finding the root of the function by Recursive Bisection. The
% root is known(?) to be bracketed between Left and Right.
TOL=5e-8;
Middle = (Left+Right)/2.0;
if(abs( (Right-Left)/Middle) < TOL)
```

```
    % Remove after routine has been debugged.
    fprintf(' Root found at %10.6f\n',Middle)
    return;
end

% Initialization of variables
fLeft = FofX(Left);
fMiddle = FofX(Middle);

if( fLeft*fMiddle <= 0.0)
    RecursiveBisect(Left, Middle); % The root is in left subinterval
else
    RecursiveBisect(Middle, Right);% The root is in right subinterval
end                                % That's it!
```

The recursive and non-recursive versions of the algorithm perform *exactly* the same calculations—it's just that the recursive version utilizes the computer to do more of the bookkeeping, rather than the programmer. Once the idea of recursion is firmly planted in your mind, it becomes a very sophisticated way to attack certain problems. It is probably not as fast to execute as the non-recursive method, but that's rarely a concern with contemporary computers.

EXERCISE 2.3

Test your understanding of the recursive bisection algorithm by repeating the previous exercise, i.e., find the root of

$$f(x) = \cos x - x \qquad (2.6)$$

between 0 and $\pi/2$.

Well, bisection works, and it may be foolproof, but it certainly can be *slow*! It's easy to determine how fast this method is. (Or slow, as the case may be.) Defining the error as the difference between the upper and lower bounds on the root, at every iteration the error is halved. If ϵ_i is the error at the i-th step, at the next step we have $\epsilon_{i+1} = \epsilon_i/2$, and the rate of convergence is said to be *linear*. Given initial brackets, we could even determine how many iterations are necessary to obtain a specific level of accuracy.

It would seem that there would be a better way to find the root, at least for a nice, smoothly varying function such as ours. And indeed, there is such a method, due to Newton. But we need to use information about the function, and how it changes— that is, derivative information. That information is most succinctly provided in a Taylor series expansion of the function. Since this expansion is so central to much of what we are doing now, and will be doing in later chapters, let's take a moment to review the essentials of the series.

2.3 Mr. Taylor's Series

In 1715 Brook Taylor, secretary of the Royal Society, published *Methodus incrementorum directa et inversa* in which appears one of the most useful expressions in much of mathematics and certainly numerical analysis. Although previously known to the Scottish mathematician James Gregory, and probably to Jean Bernoulli as well, we know it today as the **Taylor Series**. Since it will play a central role in many of our discussions, it's appropriate that we take a little time to discuss it in some detail. Let's assume that the function $f(x)$ has a continuous nth derivative in the interval $a \le x \le b$. We can then integrate this derivative to obtain

$$\int_a^{x_1} f^{[n]}(x_0) \, dx_0 = f^{[n-1]}(x_1) - f^{[n-1]}(a). \qquad (2.7)$$

Integrating again, we have

$$\int_a^{x_2} \int_a^{x_1} f^{[n]}(x_0) \, dx_0 \, dx_1 = \int_a^{x_2} \left(f^{[n-1]}(x_1) - f^{[n-1]}(a) \right) dx_1$$

$$= f^{[n-2]}(x_2) - f^{[n-2]}(a) - (x_2 - a) f^{[n-1]}(a). \qquad (2.8)$$

Continuing in this way we find, after n integrations,

$$\int_a^{x_n} \cdots \int_a^{x_1} f^{[n]}(x) \, dx_0 \cdots dx_{n-1}$$

$$= f(x_n) - f(a) - (x_n - a) f'(a)$$

$$- \frac{(x_n - a)^2}{2!} f''(a) - \frac{(x_n - a)^3}{3!} f'''(a) \cdots - \frac{(x_n - a)^{n-1}}{(n-1)!} f^{[n-1]}(a). \qquad (2.9)$$

To simplify the appearance of the expression, we now substitute x for x_n, and solve for $f(x)$ to obtain the *Taylor Series*

$$f(x) = f(a) + (x - a)f'(a) + \frac{(x - a)^2}{2!} f''(a) + \frac{(x - a)^3}{3!} f'''(a) + \cdots$$

$$+ \frac{(x - a)^{n-1}}{(n-1)!} f^{[n-1]}(a) + R_n(x), \qquad (2.10)$$

where

$$R_n(x) = \int_a^x \cdots \int_a^{x_1} f^{[n]}(x) \, dx_0 \cdots dx_{n-1}. \qquad (2.11)$$

This remainder term is often written in a different way. Using the mean value theorem of integral calculus,

$$\int_a^x q(y) \, dy = (x - a) q(\xi), \quad \text{for } a \le \xi \le x, \qquad (2.12)$$

and integrating $n - 1$ more times, the remainder term can be written as

$$R_n(x) = \frac{(x-a)^n}{n!} f^{[n]}(\xi), \tag{2.13}$$

a form originally due to Lagrange. If the function is such that

$$\lim_{n \to \infty} R_n = 0, \tag{2.14}$$

then the finite series can be extended to an infinite number of terms and we arrive at the Taylor series expression for $f(x)$.

To illustrate, consider the Taylor series expansion of $\sin x$ about the point $x = 0$:

$$\begin{aligned}
f(x) &= \sin x, & f(0) &= 0, \\
f'(x) &= \cos x, & f'(0) &= 1, \\
f''(x) &= -\sin x, & f''(0) &= 0, \\
f''' &= -\cos x, & f'''(0) &= -1,
\end{aligned} \tag{2.15}$$

$$\vdots \qquad\qquad \vdots$$

with remainder

$$R_n(x) = \begin{cases} (-1)^{n/2} \dfrac{x^n}{n!} \sin \xi, & n \text{ even}, \\[2mm] (-1)^{(n-1)/2} \dfrac{x^n}{n!} \cos \xi, & n \text{ odd}. \end{cases} \tag{2.16}$$

Since the magnitudes of the sine and cosine are bounded by one, the magnitude of the remainder satisfies the inequality

$$|R_n(x)| \le \frac{x^n}{n!}. \tag{2.17}$$

For any given x, the factorial will eventually exceed the numerator and the remainder will tend toward zero. Thus we can expand $f(x) = \sin x$ as an infinite series,

$$f(x) = f(0) + (x - 0)f'(0) + \frac{(x-0)^2}{2!} f''(0) + \frac{(x-0)^3}{3!} f'''(0) + \cdots$$

$$= x - \frac{x^3}{3!} + \frac{x^5}{5!} + \cdots . \tag{2.18}$$

This is, of course, simply the well-known approximation for the sine function.

Now, it might seem to be a small step to say that all functions that possess an infinite number of derivatives can be expressed as a Taylor series; but of course, falling off a cliff only takes a small step, too. Consider the function

$$f(x) = \begin{cases} e^{-1/x^2}, & \text{for } x \ne 0, \\ 0, & \text{for } x = 0, \end{cases}$$

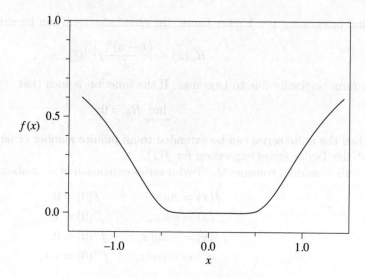

Figure 2.2   A decidedly unpleasant function!

which is plotted in Figure 2.2. This is *not* a "nasty" function—it is well-behaved, and goes smoothly to zero as $x \to 0$. In fact, it goes to zero so strongly that all its derivatives go to zero there as well. If we then try to use Taylor's series about $a = 0$, we find that $f(x) = 0 + 0 + \cdots = 0$, **everywhere!**

2.4 The Newton-Raphson Method

To appreciate some of the power of Taylor's series, we'll use it to develop Newton's method to find the zeroes of a function. (The English mathematician Joseph Raphson (1648–1715) is credited with the independent discovery of the algorithm.) Assume that we have a good "guess," so that $(x - a)$ is a small number. Then keeping just the first two terms of the Taylor series, we have

$$f(x) \approx f(a) + (x - a)f'(a). \tag{2.19}$$

We want to find that value of x for which $f(x) = 0$; setting $f(x)$ equal to zero and solving for x, we quickly find

$$x = a - \frac{f(a)}{f'(a)}. \tag{2.20}$$

To see how this works, take a look at Figure 2.3. At $x = a$ the function and its derivative, which is tangent to the function, are known. Assuming that the function doesn't differ too much from a straight line, a good approximation to where the *function* crosses zero is where the *tangent line* crosses zero. This point, being the solution to a *linear* equation, is easily found—it's given by Equation 2.20!

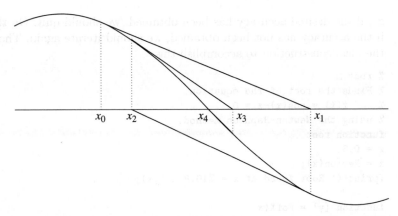

Figure 2.3   The Newton-Raphson in action. Beginning with x_0, the successive iterates move closer to the zero of the function. The location of x_4 and the actual crossing are indistinguishable on this scale.

Then this point can be taken as a new guess for the root, the function and its derivative evaluated, and so on. The idea of using one value to generate a better value is called *iteration*, and is a very practical technique that we will use often. Changing the notation a little, we can calculate the $(i + 1)$-th value x_{i+1} from the i-th value by the iterative expression

$$x_{i+1} = x_i - \frac{f(x_i)}{f'(x_i)}. \tag{2.21}$$

For the function $f(x) = \cos x - x$, we have that $f'(x) = -\sin x - 1$. We know that $\cos x = 1$ at $x = 0$, and that $\cos x = 0$ at $x = \pi/2$, so we might guess that $x = \cos x$ somewhere around $x_0 = \pi/4$. We then calculate the zero to be at

$$x_1 = \frac{\pi}{4} - \frac{\cos \pi/4 - \pi/4}{-\sin \pi/4 - 1} = 0.739536134. \tag{2.22}$$

This is a pretty good result, much closer to the correct answer of 0.739085133 than was the initial guess of $\pi/4 = 0.785398163$. And as noted, this result can be used as a new guess to calculate another approximation to the location of the zero. Thus

$$x_2 = 0.739536134 - \frac{\cos(0.739536134) - 0.739536134}{-\sin(0.739536134) - 1} = 0.739085178, \tag{2.23}$$

a result accurate to 7 significant digits.

Beginning with an initial guess x_0, the expression is iterated to generate $x_1, x_2, \ldots$, until the result is deemed sufficiently accurate. Typically we want a result that is accurate to about eight significant digits, e.g., a relative error of 5×10^{-8}. That means that after each evaluation of x_{i+1} it should be compared to

x_i; if the desired accuracy has been obtained, we should quit. On the other hand, if the accuracy has not been obtained, we should iterate again. The `while` loop is the ideal construction to accomplish this

```
% root.m
% Finds the root of the equation
%      f(x) = cos(x)-x = 0
% using the Newton-Raphson method.
function root
x = 0.8;
x = Newton(x);
fprintf(' Root found at x = %10.8f\n',x);

function [y] = FofX(x)
% This is an example of a nonlinear function whose
% root cannot be found analytically.
y = cos(x) - x;

function [y] = DERofF(x)
% This function is the derivative of "F of X."
y = -sin(x) - 1.0;

function [x] = Newton(x)
% Preliminary code for root finding with Newton-Raphson
TOL   = 5e-09;
error = 10*TOL;
%  Top of the loop
iterations = 0;
while (error > TOL)
    delta = -FofX(x)/DERofF(x);
    x = x + delta;
    iterations = iterations + 1;
    % Check for the relative error condition:
    % If too big, loop again; if small enough, end.
    error = abs( delta / x );
end
fprintf(' After %4.0f iterations\n',iterations)
```

EXERCISE 2.4

Verify that this code is functioning properly by finding (again) where $x = \cos x$. Compare the effort required to find the root with the Newton-Raphson and the bisection methods.

As we noted earlier, finding the roots of equations often occur in a larger context. For example, in Chapter 4 we will find that the zeros of Legendre functions play a special role in certain integration schemes. So, let's consider the Legendre polynomial

$$P_8(x) = \frac{6435x^8 - 12012x^6 + 6930x^4 - 1260x^2 + 35}{128}, \quad -1 \le x \le 1, \qquad (2.24)$$

and try to find its roots. Where to start? What would be a good initial guess? Since only the first derivative term was retained in developing the Newton-Raphson method, we suspect that we need to be close to a root before using it. For $|x| < 1$, we have $x^8 < x^6 < x^4 < x^2$,—let's (temporarily) ignore all the terms in the polynomial except the last two, and set this truncated function equal to zero. We thus have

$$P_8(x_0) \approx \frac{-1260x_0^2 + 35}{128} = 0 \qquad (2.25)$$

and hence

$$x_0 = \pm\sqrt{\frac{35}{1260}} = \pm\sqrt{\frac{1}{36}} = \pm\frac{1}{6}. \qquad (2.26)$$

Thus 0.167 should be an excellent guess to begin the iteration for the smallest non-negative root.

EXERCISE 2.5
Use the Newton-Raphson method to find the smallest non-negative root of $P_8(x)$.

Root-finding in general, and the Newton-Raphson method in particular, arise in various rather unexpected places. For example, how could we find the two-thirds power of thirteen, with only a 4-function hand calculator? That is, we want to find x such that

$$x = 13^{2/3}. \qquad (2.27)$$

Cubing both sides, we have

$$x^3 = 13^2 = 169 \qquad (2.28)$$

or

$$x^3 - 169 = 0. \qquad (2.29)$$

Interesting.

EXERCISE 2.6
Use the Newton-Raphson method to solve Equation 2.29 for the two-thirds root of thirteen, to 8 significant digits.

2.5 Fools Rush In...

Well, our Newton-Raphson method seems to be working so well, let's try it to find a root of the equation $f(x) = x^2 + 1 = 0$. No problem. Starting the iteration with $x_0 = 1/\sqrt{3}$, we find the first few iterates to be

$$x_0 = \quad .577350269$$
$$x_1 = -.577350269$$
$$x_2 = \quad .577350269$$
$$x_3 = -.577350269$$
$$x_4 = \quad .577350269$$
$$x_5 = -.577350269$$

Oops.

Clearly, there's a problem here. Not only are the iterates not converging, they're just flopping back and forth between $\pm 1/\sqrt{3}$. This example forces us to realize that we haven't yet thought enough about how to approach computing. Perhaps the first thing we need to realize is that the world is not always nice; sometimes things just don't go our way. While we always try to do things right, errors will always be made, and we can't expect the computer to protect us from ourselves. In particular, the computer can't do something we haven't instructed it to do—it's not smarter than we are. So, just because the computer is there and is eager to help us if we only type in the code, we must first decide if the problem is suitable for computation. Perhaps it needs to be transformed into an equivalent problem, stated differently; perhaps another algorithm should be used; or perhaps we should have realized that the problem at hand has no real roots.

> Computing is not a substitute for thinking.

As we write programs to solve problems of our interest, we'll try to anticipate various situations. This will probably require extra programming for special cases. In the problem above, we might have tried to determine if a real root existed before we tried to find it. Certainly we can't expect the program to know what we don't. What we need is a strategy toward computing, a *game plan* so to speak. The Newton-Raphson method is a robust algorithm that often works very well—it's like a high-risk *offense*, capable of aggressively finding a root. What we've missed is what every sports fan knows: while offense wins games, *defense* wins championships. We should strive to be intelligent in our computing, anticipating various possibilities, and trying to not make errors. But we should be prepared to fall short of this goal— it's simply not possible to foresee all eventualities. Reasonable people know that mistakes will occasionally be made, and take appropriate steps *before* they occur. If we can't instruct the computer how to always act correctly, let's at least instruct it how to not act incorrectly! A major key to successful programming is to

---

Compute defensively!

But how do we instruct the computer to not act incorrectly? In this case, it's pretty easy. When the iteration worked, it was very fast. But when it failed, it failed miserably. Thus we can require that the algorithm either finds a root in just a few steps, or that it quits. Of course, if it quits it should inform us that it is quitting because it hasn't found a root. (There's nothing quite as frustrating as a computer program that stops with no explanation. Or one that prints ERROR, without any indication of what kind of error or where it occurred.) The maximum number of iterates could be passed to the code fragment, but it is easier to just set a maximum that seems much greater than you would ever need, say 30 iterations. The idea is to prevent infinite loops and to provide a graceful exit for the program.

EXERCISE 2.7

Modify the displayed code on Page 54 code to keep track of the number of iterations, and to exit the loop and end after writing an appropriate message if a root is not found in 30 iterations. Test your modifications on the example above, $f(x) = x^2 + 1$, with an initial x of 0.5. You might want to print out the iterates, just to see how the search proceeds.

2.6 Rates of Convergence

We previously saw that the bisection method was *linear* in its convergence. Our experience with the Newton-Raphson scheme is that if it converges, it converges very rapidly. To quantify this statement, let's return to the Taylor series

$$f(x) = f(x_i) + (x - x_i)f'(x_i) + \frac{(x - x_i)^2}{2!}f''(x_i) + \cdots. \tag{2.30}$$

We'll assume that we're in a region where the function is well behaved and the first derivative is not small. Keeping the first two terms and setting $f(x) = 0$, we're led to the iteration

$$x_{i+1} = x_i - \frac{f(x_i)}{f'(x_i)}, \tag{2.31}$$

just as before. Recall that both x_i and x_{i+1} are approximations to the location of the root—if x is where the root *actually* is, then $\epsilon_i = x - x_i$ is a measure of the error in x_i. Subtracting x from both sides of Equation 2.31, we find

$$\epsilon_{i+1} = \epsilon_i + \frac{f(x_i)}{f'(x_i)}, \tag{2.32}$$

an expression relating the error at one iteration to the next. Let's return to the Taylor series, this time keeping the first three terms in the series. Setting $f(x) = 0$ and solving for $f(x_i)$, we find

$$f(x_i) = -\epsilon_i f'(x_i) - \frac{\epsilon_i^2}{2} f''(x_i). \tag{2.33}$$

Substituting this expression into the previous one, we find that

$$\begin{aligned}
\epsilon_{i+1} &= \epsilon_i + \frac{-\epsilon_i f'(x_i) - \frac{\epsilon_i^2}{2} f''(x_i)}{f'(x_i)} \\
&= -\frac{\epsilon_i^2 f''(x_i)}{2 f'(x_i)}. \tag{2.34}
\end{aligned}$$

If f''/f' is approximately constant near the root, then at each step the error is proportional to the *square* of the error at the previous step—if the error is initially small, it gets smaller very quickly. Such convergence is termed *quadratic*. In the Newton-Raphson iteration, each iteration essentially doubles the number of significant digits that are accurate. (It is possible, however, that the method does not converge: this might happen if the initial error is too large, for example. It's also possible that f' is near zero in the vicinity of the root, which happens if there are two roots of $f(x)$ close to one another. Could you modify the method presented here to treat that situation?)

It would be desirable to combine the slow-but-sure quality of the bisection method with the fast-but-iffy characteristic of Newton's method to come up with a guaranteed winner. With a little thought, we can do just that. Let's start with the fact (verified?) that the root is bounded between $x = a$ and $x = c$, and that the best current guess for the root is $x = b$. (Note that initially we may choose b to be either a or c.) We'll include the iteration counter, so that the code doesn't loop forever. But the critical step is to decide when to take a bisection step, and when to take a Newton-Raphson step. Clearly, we want to take a Newton-Raphson wherever possible. Since we *know* that the root is bracketed, it's clearly in our interest to only take steps that lie within those limits. Thus the crucial step is to determine if the *next Newton-Raphson guess* will be outside the bounding interval or not. If the next guess is within the bounds, then

$$a \leq b - \frac{f(b)}{f'(b)} \leq c. \tag{2.35}$$

Subtracting b from all terms, multiplying by $-f'(b)$, and subtracting $f(b)$, this inequality can be rewritten as

$$(b - a)f'(b) - f(b) \geq 0 \geq (b - c)f'(b) - f(b). \tag{2.36}$$

This inequality will be satisfied *if* the next iterate lies between a and c. An easy way of determining if this is so is to compare the product of the first term and the last term to zero. If the product is less than or equal to zero, then the next Newton-Raphson guess will fall within the known limits, and so a Newton-Raphson step should certainly be taken; if this condition is not met, a bisection step should be taken instead. Now, to attempt a judicious merger of the bisection and Newton-Raphson methods using this logic to decide which method to utilize ...

```
% moreroots.m
% On the hybrid method to find the root of an equation
function moreroots
%
x_initial = ...
x_final   = ...

[x_root, found] = Hybrid(x_initial, x_final);
if(found)fprintf(' root at x = %10.8f\n',x_root); end;
if(~found) ???   %  What IS the appropriate action???

function [y] = FofX(x)
%
%  < Define the function >
%

function [y] = DERofF(x)
%
%  < Define the derivative of the function. >
%

function [Best, found] = Hybrid(Left,Right)
% A hybrid BISECTION/NEWTON-RAPHSON method for finding the
% root of a function F, with derivative Fprime. The root
% is known to be between Left and Right, and the result
% is returned in 'Best'. If the next NR guess is within
% the known bounds, the step is accepted; otherwise, a
% bisection step is taken.
%
% The root is initially bracketed between Left and Right:
%      x :      Left        Best        Right
%       f(x):     fLeft       fBest       fRight
%       f'(x):    ---         DerfBest    ---
%
% Initialize parameters
TOL   = 5.e-3;    % A LARGE tolerance is chosen, until we know this works.
error = 10*TOL;
found = false;    % The root has NOT been found --- yet!
% Initialization of variables
```

```
fLeft  = FofX(Left);
fRight = FofX(Right);
% Verify that root is bracketed:
if (fLeft * fRight > 0), disp ('root NOT bracketed'); return, end
% Just to get started, let BEST = ...
if( abs(fLeft) <= abs(fRight))
    Best  = Left;
    fBest = fLeft;
else
    Best  = Right;
    fBest = fRight;
end
DerfBest = DERofF(Best);
% count is the number of times through the while loop
count = 0;
while (error > TOL & count <= 30)
    count = count + 1;
    % Determine Newton-Raphson or Bisection step:
    if((DerfBest*(Best-Left )-fBest)*...
            (DerfBest*(Best-Right)-fBest) <= 0)
        delta = -fBest/DerfBest;      % O.K. to take a Newton-Raphson step
        Best  = Best + delta;
    else
        delta = (Right-Left)/2.0;     % take a bisection step instead
        Best  = (Left+Right)/2.0;
    end
    % Compare the relative error to the TOLerance
    error = abs(delta/Best);
    if(error <= TOL)
        found = true;     %Error is BELOW tolerance, the ROOT HAS BEEN FOUND!
        % fprintf('root found at %10.8f\n',Best);
        return
    else
                % The relative error is too big, prepare to continue
        fBest    = FofX(Best);
        DerfBest = DERofF(Best);
        % Adjust brackets
        if(fLeft*fBest <= 0)
            Right  = Best;            % The root is in left subinterval:
            fRight = fBest;
        else
            Left  = Best;             % The root is in right subinterval:
            fLeft = fBest;
        end
    end
end
```

```
        if(error > TOL | count > 30)
            % Can only get to this point if the ERROR is TOO BIG
            % and if  COUNT is greater than 30. Time to QUIT !!!
            fprintf('Root not converged after 30 iterations.')
            return
        end
```

This looks like it just might work . . . .

However, what if it didn't? That is, we really shouldn't *presume* that a root will be found. Rather, we should assume that it *isn't* found, and proceed accordingly. (Compute defensively!) Thus we first define a flag, the variable found, and initialize it to "false." We then test to see if the root is indeed in the interval provided: if it isn't a return is immediately executed, returning control of the program to the calling routine. Only after a root has been successfully determined should the flag be set to "true." Of course, the calling routine must then test whether a root has been found, and take appropriate actions.

EXERCISE 2.8
Use the hybrid method discussed above to find the root of the equation

$$x^2 - 2x - 2 = 0,$$

given that there is a root between 0 and 3. You might find it interesting to add output statements indicating whether a Newton-Raphson or bisection step is being taken. Such statements can be a great help in writing and debugging programs, and can then be commented out when no longer needed. (And easily reinstated if a problem in the code later develops!)

2.7 Exhaustive Searching

We now have a good method for finding a root, if you first know that the root is bounded. But how do you find those bounds? Unfortunately, the answer is that there is *no good way* of finding them. The reason, of course, is that finding the bounds is a *global* problem—the root might be found *anywhere*—but finding the root, after the bounds are known, is a *local* problem. Almost by definition, local problems are always easier to solve than global ones.

So, what to do? One possibility is to graph the curve, and let your eye find the bounds. This is highly recommended, and for simple functions can be done with pencil and paper; for more complicated ones, the computer can be used to graph the function for you. But we can also investigate the function analytically. When we were finding an initial guess for the root of the Legendre function $P_8(x)$, we knew that all the roots were less than 1. As a result, $x^8 < x^6 < x^4 < x^2$, so we ignored the leading terms in the polynomial. Keeping only the two largest terms, we could exactly solve for the root of the truncated function. In a similar fashion, we can obtain a good guess for the largest root of a polynomial, if it's greater than one. To illustrate, consider the quadratic equation

$$f(x) = x^2 - 11x + 10. \tag{2.37}$$

This can of course be solved exactly, and roots found at $x = 1$ and 10. But keeping just the leading two terms, we have the truncated function

$$\bar{f}(x) = x^2 - 11x, \tag{2.38}$$

which has a root at

$$x = 11, \tag{2.39}$$

a very reasonable approximation to the root of the original function, and obtained without taking a square root. Of course, the value of the approximation is more impressive if the problem isn't quite so obvious. Consider, for example, the function

$$f(x) = x^3 - 7x^2 - 10x + 16. \tag{2.40}$$

Our approximation to the largest root is 7—but what is the exact value?

While there are shortcuts for polynomials—many more than we've mentioned—there are no similar tricks for general functions. The only method that is generally applicable is brute force, exhaustive searching. The most common strategy is to simply step along, evaluating the function at each step, and determining if the function has changed sign. If it has, then a root is located within that step; if not, the search is continued. The problem with this procedure, of course, is that the step might be so large that the function has changed sign *twice*, e.g., there are two roots in the interval, in which case this method will not detect their presence. (If derivatives are easily obtained, that information can be incorporated in the search by determining if the derivative has changed sign. If it has, that *suggests* that there might be two roots in the interval—at least, there is a minimum.)

Of course, determining an appropriate size step is as much educated guesswork as anything else. Use any and all information you have about the function, and be conservative. For example, we know that there are 4 roots of $P_8(x)$ between 0 and 1. If they were equally distributed, they might be 0.333 apart. Any search should certainly use a step at least half this, or 0.167, if not smaller.

EXERCISE 2.9

Find all the non-negative roots of $P_8(x)$. Use an exhaustive search to isolate the roots, and then use the hybrid algorithm you've developed to locate the roots themselves to a relative accuracy of 5×10^{-8}.

2.8 Look Ma, No Derivatives!

With the safeguards we've added, the hybrid Bisection/Newton-Raphson algorithm you've developed is a good one. Unfortunately, it often happens that the required derivatives are not directly available to us. (Or perhaps the function is available but is so complicated that obtaining its derivative is difficult; or having the derivative, getting it coded without errors is unlikely.) For those situations, we need a method that requires only evaluations of the function, and not its derivatives, such as the bisection method.

Well, bisection works, but it certainly can be slow! The reason, of course, is that we have *not* been very resourceful in using the information available to us. After all, we know (assume?) that the root is bounded, $a \leq \bar{x} \leq c$, and we know the value of the function at the limits of the interval. Let's use this information as best we can, and approximate $f(x)$ by the straight line passing through the known values of the function at the endpoints of the interval, $[a, f(a)]$ and $[c, f(c)]$. This leads to the *method of false position*. You can easily verify that the line is given by the equation

$$p(x) = \frac{x - c}{a - c}f(a) + \frac{x - a}{c - a}f(c) \tag{2.41}$$

and can be thought to be an *approximation* to the function $f(x)$. Being a simpler equation, its root can be easily determined: setting $p(\bar{x}) = 0$, we find

$$\bar{x} = \frac{af(c) - cf(a)}{f(c) - f(a)}. \tag{2.42}$$

This approximation is depicted graphically in Figure 2.4. Since $f(a)$ and $f(c)$ are opposite in sign, there's no worry that the denominator might vanish. It should be fairly obvious that in many common circumstances this is a considerable improvement over the bisection method. (An interesting analogy can be found in finding someone's phone number in the telephone book. To find Arnold Aarons' telephone number, the "bisection" method would first look under M, halfway in the book. It would then divide the interval in half, and look under G, about a quarter of the way through the book, and so on. In contrast, the method of false position would expect to find Arnold's name early in the phone book, and would start looking only a few pages into it.)

After making the guess, the iteration proceeds by determining which subinterval contains the root and adjusting the bounds a and c appropriately. Since only one of the endpoints is changed, it is entirely possible, even likely, that one of these points will be fixed. (Is this statement obviously true? If not, look at Figure 2.4 once again.) For example, the method might converge to the root from above, so that each iteration leaves c closer and closer to the root, *but never changes a!* What are important are the successive guesses, and the difference in them (á là Newton-Raphson) rather

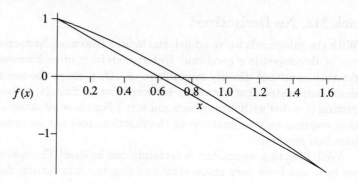

Figure 2.4   The function $f(x) = \cos x - x$ and its linear approximation, $p(x)$.

than the difference between the bounds. Thus you must keep track of x_i and x_{i+1} as well as a and c.

Beginning with your existing bisection code, only a few changes are necessary to transform it into a False Position code. The first, of course, is to modify the expression for the root: instead of the variable Middle, we'll use NewGuess, and define it according to Equation 2.42. Also, we need to keep tabs on the successive approximations: we'll use OldGuess as the previous approximation. An outline of the code might look like

```
function [NewGuess] = false(Left,Right)
%  <prepare for looping: set initial values, etc. To
%  get started, must assign some value to OldGuess.>

OldGuess = Right;

%  <Top of the loop>

while (error > TOL & iterations < 30)
    NewGuess = (Left*fRight-Right*fLeft)/(fRight-fLeft);
    fGuess = FofX(NewGuess);

    error = abs((NewGuess-OldGuess)/NewGuess);

    %  <determine which interval contains the root and redefine
    %  Left and Right accordingly>

    OldGuess = NewGuess;
end

%  <print a message if the error is still large and the iteration limit is
%  exceeded>
```

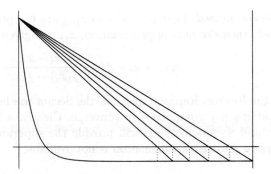

Figure 2.5   An example illustrating that the convergence of the method of false position can be lethargic.

EXERCISE 2.10

Modify your old bisection code to use the method of false position. Use the new code to find the root of $f(x) = x - \cos x = 0$, and compare the effort required, i.e., the number of iterations, to that of the bisection method.

The method of false position appears to be an obvious improvement over the bisection method, but there are some interesting situations in which that's not so. Consider the example in Figure 2.5. Although the root is bracketed, the bounds aren't close enough to the root to justify a linear approximation for the function. In this case, the method of false position might actually require *more* function evaluations than bisection.

We can rewrite Equation 2.42 as

$$\bar{x} = a - f(a)\frac{c - a}{f(c) - f(a)}, \tag{2.43}$$

which looks suspiciously like Newton-Raphson with the derivative approximated by

$$f'(a) \approx \frac{f(c) - f(a)}{c - a}. \tag{2.44}$$

Recall, however, that one of the endpoints will be fixed as we approach the root. That is, c might be fixed as a approaches the root. Then $c - a$ approaches a constant, but not zero. Although Equation 2.44 looks something like a derivative, this expression *does not* approach the actual derivative in the limit.

However, the successive iterative approximations do approach one another, so that *they* can be used to approximate the derivative. Using the previous two iterations for the root to approximate the derivative appearing in Newton's method gives us the *Secant method*. That is, if x_i and x_{i-1} are the previous two approximations to the root, then the next approximation, x_{i+1}, is given as

$$x_{i+1} = x_i - f(x_i)\, \frac{x_i - x_{i-1}}{f(x_i) - f(x_{i-1})}. \tag{2.45}$$

As with the Newton-Raphson method, the Secant method works very well when it works, but it's not guaranteed to converge. Clearly, a hybrid combination of the Bisection and Secant methods will provide the superior method for finding roots when explicit derivative information is not available.

EXERCISE 2.11

Replace Newton-Raphson by Secant in the Hybrid code, so that only function evaluations—no derivatives—are used to find the root of a function. Use this method to find a root of $f(x) = \sin x - x/2 = 0$ between $\pi/2$ and π.

• **2.9 Accelerating the Rate of Convergence**

For the exercises you've seen so far, and for many similar problems, the speed with which the computer finds a root is not really an issue: The time required to find a solution has all been in the development, writing, and debugging of the computer program, not in the actual calculation. But effort spent in developing good, reliable methods is spent only once—you're now learning how to find roots, and that effort shouldn't be duplicated in the future. In fact, you should regard your current effort as an investment for the future, to be paid off when you desperately need a solution to a particular problem, and realize you already have all the tools needed to obtain it.

In the "real world" we usually find that the problems that interest us become more complicated, and the functions get harder to evaluate. As a result, the time required to calculate a solution gets longer. Thus the efficiency of a root finder should be discussed in terms of the number of function evaluations required, not in the complexity of the root-finding algorithm. For example, perhaps the "function" whose zero you're trying to find is actually a multidimensional integral that requires an hour of supercomputer time to evaluate. Not having a supercomputer at your disposal, that's fifty hours on your local mainframe, or ten days on your microcomputer. Very quickly, you realize that life will pass you by if you can't find that root Real Soon Now! And a few extra multiplications to find that root, at microseconds each, don't add much to the total time involved.

Thus we want a root, and we want it with as few function, and/or derivative evaluations as possible. The key is to realize that we've been all too eager to discard expensive, hard-to-obtain information—let's see if we can't use some of those function evaluations that we've been throwing away. For concreteness, let's look at the Secant method a little more closely.

> The harder information is to obtain, the more reluctant we should be to discard it.

In the Hybrid Bisection/Secant method we've developed, a linear approximation is used to obtain the next approximation to the root, and then the endpoints of the interval are adjusted to keep the root bounded. By using three points, which we have, a quadratic could be fitted to the function. We would then have a quadratic approximation for the root rather than a linear one, and *with no additional function evaluations*. Sounds good.

Consider the points x_0, x_1, and x_2, and the function evaluated at these points. We can think of these as three successive approximations to the root of the function $f(x)$. The quadratic

$$p(x) = a(x - x_2)^2 + b(x - x_2) + c \tag{2.46}$$

will pass through these points if

$$c = f(x_2),$$
$$b = \frac{(x_0 - x_2)^2[f(x_1) - f(x_2)] - (x_1 - x_2)^2[f(x_0) - f(x_2)]}{(x_0 - x_1)(x_0 - x_2)(x_1 - x_2)},$$
$$a = \frac{(x_1 - x_2)[f(x_0) - f(x_2)] - (x_0 - x_2)[f(x_1) - f(x_2)]}{(x_0 - x_1)(x_0 - x_2)(x_1 - x_2)}. \tag{2.47}$$

The next approximation to the root, x_3, is then found by setting $p(x_3) = 0$ and solving the *quadratic* equation to find

$$x_3 - x_2 = \frac{-b \pm \sqrt{b^2 - 4ac}}{2a}. \tag{2.48}$$

We expect (or, at least, we hope) that we are converging to the root, so that $x_3 - x_2$ is small in magnitude. But according to Equation 2.48, this will only happen if $-b$ and $\pm\sqrt{b^2 - 4ac}$ are nearly equal in magnitude and opposite in sign. That is, the small magnitude will be achieved by taking the difference between two nearly equal numbers, not a very sound practice. Rather than evaluating the root by Equation 2.48, let's develop an alternate form that has better numerical characteristics.

Let's assume for the moment that $b \geq 0$—then the root will be associated with the plus sign in the expression, and we can rewrite Equation 2.48 as

$$x_3 - x_2 = \left(\frac{-b + \sqrt{b^2 - 4ac}}{2a}\right)\left(\frac{-b - \sqrt{b^2 - 4ac}}{-b - \sqrt{b^2 - 4ac}}\right)$$
$$= \frac{b^2 - (b^2 - 4ac)}{2a(-b - \sqrt{b^2 - 4ac})} = -\frac{2c}{b + \sqrt{b^2 - 4ac}}, \quad b \geq 0. \tag{2.49}$$

For $b < 0$, the same reasoning leads to

$$x_3 - x_2 = \left(\frac{-b - \sqrt{b^2 - 4ac}}{2a} \right) \left(\frac{-b + \sqrt{b^2 - 4ac}}{-b + \sqrt{b^2 - 4ac}} \right)$$

$$= \frac{b^2 - (b^2 - 4ac)}{2a(-b + \sqrt{b^2 - 4ac})} = \frac{2c}{-b + \sqrt{b^2 - 4ac}}, \quad b < 0. \qquad (2.50)$$

It should be fairly clear that the hybrid Bisection/Secant method can easily be modified to incorporate this quadratic approximation to find the root. The quadratic approximation itself is due to Müller; coupling it with the bisection method is due to Brent. The result is a robust, virtually failsafe method of finding roots using only function evaluations.

EXERCISE 2.12

Modify your code to include this accelerated method. Verify that it's functioning correctly by finding x such that

$$\cos x = x \sin x. \qquad (2.51)$$

Before leaving this section, let's see if we can't extract a little more information from our expression for the root. Differentiating (2.46), we find that

$$p'(x) = 2a(x - x_2) + b, \qquad (2.52)$$

so that

$$p'(x_2) = b. \qquad (2.53)$$

Near the root, we'll assume that the derivative is nonzero, while the function itself is small. That is, $b = p'(x_2) \neq 0$ while $c = p(x_2) \approx 0$. We can then write

$$x_3 - x_2 = -\frac{2c}{b + \sqrt{b^2 - 4ac}} = -\frac{2c}{b + b\sqrt{1 - 4ac/b^2}}, \quad b \geq 0, \qquad (2.54)$$

where $4ac/b^2$ is a small term. Making small argument expansions, we find

$$x_3 - x_2 \approx -\frac{2c}{b + b(1 - 2ac/b^2 + \cdots)} \approx -\frac{2c}{2b} \frac{1}{1 - ac/b^2}$$

$$\approx -\frac{c}{b}(1 + \frac{ac}{b^2} + \cdots) \approx -\frac{c}{b} - \frac{ac^2}{b^3}$$

$$= -\frac{f(x_2)}{f'(x_2)} - \frac{f''(x_2)f^2(x_2)}{2[f'(x_2)]^3}. \qquad (2.55)$$

The first term we recognize as just the Newton-Raphson expression—the second is a *correction term*, partially accounting for the nonlinearity of the actual function. That is, a quadratic contribution. (We could have arrived at this result by considering the next higher order in the Taylor series leading to the Newton-Raphson approximation to the root in the first place.) That is, using

$$f(x) \approx f(a) + (x-a)f'(a) + \frac{(x-a)^2}{2}f''(a) \qquad (2.56)$$

instead of Equation 2.19. The usual solution for the root would have been

$$x = a + \frac{-f'(a) \pm \sqrt{f'^2(a) - 2f(a)f''(a)}}{f''(a)}. \qquad (2.57)$$

The same considerations as previously made, with regard to calculating a small number as the difference between two larger ones, would lead to the exact expressions

$$x = a - \frac{2f(a)}{f'(a) + \sqrt{f'^2(a) - 2f(a)f''(a)}}, \quad f'(a) \geq 0 \qquad (2.58)$$

and

$$x = a - \frac{2f(a)}{f'(a) - \sqrt{f'^2(a) - 2f(a)f''(a)}}, \quad f'(a) < 0, \qquad (2.59)$$

which can be useful in their own right. Making the appropriate small argument expansions would lead to Equation 2.55.

Yet another way of arriving at this result is to simply use the usual Newton-Raphson result in Equation 2.56. That is, we know that

$$x - a \approx -f(a)/f'(a), \qquad (2.60)$$

so that

$$(x - a)^2 \approx f^2(a)/f'^2(a). \qquad (2.61)$$

Using this approximation, the equation $f(x) = 0$ becomes

$$f(a) + (x-a)f'(a) + \frac{f^2(a)}{2f'^2(a)}f''(a) = 0, \qquad (2.62)$$

a linear equation for $x - a$ with solution

$$x - a = -\frac{f(a)}{f'(a)} - \frac{f^2(a)f''(a)}{2f'^3(a)}, \qquad (2.63)$$

which is just Equation 2.55, again!

No matter how it is obtained, Equation 2.55 has an interesting geometrical interpretation. Rather than simply putting a straight line through $[x_2, f(x_2)]$, the line is drawn through a point that is moved up or down to compensate for the shape of the function, as seen in Figure 2.6. The line that's drawn is still linear, but the curvature of the function has been taken into account.

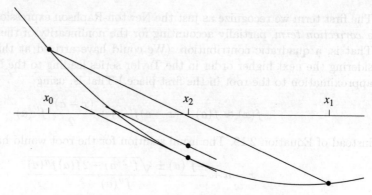

Figure 2.6   Accelerating the rate of convergence.

2.10 MATLAB's Root Finding Routines

As noted in the introduction to this chapter, MATLAB has it's own root-finding routines. For nonlinear functions,

```
fzero('exp(-x)-x', 0.4)
```

will find the zero of $f(x) = e^{-x} - x$ using the given initial value of 0.4. For a previously defined user function myF, the root could be found with

```
fzero('myF(x)', guess)
```

where **guess** is an initial estimate of the location of the root.

For polynomials, the native MATLAB command is roots(vector), where vector is a row vector containing the coefficients of the polynomial. That is, for

$$p(x) = x^4 - 53x^3 + 1026x^2 - 8568x + 25920,$$

the roots can be found with the command

```
roots([1 -53 1026 -8568 25920])
```

2.11 A Little Quantum Mechanics Problem

Our interest is not in numerical methods *per se*, but in investigating physical processes and solving physical problems. The only reason we've been looking at the roots of equations is because there are problems of interest to us that present themselves in this way. One such problem arises in quantum mechanics, and is routinely used for illustration in elementary textbooks: finding the eigenvalues of the finite square well.

Newton's equations of motion play a fundamental role in classical mechanics; in quantum mechanics, that role is played by the Schrödinger equation,

$$-\frac{\hbar^2}{2m}\frac{d^2\psi}{dx^2} + V(x)\psi(x) = E\psi(x).$$ (2.64)

This is the equation that determines "all there is to know" about the one dimensional problem of a particle of mass m moving in the potential $V(x)$. In this equation, $\hbar$ is a fundamental constant due to Planck, E is the total energy, and ψ is the *wavefunction* of the system. ψ is the unknown quantity that you're solving for, the "solution" to the Schrödinger equation. Once ψ is determined, all the observable quantities pertaining to the system can be calculated. In particular, $\psi^*\psi\,dx$ is the probability of finding the particle between x and $x + dx$.

Now here comes the hard part: it can happen that E is unknown as well! It would seem that there are too many unknowns in the Schrödinger equation for us to solve the problem, and that would be true except for certain physical constraints that we impose. Let's consider a specific example, the infinite square well (Figure 2.7).

In this case, the potential is zero between $-a$ and a, but infinite outside that region. The Schrödinger equation can be solved in the interior of the well with the general result that

$$\psi(x) = A\sin kx + B\cos kx,$$ (2.65)

where

$$k = \sqrt{\frac{2mE}{\hbar^2}}.$$ (2.66)

Outside the interval $-a \le x \le a$, the potential is infinite and so we shouldn't expect to find the particle there. If the particle can't be found there, then the wavefunction is zero in that region. Since we also expect that the probability of

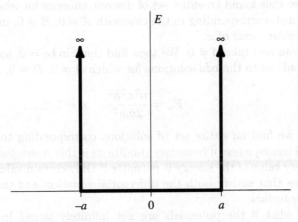

Figure 2.7   The infinite square well.

finding a particle is a continuous function, we require that the wavefunction vanishes at $\pm a$. That is, the *physics* of the problem *requires* that the wavefunction vanish at these points. We have thus established *boundary conditions* that must be satisfied by any mathematical solution in order to be physically correct.

Now we need to *impose* these boundary conditions upon the general solution. At $x = -a$, we *require* that

$$-A \sin ka + B \cos ka = 0, \tag{2.67}$$

while at $x = +a$, we require that

$$A \sin ka + B \cos ka = 0. \tag{2.68}$$

We now add and subtract these two equations to obtain

$$B \cos ka = 0 \tag{2.69}$$

and

$$A \sin ka = 0. \tag{2.70}$$

Consider the second equation, $A \sin ka = 0$. This can be accomplished in one of two ways: either A or $\sin ka$ is identically zero. Let's take $A = 0$. Then, if the wavefunction is to be at all interesting, $B \neq 0$. But $B \cos ka = 0$, and if $B \neq 0$, then we must have $\cos ka = 0$. The only way the cosine can vanish is if the argument is equal to $\pi/2, 3\pi/2, \ldots$. That is, we've found that the boundary condition can be met if

$$ka = \sqrt{\frac{2mE}{\hbar^2}} \, a = (n + 1/2)\pi, \quad n = 0, 1, \ldots \tag{2.71}$$

or

$$E_n = \frac{(n + 1/2)^2 \pi^2 \hbar^2}{2ma^2}, \quad n = 0, 1, \ldots \tag{2.72}$$

We have thus found an entire set of discrete energies for which the boundary condition is met, corresponding to the case with $A = 0$, $B \neq 0$, in which all the solutions are *even* functions of x.

We can also take $A \neq 0$. We then find that $\sin ka = 0$, so that $ka = 0, \pi, 2\pi, \ldots$. This leads us to the *odd* solutions for which $A \neq 0$, $B = 0$, and

$$E_n = \frac{n^2 \pi^2 \hbar^2}{2ma^2}, \quad n = 1, 2, \ldots \tag{2.73}$$

Again, we find an entire set of solutions corresponding to a particular parity. A general consequence of boundary conditions is this *restriction* to a set of solutions— not every value of the energy is permitted! Only certain values of the energy lead to solutions that satisfy both the differential equation *and* the boundary conditions: the *eigenvalues*.

But what if the potentials are not infinitely large? In the *finite square well* problem, we identify three different regions (see Figure 2.8).

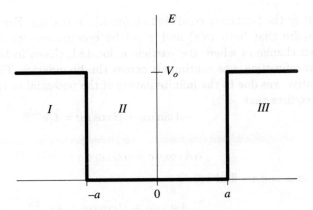

Figure 2.8   The finite square well.

We will only concern ourselves with states of the system that are localized, having energy less than V_o. In region I, the Schrödinger equation is

$$\frac{d^2\psi}{dx^2} - \frac{2m}{\hbar^2}(V_o - E)\psi = 0, \tag{2.74}$$

which has as a general solution

$$\psi_I(x) = Ce^{\beta x} + De^{-\beta x}, \quad \text{where } \beta = \sqrt{2m(V_o - E)}/\hbar^2. \tag{2.75}$$

We might be tempted to require both C and D to be zero so that the wavefunction would be zero and there would be no possibility of finding the particle in region I. *But this is inconsistent with experiment!* Sometimes, it's not easy being a physicist. One of the real surprises of quantum mechanics is that the wavefunction for a particle can be nonzero in places that classical mechanics would not allow the particle to be: region I is such a *classically forbidden* region. What we do find, however, is that the farther into the classically forbidden region we look, the less likely it is to find the particle. That is, the wavefunction must *decrease* as it goes into the barrier. (For the infinite square well, this decrease must occur immediately, i.e., there's a discontinuity in the derivative of the wavefunction.) The correct boundary condition is then that D must identically vanish, else the probability would *increase* as the forbidden region was penetrated, contrary to the above discussion.

In region II the general solution is

$$\psi_{II} = A \sin \alpha x + B \cos \alpha x, \quad \alpha = \sqrt{\frac{2mE}{\hbar^2}}, \tag{2.76}$$

while in region III it must be

$$\psi_{III} = Fe^{-\beta x} \tag{2.77}$$

to satisfy the boundary condition on forbidden regions. Furthermore, we are going to require that both $\psi(x)$ and $\psi'(x)$ be continuous—we don't expect to find a sudden change in where the particle is located. (Even in the infinite square well, the wavefunction was continuous across the boundaries. The discontinuity of the derivative was due to the infinite nature of the potential at that point.) At $x = -a$, this requires that

$$-A \sin \alpha a + B \cos \alpha a = C e^{-\beta a} \tag{2.78}$$

and

$$\alpha A \cos \alpha a + \alpha B \sin \alpha a = \beta C e^{-\beta a} \tag{2.79}$$

while at $x = a$ we find

$$A \sin \alpha a + B \cos \alpha a = F e^{-\beta a} \tag{2.80}$$

and

$$\alpha A \cos \alpha a - \alpha B \sin \alpha a = -\beta F e^{-\beta a}. \tag{2.81}$$

After some algebra, we again find two cases, according to the parity of the solution:

$$\text{Even States: } A = 0, \quad B \neq 0, \quad C = F, \quad \alpha \tan \alpha a = \beta. \tag{2.82}$$

$$\text{Odd States: } A \neq 0, \quad B = 0, \quad C = -F, \quad \alpha \cot \alpha a = -\beta. \tag{2.83}$$

This is the result most often displayed in textbooks. We see that the original problem of finding the energies and wavefunctions of the finite square well has evolved into the problem of finding the roots of a transcendental equation. And that's a problem we know how to solve!

2.12 Computing Strategy

When we're first presented with a substantial problem, such as this one, it is easy to become overwhelmed by its complexity. In the present case, the goal is to find the energies and wavefunctions of the finite square well, but we're not going to get there in one step. While we always want to remember where we're going, we need to break the original problem into several smaller chunks of a more manageable size, and solve them one at a time. This is the "modularization" we spoke of earlier, and we see a strong correlation between the process of solving the physical problem, and the writing of computer code that addresses a particular piece of the problem.

Our "main program" will initialize some variables, and then call one of the root-finding functions to actually find the root. It's in this main program that any issues of a global nature, issues that will pertain to the program as a whole, should be addressed. And in this project, we have such an issue: units.

In physics, we are accustomed to quantities such as mass having two attributes: their magnitude *and* their unit. Saying that a particle has mass 2 doesn't tell us much; 2 kilograms, or 2 metric tons? The computer, however, only knows magnitudes—it is up to the *computor* to keep the units straight. Sometimes this is easy, and sometimes not. In the current problem, we have attributes such as mass, distance, and energy to be considered. For macroscopic objects, expressing these attributes in kilograms, meters, and joules is natural, but these are extremely large units in which to express quantum mechanical entities. For example, the mass of the electron is about 9.11×10^{-31} kilograms—a perfectly good number, but rather small. It's best to use units that are natural to the problem at hand: for the square well problem, electron masses, nanometers, and eV's are an appropriate set to use. Using $\hbar = 6.5821220 \times 10^{-16}$ eV-sec, we can then write

$$\hbar^2 = 0.076199682 \, m_e \, \mathrm{eV \, nm}^2. \tag{2.84}$$

It's no accident that the numerical factor that appears here is roughly on the order of one—in fact, that's one of the reasons for this choice of units, which work nicely for this problem.

(This is certainly not the only reasonable choice to be made. In fact, for those who routinely work in atomic and molecular physics or in quantum chemistry, a quite different choice is often made: so called *atomic units*. In these units, the electron mass and $\hbar$ are both one. This makes the unit of length equal to the Bohr radius, $a_o = 5.2917720859 \times 10^{-2}$ nm, and the unit of energy the Hartree, $H = 27.2113845 \, \mathrm{eV}$. With this choice, virtually all the units "disappear" from the Schrödinger Equation, which definitely has its advantages.)

Let's imagine that we are to find the energy of the lowest state having even parity. Then we would rewrite Equation 2.82 as

$$f(E) = \alpha \tan \alpha a - \beta = 0, \tag{2.85}$$

$$\text{where} \quad \alpha = \sqrt{\frac{2mE}{\hbar^2}} \quad \text{and} \quad \beta = \sqrt{2m(V_o - E)/\hbar^2}. \tag{2.86}$$

Now, the root-finders we've developed expect—actually, they demand!—that the root be bracketed. At this point, we have no idea where to start looking for the root, except that the root must lie between zero and the top of the well. An exhaustive search, simply calculating the function at several energies, say every 0.1 eV up to 10 eV, could be conducted, but we would like to find the root with as few function evaluations as possible. A general strategy is to look for "special points" where the function has known forms. At $E = 0$, the function is easily evaluated as $f(0) = -\sqrt{2mV_o/\hbar^2}$. We also recognize that it goes to infinity as the argument of the tangent goes to $\pi/2$. In fact, the repetitive nature of the tangent function suggests to us that there might be several roots, one during each cycle of the function.

> Use analytic results to establish limiting cases.

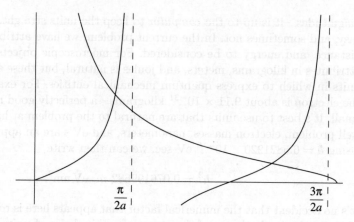

Figure 2.9   A plot of the functions $\tan \alpha a$ and β/α versus α.

In Figure 2.9, we've plotted $\tan \alpha a$ and β/α, for the case of $V_o = 10$ eV, $a = 0.3$ nm, and $m = 1\ m_e$. While $\tan \alpha a$ contains about 1.5 cycles in this range, β/α decreases from infinity at $\alpha = 0$ to zero at $\alpha = \sqrt{2mV_o/\hbar^2}$. The figure clearly indicates a root lying in the range $0 < E < \frac{\pi^2 \hbar^2}{8ma^2} \approx 1.045$ eV. (The one-dimensional square well *always* has a root, and hence at least one bound state always exists. This is *not* the case for three dimensions.)

> Simple plots can help us visualize what's going on.

We now have rigorously bracketed the root during each cycle of the tangent function, but we're not quite ready to start. The difficulty is that we never want the computer to actually evaluate an infinity—which is exactly what the computer will try to do if instructed to evaluate the tangent at $\alpha a = \pi/2$. We could set the upper bound at some slightly smaller value, say 0.999999 the upper limit of the energy. But if this value is too small, the root would not be bounded. Instead of trying to "patch the code" or to make it work, let's see if we can find the true origin of the difficulty.

When boundary conditions were imposed, we found that for even states

$$B \cos \alpha a = C e^{-\beta a} \qquad (2.87)$$

and

$$\alpha B \sin \alpha a = \beta C e^{-\beta a}. \qquad (2.88)$$

We then wrote this requirement as

$$\alpha \tan \alpha a = \beta, \qquad (2.89)$$

but it could just as easily have been written as

$$\beta \cos \alpha a = \alpha \sin \alpha a. \tag{2.90}$$

In fact, Equation 2.90 is just a statement of the matching condition, with common terms eliminated. To obtain Equation 2.89 from 2.90 we had to divide by $\cos ka$—our infinity problem originates here, when $ka = \pi$ and we're dividing by zero! We can totally avoid the infinity problem, and simultaneously improve the correspondence between computer code and the mathematical boundary conditions, by replacing the transcendental equations 2.82 and 2.83 by

$$\text{Even States: } A = 0, \quad B \neq 0, \quad C = F, \quad \beta \cos \alpha a = \alpha \sin \alpha a. \tag{2.91}$$

$$\text{Odd States: } A \neq 0, \quad B = 0, \quad C = -F, \quad \alpha \cos \alpha a = -\beta \sin \alpha a. \tag{2.92}$$

In analogy to Figure 2.9, we could now plot $\beta \cos \alpha a$ and $\alpha \sin \alpha a$ versus α. The curves would cross at exactly the same points as do β/α and $\tan \alpha a$, but would be preferable in the sense that they have no singularities in them. However, having the capability of the computer to plot for us creates many options. For instance, there's no longer any reason to be using α as the independent variable—while α is a convenient variable for humans, the computer would just as soon use the energy directly! This facilitates a more straightforward approach to the solution of the problem before us.

All we have left to do is to code the function itself. It's no accident that this is the last step in the process of developing a computer program to solve our physical problem—although clearly important to the overall goal, it's at the end of the logical chain, not the beginning. For the even parity solutions, the function might be coded something like this:

```
% plot_even
% plot a function for the even condition in a finite square well.

function plot_even
%
< plot the function even(x) >

function [F_even] = even(E)
% This FUNCTION evaluates the EVEN condition for the
% finite square well,
% F(E) = beta * cosine(alpha*a) - alpha * sine(alpha*a)
% for a well with DEPTH V0 and WIDTH 2A.
% Mass is expressed in electron masses.
% Energy is expressed in eV.
% Distance is expressed in nanometers.
%
% Specify constants:
a   = ?
V0  = ?
```

```
Mass = ?
h_bar_SQ = 0.076199682;
% Evaluate the function and return.
alpha = sqrt(2*Mass*E/h_bar_SQ);
beta  = sqrt(2*Mass*(VO-E)/h_bar_SQ);
F_even = beta*cos(alpha*a)-alpha*sin(alpha*a);
```

EXERCISE 2.13

Using $a = 0.3$ nm, $m = 1\ m_e$, and $V_o = 10$ eV, plot the function

$$f(E) = \beta \cos \alpha a - \alpha \sin \alpha a$$

as a function of energy.

All that's left is to solve the original problem!

EXERCISE 2.14

Find the lowest even and lowest odd solutions to the square well problem, with $a = 0.3$ nm, $m = 1\ m_e$, and $V_o = 10$ eV. Plot the potential, and the wavefunctions associated with these eigenvalues. (The convention is to align the zero baseline of the wavefunction with the energy eigenvalue.) Of course, you should augment your plot with appropriate labeling, a title, and so forth.

It's quite common in physics that the solution to one problem just leads to more questions. You've now found the lowest energies of the square well for a particular width parameter a, but doesn't that make you wonder how the energies would *change* with a? Or with V_o?

EXERCISE 2.15

Investigate the dependence of the lowest two eigenvalues (energies) of the square well upon V_o (with a fixed at 0.3 nm) and a (with V_o fixed at 10 eV), and plot your results. What is the smallest width that will support two bound states?

And what would happen if you had not one square well, but two? Of course, you would need to develop different solutions than the ones used here, with five regions of interest instead of three, but the process would be the same. Clearly, however, the algebra would become tedious and error-prone. This is unfortunate, as the double square well (Figure 2.10) exhibits some interesting behavior, not seen in the single square well problem. How do the lowest energies of even and odd parity change as the distance between the wells change? What do the eigenfunctions look like?

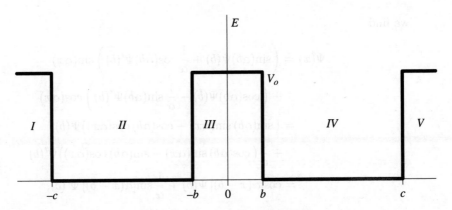

Figure 2.10   The double square well.

From physical reasoning, how must the lowest eigenvalues and their wavefunctions behave in the limit that the distance between the wells vanishes?

2.13 The Propagator Method

Before addressing the double square well problem, let's develop an alternate approach to the single well problem, based on the concept of a *propagator*. First, let's revisit the single well.

Let's assume that we have the solution $\Psi(b)$ and its derivative $\Psi'(b)$ at the left side of the well, $x = b$. The region between b and c is a classically allowed region, so in this region the solution is just

$$\Psi = A\sin(\alpha x) + B\cos(\alpha x) \tag{2.93}$$

and hence

$$\Psi' = A\alpha\cos(\alpha x) - B\alpha\sin(\alpha x). \tag{2.94}$$

Requiring this solution to match the known values of Ψ and Ψ' at b yields two equations that we can solve for the unknown values of A and B:

$$A = \sin(\alpha b)\Psi(b) + \frac{1}{\alpha}\cos(\alpha b)\Psi'(b),$$

$$B = \cos(\alpha b)\Psi(b) - \frac{1}{\alpha}\sin(\alpha b)\Psi'(b). \tag{2.95}$$

This doesn't look particularly appealing, and it's going to get worse before it gets better! Substituting these expressions for A and B into Equation 2.93 for $\Psi(x)$, we find

$$\Psi(x) = \left(\sin(\alpha b)\Psi(b) + \frac{1}{\alpha}\cos(\alpha b)\Psi'(b) \right) \sin(\alpha x)$$

$$+ \left(\cos(\alpha b)\Psi(b) - \frac{1}{\alpha}\sin(\alpha b)\Psi'(b) \right) \cos(\alpha x)$$

$$= \left(\sin(\alpha b)\sin(\alpha x) + \cos(\alpha b)\cos(\alpha x) \right)\Psi(b)$$

$$+ \frac{1}{\alpha}\left(\cos(\alpha b)\sin(\alpha x) - \sin(\alpha b)\cos(\alpha x) \right)\Psi'(b)$$

$$= \cos[\alpha(x - b)]\,\Psi(b) + \frac{1}{\alpha}\sin[\alpha(x - b)]\,\Psi'(b), \qquad (2.96)$$

and for the derivative we find

$$\Psi'(x) = -\alpha\sin[\alpha(x - b)]\,\Psi(b) + \cos[\alpha(x - b)]\,\Psi'(b). \qquad (2.97)$$

This is certainly simpler than what we had, but it takes on even greater elegance when we write it in matrix form,

$$\begin{bmatrix} \Psi(x) \\ \Psi'(x) \end{bmatrix} = \begin{bmatrix} \cos[\alpha(x - b)] & \frac{1}{\alpha}\sin[\alpha(x - b)] \\ -\alpha\sin[\alpha(x - b)] & \cos[\alpha(x - b)] \end{bmatrix} \begin{bmatrix} \Psi(b) \\ \Psi'(b) \end{bmatrix}$$

$$= P_{allowed} \begin{bmatrix} \Psi(b) \\ \Psi'(b) \end{bmatrix}, \qquad (2.98)$$

where

$$P_{allowed} = \begin{bmatrix} \cos[\alpha(x - b)] & \frac{1}{\alpha}\sin[\alpha(x - b)] \\ -\alpha\sin[\alpha(x - b)] & \cos[\alpha(x - b)] \end{bmatrix}. \qquad (2.99)$$

It's in this form that we see the matrix "propagating" the solution from b to x. That is, the "solution" (both Ψ and Ψ') is "propagated," or carried forward, from b to x by this matrix multiplication. It's also noteworthy that the propagation matrix depends only upon the distance $x - b$, and not on x or b themselves.

At this point, we're ready to solve our problem. There are several different ways we could proceed; for example, we could place the potential symmetrically about the origin, thus taking full advantage of the symmetry of the problem. We would then propagate the solution from $-\infty$ up to 0 and require that $\Psi'(0) = 0$ for the even states, and $\Psi(0) = 0$ for the odd states. A problem's symmetry can often be used in this way to simplify the solution, but it isn't *necessary*. We'll demonstrate this by developing a method that doesn't utilize the symmetry of the problem—but in so doing our solutions will no longer naturally fall into an even/odd category.

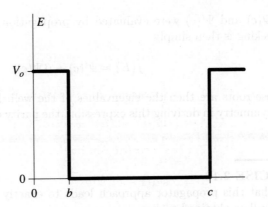

Figure 2.11   Another single well.

Let's begin in the region left of the well in Figure 2.11, $x < b$. In this region we know that the solution must be

$$\Psi(x) = Ge^{\beta x} \qquad (2.100)$$

so that

$$\Psi'(x) = G\beta e^{\beta x}. \qquad (2.101)$$

The overall normalization isn't important; what *is* important is the relationship between Ψ and Ψ', namely that

$$\Psi'(x) = \beta\,\Psi(x), \qquad x < b. \qquad (2.102)$$

From continuity, this must be true at $x = b$ as well. Computationally, we can choose any nonzero value for Ψ—let's choose $\Psi(b) = 1$, and Equation 2.102 gives $\Psi'(b) = \beta$. We then propagate the solution (and its derivative) from b to c, using the free propagator of Equation 2.98.

For $x > c$, we know the solution is exponentially decaying,

$$\Psi(x) = Ge^{-\beta x}, \qquad (2.103)$$

so that

$$\Psi'(x) = -G\beta e^{-\beta x} \qquad (2.104)$$

and

$$\Psi'(x) = -\beta\,\Psi(x), \qquad x > c. \qquad (2.105)$$

The matching condition at $x = c$ that the acceptable wavefunction must satisfy is then

$$\Psi'(c) = -\beta\,\Psi(c) \qquad (2.106)$$

where $\Psi(c)$ and $\Psi'(c)$ were evaluated by propagation. The function whose roots we're seeking is then simply

$$f(E) = \Psi'(c) + \beta\,\Psi(c), \tag{2.107}$$

and those roots are then the eigenvalues of the well. Note that since we did not invoke symmetry in deriving this expression, the parity of the solution doesn't enter in.

EXERCISE 2.16
Verify that this propagator approach leads to exactly the same solutions for the square well as obtained earlier.

2.14 The Double Well

Now consider a system composed of two wells, separated by some distance, as in Figure 2.12. If this distance is large, then the wells are isolated and the allowed energies of the system are the same as for a single well. But if the distance is not too large the wavefunction of one well can penetrate the barrier into the other well, so that the two wells interact. A major advantage of the propagator approach is that it is easily applied to this case, with virtually no increase in difficulty, while the "matching boundary conditions" approach leads to greater and greater complexity. (Note, of course, that these two approaches are actually the same, it's just that the algebra has been rearranged to *appear* less complicated.)

We already know how to propagate the solution in the allowed region. The appropriate propagator for the forbidden region can be derived in exactly the same manner.

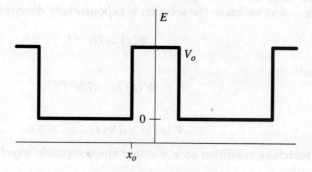

Figure 2.12   A double well.

EXERCISE 2.17

Show that the propagator for the forbidden region is

$$P_{forbidden} = \begin{bmatrix} \cosh[\beta(x - x_o)] & \frac{1}{\beta}\sinh[\beta(x - x_o)] \\ \beta\sinh[\beta(x - x_o)] & \cosh[\beta(x - x_o)] \end{bmatrix}. \qquad (2.108)$$

The procedure for propagating the wavefunction should be clear: as before, start in the forbidden region to the left of all wells. If the wells are identical, we can use the symmetry of the problem to cut the work somewhat. With the propagator for the allowed region, find the wavefunction (and its derivative) across the first well, and then propagate with the forbidden region propagator to the origin, where the parity of the wavefunction is used to determine if the wavefunction or its derivative should be zero. If the wells are not identical, propagate through the allowed region, all the way through the forbidden region, and then through the second allowed region, matching up with the known behavior at the right side of the second well.

EXERCISE 2.18

Solve for all the energies of the double well, with $V_o = 10\,\text{eV}$ and the well width, W, being 0.6 nm as before. (Our earlier a was half the well width.) Let the separation between the wells, S, be 0.2 nm. Then vary the distance between the wells, and plot the lowest two energies of the system versus separation distance.

● **2.15 A One-Dimensional Crystal**

As we add more wells to our problem, as indicated in Figure 2.13, we are in fact developing a one-dimensional model of a crystal. Imagine that we're interested in a model having N identical wells of width W, separated by the same barrier width S.

Starting at the far left, we have a sequence of a well followed by a barrier, repeated N times. The solution can be propagated through this system of wells

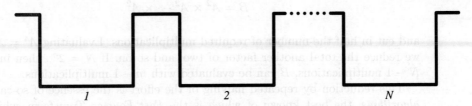

Figure 2.13   The N-square well potential.

and barriers, and finally matched with the exponentially decaying solution at the far right. Alternatively, we could place the origin at the geometric center, integrate up to the origin, and apply parity restrictions to determine the eigenvalues.

The only remaining difficulty lies with the "global" search strategy. The energy levels of the single well are separated by many eV, so that a 0.1 eV search region was sufficiently small. But with the multiple well system, we're seeing a splitting of the energy levels, and this splitting is much smaller than the difference between the basic energy levels. For the double well, this splitting was on the order of 0.1 eV— since the two states were of opposite parity, we didn't have a problem. But with the many well system, we might. To be "safe," let's choose the search increment to be $0.1/N$, for a system of N wells.

EXERCISE 2.19

Modify your code to treat this many well problem. Use your program to investigate the energy structure of the model crystal with increasing N. What can you say about the limit as $N \to \infty$?

2.16 A Note on *Fast* Algorithms

When investigating an N well problem, it would seem that we would need to perform (on the order of) N matrix multiplications. But this is not the case. In fact, to multiply N identical matrices, all we need is (on the order of) $\ln(N)$ multiplications! (In this discussion, we take the matrix A to be the propagator from the left of one well to the left of the next well, e.g., the product of the propagators for allowed and forbidden regions.)

Consider the expression

$$B = A \times A \times A \ldots A \times A.$$

By evaluating $A^2 = A \times A$, we can evaluate B as

$$B = A^2 \times A^2 \cdots \times A^2$$

and cut in half the number of required multiplications. Evaluating $A^4 = A^2 \times A^2$, we reduce the total another factor of two, and so on. If $N = 2^m$, then instead of $N - 1$ multiplications, B can be evaluated with $m - 1$ multiplications.

This reduction by repeated halving of the effort is the essence of so-called *fast algorithms*, the best known of which is the *Fast Fourier Transform*, which we'll investigate later.

2.17 Impurities

The propagator approach allows us to investigate the role of impurities in the crystal lattice. That is, what happens if the wells are not all identical? In particular, what if one well is substantially different from the others?

In this situation, the potential is not symmetric and as a result the wavefunctions are not of definite parity. Thus the wavefunction must be propagated through all the wells, and matched to the exponentially decaying solution in the forbidden region at the far right. The condition to be met is then

$$\frac{\Psi_{propagated}(E)}{\Psi'_{propagated}(E)} = -\beta, \tag{2.109}$$

where $\Psi_{propagated}(E)$ and $\Psi'_{propagated}(E)$ are the results of the numerical propagation of the wavefunction through all the wells. The function of interest, whose roots are then the eigenvalues, can be written as

$$f(E) = \Psi_{propagated}(E) + \beta * \Psi'_{propagated}(E). \tag{2.110}$$

Since the energy differences between these states will become increasingly smaller as N increases, considerable care should be exercised in finding these eigenvalues.

EXERCISE 2.20

Add an "impurity" to your N-well model. What happens to the energies of the crystal as the depth of this well is changed?

This exercise is far from "academic." In the real world, corundum is a crystal of aluminum oxide, Al_2O_3. It's very hard, 9.0 on the Mohs scale of mineral hardness, and is used as an industrial abrasive and on sandpaper. But if a small fraction of the aluminum ions are replaced by chromium, the result is the gemstone ruby. Furthermore, the electronic structure, e.g., the location of the energy levels, is such that ruby was used to make the first laser. (The lasing transition is between an excited state and the ground state of the chromium ion.)

2.18 The Kronig-Penney Model

A slightly different model of a crystal is obtained by applying *periodic boundary conditions* to the sequence of wells. Instead of the sequence being linear, think of "the wells" as being in a ring so that the "last" one is next to the "first" one. (See Figure 2.14.)

Rather than propagating the solution through the entire periodic array, we need only consider the propagation through one lattice cell, i.e., through one well and

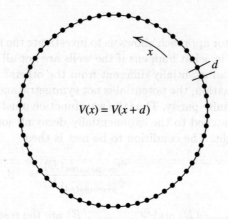

Figure 2.14 N-square well potentials arranged in a ring.

one barrier. For these propagations, we can use our known propagators,

$$P_{allowed} = \begin{bmatrix} \cos \alpha W & \dfrac{1}{\alpha} \sin \alpha W \\ -\alpha \sin \alpha W & \cos \alpha W \end{bmatrix}, \tag{2.111}$$

$$P_{forbidden} = \begin{bmatrix} \cosh \beta S & \dfrac{1}{\beta} \sinh \beta S \\ \beta \sinh \beta S & \cosh \beta S \end{bmatrix}, \tag{2.112}$$

where we've denoted the width of the well as W and the width of the barrier as S. Then at $d = W + S$, one cell width,

$$\begin{bmatrix} \Psi(d) \\ \Psi'(d) \end{bmatrix} = \begin{bmatrix} \cosh \beta S & \dfrac{1}{\beta} \sinh \beta S \\ \beta \sinh \beta S & \cosh \beta S \end{bmatrix} \begin{bmatrix} \cos \alpha W & \dfrac{1}{\alpha} \sin \alpha W \\ -\alpha \sin \alpha W & \cos \alpha W \end{bmatrix} \begin{bmatrix} \Psi(0) \\ \Psi'(0) \end{bmatrix}$$

$$= \begin{bmatrix} \cosh \beta S \cos \alpha W - \dfrac{\alpha}{\beta} \sinh \beta S \sin \alpha W & \dfrac{1}{\alpha} \cosh \beta S \sin \alpha W + \dfrac{1}{\beta} \sinh \beta S \cos \alpha W \\ \beta \sinh \beta S \cos \alpha W - \alpha \cosh \beta S \sin \alpha W & \dfrac{\beta}{\alpha} \sinh \beta S \sin \alpha W + \cosh \beta S \cos \alpha W \end{bmatrix}$$

$$\times \begin{bmatrix} \Psi(0) \\ \Psi'(0) \end{bmatrix}. \tag{2.113}$$

For potentials that are periodic, the wavefunction must reflect that periodicity. The matching condition at the cell boundary is that the wavefunction is the same, except for a phase factor, as at the previous cell boundary. That is,

$$\Psi(x + d) = e^{ikd}\Psi(x), \tag{2.114}$$

where d is the size of the cell and k is the *reciprocal lattice vector*. Then we also have

$$\Psi(x + Nd) = e^{iNkd}\Psi(x), \tag{2.115}$$

so that $e^{iNkd} = 1$. Thus

$$k = \frac{2\pi n}{Nd}, \qquad n = 0, \pm 1, \dots, \pm N. \tag{2.116}$$

Using this condition, along with the usual matching condition between the allowed and forbidden regions, we find that the requirement is that

$$\cosh \beta S \cos \alpha W + \frac{\beta^2 - \alpha^2}{2\alpha\beta} \sinh \beta S \sin \alpha W = \cos kd. \tag{2.117}$$

EXERCISE 2.21
Verify that the matching conditions do indeed lead to Equation 2.117. (Recall that if $\mathbf{A}$ is a matrix and $\mathbf{x}$ a vector, the equation $\mathbf{Ax} = 0$ has a non-trivial solution if and only if $\det \mathbf{A} = 0$.)

Consider the RHS of Equation 2.117. For a particular value of n, for an N-well model, the cosine is a constant between -1 and 1, and the equation can be solved to find the energy at which the LHS is equal to this constant, e.g., the curves cross. This is the situation depicted in Figure 2.15, in which $\cos kd = 0.6$.

Clearly, there are a discrete number of curve crossings, and hence a discrete number of allowed energies. However, we need to solve the problem again, with a different value of n, which will give us a new set of energies. As N increases, as we consider a larger and hence more realistic model of the crystal, the difference between the energies becomes infinitesimal, and the discrete set of energies becomes a continuum, as depicted in Figure 2.16. The regions having allowed energies are the energy bands. But not all energies are possible, since the LHS of Equation 2.117 is outside the limits of the cosine, leading to the band gaps between the energy bands.

EXERCISE 2.22
Determine where the edge of the energy bands are for our sequence of wells, separated by a distance $S = 0.04\,\text{nm}$. That is, solve Equation 2.117 with $\cos kd = \pm 1$. How do the energy bands change if V_o is increased? If W is increased? If S is increased?

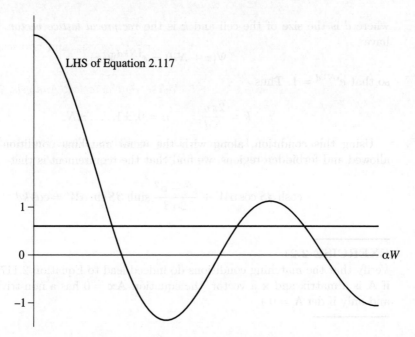

Figure 2.15   The left and right sides of Equation 2.117, plotted versus αW. ($V_o = 10\,\text{eV}$, $W = 0.6\,\text{nm}$, and $S = 0.04\,\text{nm}$.)

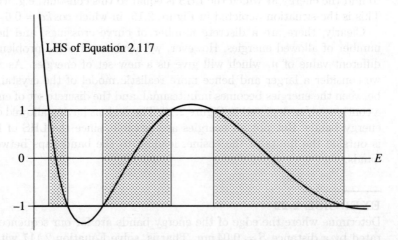

Figure 2.16   The left and right sides of Equation 2.117, plotted versus E. The shaded areas are the allowed energy bands, separated by the band gaps. Plotting versus E has the effect of "stretching" the curve, compared to Figure 2.15. As a result, the energy bands increase in width as the energy increases.

2.19 References

Root finding is a standard topic of numerical analysis, and is discussed in many such texts, including

Anthony Ralston, *A First Course in Numerical Analysis*, McGraw–Hill, New York, 1965.

Richard L. Burden and J. Douglas Faires, *Numerical Analysis*, Prindle, Weber, & Schmidt, Boston, 1985.

Curtis F. Gerald and Patrick O. Wheatley, *Applied Numerical Analysis*, Addison–Wesley, Reading, 1989.

Although somewhat dated, the following text is particularly commendable with regard to the author's philosophy of computation,

Forman S. Acton, *Numerical Methods That Work*, Harper & Row, New York, 1970.

The modifications of Brent and Müller are discussed in

J. Stoer and R. Bulirsch, *Introduction to Numerical Analysis*, Springer–Verlag, New York, 1980.

The Kronig-Penney model is discussed in many undergraduate quantum mechanics texts. The definitive advanced reference is

Charles Kittel, *Introduction to Solid State Physics, Seventh Edition*, John Wiley & Sons, Inc., New York, 1996.

3

Interpolation and Approximation

In the last chapter, we noted that an *approximation* to a function was useful in finding its root, even though we had the exact function at our disposal. Perhaps a more common circumstance is that we don't know the exact function, but build our knowledge of it as we acquire more information about it, one point at a time. In either case, it's important for us to incorporate the information we have into an approximation that is useful to us. Presumably, as we gather more information, the better our approximation becomes.

In this chapter, several ways to approximate a function and its derivatives are investigated. With *interpolation*, an approximating polynomial is found that exactly describes the function being approximated at a set of specified points. Lagrange and Hermite interpolation are discussed, and the use of cubic splines is developed. Application of Taylor's series methods to the evaluation of derivatives is also discussed, as is the important technique of Richardson extrapolation. *Curve fitting*, which approximates a function in a general sense, without being constrained to agree with the function at every point, is discussed—the method of least squares is developed in this regard. Along the way, a need to solve sets of linear equations is encountered and so a method to solve them is developed. In passing, we note that functions can be expressed in terms of other functions, and that sets of orthogonal functions are particularly convenient in this regard. Finally, the method of least squares fitting using non-polynomial functions is developed, leading us to consider minimization methods in multiple dimensions.

3.1 Lagrange Interpolation

While Taylor's series can be used to approximate a function at x if the function and its derivatives are known at some point, a method due to Lagrange can be used to approximate a function if only the function is known, although it must be known at several points. We can derive *Lagrange's interpolating polynomial* $p(x)$ from a

Taylor's series by expressing the function at x_1 and x_2 in terms of the function and its derivatives at x,

$$f(x_1) = f(x) + (x_1 - x)f'(x) + \cdots ,$$
$$f(x_2) = f(x) + (x_2 - x)f'(x) + \cdots . \qquad (3.1)$$

We would like to truncate the series and retain only the first two terms. But in so doing, the *equality* would be compromised. However, we can introduce *approximations* to the function and its derivative such that an equality is retained. That is, we introduce the new function $p(x)$ and its derivative such that

$$f(x_1) = p(x) + (x_1 - x)p'(x)$$

and

$$f(x_2) = p(x) + (x_2 - x)p'(x). \qquad (3.2)$$

Clearly, $p(x)$ is equal to $f(x)$ at x_1 and x_2, and is perhaps a reasonable approximation in their vicinity. We then have two equations in the two unknowns $p(x)$ and $p'(x)$; solving for $p(x)$, we find

$$p(x) = \frac{x - x_2}{x_1 - x_2} f(x_1) + \frac{x - x_1}{x_2 - x_1} f(x_2), \qquad (3.3)$$

a linear function in x. This is nothing more than the equation of the line passing through the points $[x_1, f(x_1)]$ and $[x_2, f(x_2)]$, and could have been found by other means. In fact, we used this equation in Chapter 2 in developing the method of false position.

But the *form* of Equation 3.3 is very convenient, and interesting. For example, it says that the contribution of $f(x_2)$ to the approximation is weighted by a given factor, $(x - x_1)/(x_2 - x_1)$, which depends upon the distance x is away from x_1. As x varies between x_1 and x_2, this factor increases (linearly) from 0 to 1, so that the importance of $f(x_2)$ to the approximation varies from "irrelevant" to "sole contributor." At the same time, the factor multiplying $f(x_1)$ behaves in a complementary way, decreasing linearly as x varies between x_1 to x_2.

A higher-order approximation can easily be obtained by retaining more terms in the series expansion. Of course, if another term is retained, the function must be known at an additional point as well. For example, the three equations

$$f(x_1) = f(x) + (x_1 - x)f'(x) + \frac{(x_1 - x)^2}{2} f''(x) + \cdots ,$$

$$f(x_2) = f(x) + (x_2 - x)f'(x) + \frac{(x_2 - x)^2}{2} f''(x) + \cdots ,$$

$$f(x_3) = f(x) + (x_3 - x)f'(x) + \frac{(x_3 - x)^2}{2} f''(x) + \cdots . \qquad (3.4)$$

can be truncated, the functions replaced by their approximations, and the equations solved to yield the quadratic interpolating polynomial

$$p(x) = \frac{(x - x_2)(x - x_3)}{(x_1 - x_2)(x_1 - x_3)} f(x_1) + \frac{(x - x_1)(x - x_3)}{(x_2 - x_1)(x_2 - x_3)} f(x_2)$$

$$+ \frac{(x - x_1)(x - x_2)}{(x_3 - x_1)(x_3 - x_2)} f(x_3). \tag{3.5}$$

Again, we see that $p(x_j) = f(x_j)$. Earlier, we obtained $p(x)$ by writing $p(x) = ax^2 + bx + c$ and determining a, b, and c by requiring that the approximation be equal to the function at three points. Since there is one and only one quadratic function passing through any three points, the interpolating polynomial of Equation 3.5 must be identical to the one we found earlier, although it certainly doesn't look the same.

Equations 3.3 and 3.5 suggest that a general interpolating polynomial of order $(N - 1)$ might be written as

$$p(x) = \sum_{j=1}^{N} l_{j,N}(x) f(x_j), \tag{3.6}$$

where the function $f(x)$ is known at the N points x_j and

$$l_{j,N}(x) = \frac{(x - x_1)(x - x_2) \cdots (x - x_{j-1})(x - x_{j+1}) \cdots (x - x_N)}{(x_j - x_1)(x_j - x_2) \cdots (x_j - x_{j-1})(x_j - x_{j+1}) \cdots (x_j - x_N)} \tag{3.7}$$

is the coefficient of $f(x_j)$. Note that

$$l_{j,N}(x_i) = \begin{cases} 1, & i = j, \\ 0, & i \neq j \end{cases}$$

a relation that is compactly expressed in terms of the Kronecker delta,

$$l_{j,N}(x_i) = \delta_{i,j}. \tag{3.8}$$

This approximation to $f(x)$ is known as the Lagrange interpolating polynomial. It can be extended to more points—later we will argue that this is not a good practice, however.

Once upon a time—before the widespread availability of computers—interpolation was an extremely important topic. Values of special functions of interest to mathematical physics, such as Bessel functions, were laboriously calculated and entered into tables. When a particular value of the function was desired, interpolation was used on the tabulated values. Sophisticated, specialized methods were developed to perform interpolation of tabular data in an accurate and efficient manner.

Today, it is more likely to have a function evaluated as needed, rather than interpolated, so that the importance of interpolation with respect to tabular data is somewhat diminished. But the topic of interpolation is still important, because sometimes the data is simply not available at the points of interest. Certainly, this often happens with experimental data. (Depending upon the circumstances, there might be more appropriate ways to analyze experimental data, however.) Interpolation also provides a theoretical basis for the discussion of other topics, such as differentiation and integration.

3.2 The Airy Pattern

When light enters a telescope, only that which falls upon the lens (or mirror) is available to the astronomer. The situation is equivalent to an infinitely large screen, with a circular hole the size of the lens (or mirror) cut in it. And we all know that when light passes through an aperture like that, it suffers diffraction. For a circular aperture, the resulting pattern of light and dark rings is known as the Airy pattern, named after Sir George Airy, the Astronomer Royal, who first described it in 1835. This diffraction distorts the image of even a point source of light, although this distortion is usually small compared to other sources of distortion. Only in the best of telescopes have these other sources been eliminated to the point that the quality of the image is *diffraction limited*. In this instance, the intensity of the light is described by the function

$$I = I_o \left[\frac{2 J_1(\rho)}{\rho} \right]^2, \tag{3.9}$$

where I_o is intensity of the incident light and $J_1(\rho)$ is the Bessel function of order 1. (The center of the image is at $\rho = 0$.) The Bessel function has many interesting characteristics, and is often studied in mathematical physics courses and discussed at length in textbooks. A few values of the Bessel function are listed in Table 3.1.

EXERCISE 3.1

Using pencil and paper, estimate $J_1(5.5)$ by linear, quadratic, and cubic interpolation.

You probably found the computations in Exercise 3.1 to be tedious—certainly, they are for high-order approximations. One of the advantages of the Lagrange

Table 3.1   Bessel Functions

ρ	$J_0(\rho)$	$J_1(\rho)$	$J_2(\rho)$
0.0	1.00000 00000	0.00000 00000	0.00000 00000
1.0	0.76519 76866	0.44005 05857	0.11490 34849
2.0	0.22389 07791	0.57672 48078	0.35283 40286
3.0	−0.26005 19549	0.33905 89585	0.48609 12606
4.0	−0.39714 98099	−0.06604 33280	0.36412 81459
5.0	−0.17759 67713	−0.32757 91376	0.04656 51163
6.0	0.15064 52573	−0.27668 38581	−0.24287 32100
7.0	0.30007 92705	−0.00468 28235	−0.30141 72201
8.0	0.17165 08071	0.23463 63469	−0.11299 17204
9.0	−0.09033 36112	0.24531 17866	0.14484 73415
10.0	−0.24593 57645	0.04347 27462	0.25463 03137

approach is that its coding is very straightforward. The crucial fragment of the code, corresponding to Equations 3.3 and 3.5, might look like

```
% lagrange.m
% Code fragment for Lagrange interpolation using N points.
% The approximation P is required at xx, using the tabulated
% values x(j) and f(j).
%
y = 0.0;
for j = 1:N
    % Evaluate the j-th coefficient
    Lj = 1.0;
    for k = 1:N
        if(j ~= k)
            Lj = Lj * (xx-x(k) )/( x(j)-x(k) );
        end
    end
    % Add contribution of j-th term to the polynomial
    y = y + Lj * f(j);
    ...
```

We should point out that products need to be initialized to 1, just as sums need to be initialized to 0. This fragment has one major flaw—what happens if any two of the x_i are the same? While this doesn't happen in the present example, it's a possibility that should be addressed in a general interpolation program.

In the previous exercise, which ρ values did you use in your linear interpolation? Nothing we've said so far would prevent you from having used $\rho = 0$ and 1, but you probably used $\rho = 5$ and 6, didn't you? You know that at $\rho = 5$ the approximating function is exact. As you move away from 5, you would expect there to be

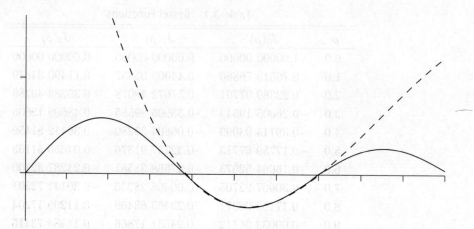

Figure 3.1   The Bessel function $J_1(\rho)$ and the cubic Lagrange polynomial approximation to it, using the tabular data at $\rho = 4, 5, 6,$ and 7.

a difference between the exact function and the approximation, but this difference (i.e., error) must become zero at $\rho = 6$. So if you use tabulated values at points that surround the point of interest, the error will be kept to a minimum.

The converse is particularly illuminating. Using the interpolating polynomial to *extrapolate* to the region exterior to the points sampled can lead to disastrous results, as seen in Figure 3.1. Here the cubic interpolation formula derived from sampling ρ at 4, 5, 6, and 7 is plotted versus the true $J_1(\rho)$. Between 5 and 6, and even between 4 and 7, the approximation is very good. But there's only so much flexibility in a cubic function, and so the interpolating polynomial must eventually fail as we use it outside that region. An extreme example is in fitting a periodic function, such as a cosine, with a polynomial. An N-th degree polynomial only has $(N-1)$ extrema, and so cannot possibly follow the infinite oscillations of a periodic function.

One would think that by increasing the order of the polynomial, we could improve the fit. And to some extent, we can. Over some specific region, say $5 \le \rho \le 6$, a cubic fit will almost surely be better than a linear one. But as we consider higher-order approximations, we see less of an improvement. The reason, of course, is that the higher-order polynomials require more points in their determination. These points are *farther* from the region of interest, and so do little to enhance the quality of the approximation.

And there is another factor, particularly for evenly-spaced data—a high-order interpolating polynomial necessarily has "a lot of wiggle in it," even if it doesn't belong! For example, consider the function

$$f(x) = \frac{1 + \tanh 2\alpha x}{2}.$$ (3.10)

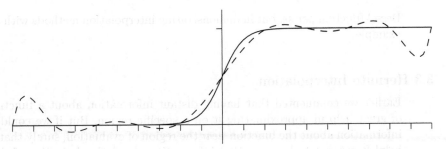

Figure 3.2   An example of the failure of a high-order interpolating polynomial.

This function has some interesting characteristics. As $\alpha \to \infty$, $f(x)$ becomes zero for $x < 0$ and unity for $x > 0$. That is, it tends toward the Heaviside step function! For $\alpha = 5$, $f(x)$ is plotted in Figure 3.2 on the interval $-1 \le x \le 1$. The curve is smooth and well-behaved, although it does possess a "kink" at $x = 0$—one that tends toward a discontinuity as $\alpha \to \infty$. We've also plotted the Lagrange interpolating polynomial obtained from using 11 evenly-spaced points in this interval. Clearly, the approximation is failing, particularly at the ends of the interval.

EXERCISE 3.2
Use a 21-point interpolating polynomial to approximate the function in Equation 3.10. Plot the approximation and the function on the interval $-1 \le x \le 1$, as in Figure 3.2. Does the higher-order approximation help?

Experience suggests that the high-order approximations aren't very useful. Generally speaking, a cubic approximation, with the points chosen so as to surround the desired point of evaluation, usually works pretty well. In developing an appropriate computer routine, you need to develop an "automatic" way of surrounding the point, and make a special provision for the two ends of the table.

EXERCISE 3.3
Using the `function` as described above to interpolate on the table of Bessel functions, write a computer program to evaluate the relative intensity I/I_o as a function of ρ across the Airy diffraction pattern, and plot it. To generate a "pleasing" display, you should evaluate the intensity at 0.1 increments in ρ.

Since the Bessel function plays a prominent role in several areas of physics, MATLAB has included it in the special functions it has built in, such as the factorial function we've encountered earlier. Clearly, our interest is not in evaluating the

Bessel function *per se*, but in demonstrating interpolation methods with a nontrivial example.

3.3 Hermite Interpolation

Earlier we commented that having distant information about a function was not of great help in approximating it on a specific region. But if we could have more information about the function *near* the region of evaluation, surely that must be of help! It sometimes happens that information about the derivative of the function, as well as the function itself, is available to us. If it is available, then we should certainly use it!

In the present example, we have a table of Bessel functions of various orders at certain tabulated points. But the Bessel functions have some special properties. (Again, the interested reader is encouraged to peruse a suitable reference.) For example,

$$J_o'(x) = -J_1(x), \tag{3.11}$$

and

$$J_n'(x) = \frac{J_{n-1}(x) - J_{n+1}(x)}{2}. \tag{3.12}$$

So we do have information about the function and its derivative! For this general case, we propose the interpolation polynomial

$$p(x) = ax^3 + bx^2 + cx + d \tag{3.13}$$

and determine a, b, c, and d by requiring that

$$p(x_1) = f(x_1), \quad p(x_2) = f(x_2),$$
$$p'(x_1) = f'(x_1), \quad \text{and} \quad p'(x_2) = f'(x_2). \tag{3.14}$$

This interpolating polynomial will be continuous, as was the Lagrange interpolating polynomial, and its first derivative will also be continuous! With some effort, we can determine the appropriate coefficients and find

$$p(x) = \frac{\left[1 - 2\dfrac{x - x_1}{x_1 - x_2}\right](x - x_2)^2}{(x_1 - x_2)^2}f(x_1) + \frac{\left[1 - 2\dfrac{x - x_2}{x_2 - x_1}\right](x - x_1)^2}{(x_1 - x_2)^2}f(x_2)$$

$$+ \frac{(x - x_1)(x - x_2)^2}{(x_1 - x_2)^2}f'(x_1) + \frac{(x - x_2)(x - x_1)^2}{(x_1 - x_2)^2}f'(x_2). \tag{3.15}$$

In this example, we've only considered Hermite cubic interpolation, but it should be clear that we could devise other polynomials, depending upon the information we have available. For example, if we knew the function at N points and the derivative at r points, we could construct a polynomial of order $N + r - 1$ satisfying the $N + r$ conditions. The more frequent circumstance is that we know the function and its derivative at N points. Using all the information at our disposal, we write the general Hermite interpolating polynomial as

$$p(x) = \sum_{j=1}^{N} h_{j,N}(x) f(x_j) + \sum_{j=1}^{N} \bar{h}_{j,N}(x) f'(x_j), \qquad (3.16)$$

where h and $\bar{h}$ are (as yet) undetermined polynomials. With some effort, we can find that

$$h_{j,N} = \left[1 - 2(x - x_j) l'_{j,N}(x_j) \right] l^2_{j,N}(x) \qquad (3.17)$$

and

$$\bar{h}_{j,N}(x) = (x - x_j) l^2_{j,N}(x), \qquad (3.18)$$

where the $l_{j,N}(x)$ were defined in association with the Lagrange polynomial. The Hermite polynomials are termed osculating, by the way, since they are constructed so as to just "kiss" at the points x_j.

EXERCISE 3.4

Using Hermite interpolation, evaluate the relative intensity I/I_o, and compare to the results of the previous exercise. In conjunction with a root-finder, determine the ρ-value for which the intensity is zero, i.e., find the location of the first dark fringe in the diffraction pattern.

It is also possible to construct approximations using higher derivatives. The Bessel functions, for example, satisfy the differential equation

$$x^2 J_n'' + x J_n' + (x^2 - n^2) J_n = 0, \qquad (3.19)$$

so that if we have a table of J_n's, we can find both J_n' and J_n''. A 5-th order approximating polynomial could then be determined, for example, passing through two points. Since this information is "local" to the region being approximated, these high-order approximations do not suffer the unstable behavior of the high-order Lagrange polynomials.

3.4 Cubic Splines

If derivatives are available, then Hermite interpolation can—and probably should—be used. That will guarantee that the function and its first derivative will be continuous. More often than not, however, the derivatives are not available. While the Lagrange interpolating polynomial can certainly be used, it has one very undesirable characteristic: its derivative is not continuous. Let's imagine that we're using the points x_1, x_2, x_3, and x_4 and interpolating in the region $x_2 \leq x \leq x_3$. As x varies from x_2 to x_3, the function and its derivatives vary smoothly. But as x increases beyond x_3, we change the points used in the interpolation in order to keep x "surrounded." This shifting of interpolation points is done for a good reason, as discussed earlier, but look at the consequence: since we now have a different set of interpolation points, we have a different approximating polynomial. Although the *function* will be continuous, the *derivatives* will suffer a discontinuous change. Not a particularly attractive feature.

It would be desirable to have an approximating function that had continuous derivatives. And in fact, we can construct such a function. Let's define $p(x)$ as the cubic interpolating function used in the region $x_j \leq x \leq x_{j+1}$, which can be written as

$$p(x) = a_j(x - x_j)^3 + b_j(x - x_j)^2 + c_j(x - x_j) + d_j. \tag{3.20}$$

Requiring this approximation to be exact at $x = x_j$ gives us

$$p(x_j) = f(x_j) = d_j. \tag{3.21}$$

This approximation should also be exact at $x = x_{j+1}$, so that

$$p_{j+1} = a_j h_j^3 + b_j h_j^2 + c_j h_j + p_j, \tag{3.22}$$

where we've introduced the notation

$$p_j = p(x_j) \qquad \text{and} \qquad h_j = x_{j+1} - x_j. \tag{3.23}$$

The derivatives of our cubic approximation are

$$p'(x) = 3a_j(x - x_j)^2 + 2b_j(x - x_j) + c_j \tag{3.24}$$

and

$$p''(x) = 6a_j(x - x_j) + 2b_j. \tag{3.25}$$

For the second derivative at $x = x_j$ we have

$$p''(x_j) = p_j'' = 2b_j \tag{3.26}$$

so that

$$b_j = \frac{p_j''}{2}, \tag{3.27}$$

while at $x = x_{j+1}$ we have

$$p''_{j+1} = 6a_j h_j + 2b_j \qquad (3.28)$$

and hence

$$a_j = \frac{1}{6}\frac{p''_{j+1} - p''_j}{h_j}. \qquad (3.29)$$

From Equation 3.22, we then find that

$$c_j = \frac{p_{j+1} - p_j}{h_j} - \frac{h_j p''_{j+1} + 2h_j p''_j}{6}. \qquad (3.30)$$

With the coefficients of the polynomial known, at least in terms of the p''_j, we can write

$$p(x) = p_j + \left[\frac{p_{j+1} - p_j}{h_j} - \frac{h_j p''_{j+1}}{6} - \frac{h_j p''_j}{3}\right](x - x_j) + \frac{p''_j}{2}(x - x_j)^2$$

$$+ \frac{p''_{j+1} - p''_j}{6h_j}(x - x_j)^3, \qquad x_j \le x \le x_{j+1}, \qquad (3.31)$$

and

$$p'(x) = \frac{p_{j+1} - p_j}{h_j} - \frac{h_j p''_{j+1}}{6} - \frac{h_j p''_j}{3} + p''_j(x - x_j)$$

$$+ \frac{p''_{j+1} - p''_j}{2h_j}(x - x_j)^2, \qquad x_j \le x \le x_{j+1}. \qquad (3.32)$$

These expressions tell us that the function and its derivative can be approximated from the p_j and the p''_j. Of course, we already know the p_j. To determine the p''_j, we consider the derivative in the *previous* interval. Replacing j by $j-1$ in Equation 3.32, we have

$$p'(x) = \frac{p_j - p_{j-1}}{h_{j-1}} - \frac{h_{j-1} p''_j}{6} - \frac{h_{j-1} p''_{j-1}}{3} + p''_{j-1}(x - x_{j-1})$$

$$+ \frac{p''_j - p''_{j-1}}{2h_{j-1}}(x - x_{j-1})^2, \qquad x_{j-1} \le x \le x_j. \qquad (3.33)$$

We now require that Equations 3.33 and 3.32 yield exactly the same value of the derivative at $x = x_j$, so that

$$\frac{p_j - p_{j-1}}{h_{j-1}} - \frac{h_{j-1} p''_j}{6} - \frac{h_{j-1} p''_{j-1}}{3} + p''_{j-1} h_j + \frac{p''_j - p''_{j-1}}{2h_{j-1}} h_{j-1}^2$$

$$= \frac{p_{j+1} - p_j}{h_j} - \frac{h_j p''_{j+1}}{6} - \frac{h_j p''_j}{3}. \qquad (3.34)$$

Moving the (unknown) p_j'' to the left side of the equation and the (known) p_j to the right, we find

$$h_{j-1}p_{j-1}'' + (2h_j + 2h_{j-1})p_j'' + h_j p_{j+1}''$$

$$= 6\left(\frac{p_{j+1} - p_j}{h_j} - \frac{p_j - p_{j-1}}{h_{j-1}}\right), \qquad j = 2, \ldots, N-1. \qquad (3.35)$$

This gives us $(N-2)$ equations for the N unknown p_j''—we need two more equations to determine a unique solution. These additional equations may come from specifying the derivative at the end points, i.e., at $x = x_1$ and x_N. From Equation 3.32, we find

$$2h_1 p_1'' + h_1 p_2'' = 6\frac{p_2 - p_1}{h_1} - 6p_1', \qquad (3.36)$$

while from Equation 3.33 we find

$$h_{N-1}p_{N-1}'' + 2h_{N-1}p_N'' = -6\frac{p_N - p_{N-1}}{h_{N-1}} + 6p_N'. \qquad (3.37)$$

All these equations can be written in matrix form as

$$\begin{bmatrix} 2h_1 & h_1 & & & & \\ h_1 & 2(h_1 + h_2) & h_2 & & & \\ & h_2 & 2(h_2 + h_3) & h_3 & & \\ & & & \ddots & & \\ & & & h_{N-2} & 2(h_{N-2} + h_{N-1}) & h_{N-1} \\ & & & & h_{N-1} & 2h_{N-1} \end{bmatrix} \begin{bmatrix} p_1'' \\ p_2'' \\ p_3'' \\ \vdots \\ p_{N-1}'' \\ p_N'' \end{bmatrix}$$

$$= \begin{bmatrix} 6\dfrac{p_2 - p_1}{h_1} - 6p_1' \\ 6\dfrac{p_3 - p_2}{h_2} - 6\dfrac{p_2 - p_1}{h_1} \\ 6\dfrac{p_4 - p_3}{h_3} - 6\dfrac{p_3 - p_2}{h_2} \\ \vdots \\ 6\dfrac{p_N - p_{N-1}}{h_{N-1}} - 6\dfrac{p_{N-1} - p_{N-2}}{h_{N-2}} \\ -6\dfrac{p_N - p_{N-1}}{h_{N-1}} + 6p_N' \end{bmatrix} \qquad (3.38)$$

Is it obvious why the matrix is termed *tridiagonal*?

The derivatives at the end points are not always known, however. The most common recourse in this instance is to use the so-called _natural spline_, obtained by setting the second derivatives to zero at $x = x_1$ and $x = x_N$. This forces the approximating function to be linear at the limits of the interpolating region. In this case the equations to be solved are

$$
\begin{bmatrix}
1 & & & & & \\
& 2(h_1 + h_2) & h_2 & & & \\
& h_2 & 2(h_2 + h_3) & h_3 & & \\
& & & \ddots & & \\
& & & h_{N-2} & 2(h_{N-2} + h_{N-1}) & \\
& & & & & 1
\end{bmatrix}
\begin{bmatrix}
p_1'' \\
p_2'' \\
p_3'' \\
\vdots \\
p_{N-1}'' \\
p_N''
\end{bmatrix}
$$

$$
=
\begin{bmatrix}
0 \\
6\dfrac{p_3 - p_2}{h_2} - 6\dfrac{p_2 - p_1}{h_1} \\
6\dfrac{p_4 - p_3}{h_3} - 6\dfrac{p_3 - p_2}{h_2} \\
\vdots \\
6\dfrac{p_N - p_{N-1}}{h_{N-1}} - 6\dfrac{p_{N-1} - p_{N-2}}{h_{N-1}} \\
0
\end{bmatrix}.
\tag{3.39}
$$

Again, the equations are of a tridiagonal form. This is the simplest form that allows for a second derivative. Since many of the important equations of physics are second-order differential equations, tridiagonal systems like these arise frequently in computational physics. Before proceeding with our problem of determining cubic splines, let's investigate the general solution to systems of equations of this form.

3.5 Tridiagonal Linear Systems

Linear algebraic systems are quite common in applied problems. In fact, since they are relatively easy to solve, one way of attacking a difficult problem is to find some way to write it as a linear one. In the general case, where a solution to an arbitrary set of simultaneous linear equations is being sought, Gaussian elimination with partial pivoting is a common method of solution and will be discussed later in this chapter. For tridiagonal systems, Gaussian elimination takes on a particularly simple form, which we discuss here.

Let's write a general tridiagonal system as

$$
\begin{bmatrix}
b_1 & c_1 & & & & \\
a_2 & b_2 & c_2 & & & \\
& a_3 & b_3 & c_3 & & \\
& & & \ddots & & \\
& & & a_{N-1} & b_{N-1} & c_{N-1} \\
& & & & a_N & b_N
\end{bmatrix}
\begin{bmatrix}
x_1 \\ x_2 \\ x_3 \\ \vdots \\ x_{N-1} \\ x_N
\end{bmatrix}
=
\begin{bmatrix}
r_1 \\ r_2 \\ r_3 \\ \vdots \\ r_{N-1} \\ r_N
\end{bmatrix}.
\tag{3.40}
$$

The b_j, $j = 1, \ldots, N$ lie on the main diagonal. On the subdiagonal lie the a_j, for which j ranges from 2 to N, while the c_j lie above the main diagonal, with $1 \leq j \leq N - 1$. Alternatively, we can write Equation 3.40 as a set of simultaneous equations,

$$
\begin{aligned}
b_1 x_1 + c_1 x_2 \qquad\qquad\qquad\qquad\qquad &= r_1 \\
a_2 x_1 + b_2 x_2 + c_2 x_3 \qquad\qquad\qquad &= r_2 \\
a_3 x_2 + b_3 x_3 + c_3 x_4 \qquad\qquad &= r_3 \\
&\;\;\vdots \\
a_{N-1} x_{N-2} + b_{N-1} x_{N-1} + c_{N-1} x_N &= r_{N-1} \\
a_N x_{N-1} + b_N x_N &= r_N
\end{aligned}
\tag{3.41}
$$

The general way to solve such sets of equations is to combine the equations in such a way as to eliminate some of the variables. Let's see if we can eliminate x_1 from the first two equations. Multiply the first equation by a_2/b_1, and subtract it from the second, and use this new equation in place of the original second equation to obtain the set

$$
\begin{aligned}
b_1 x_1 + c_1 x_2 \qquad\qquad\qquad\qquad\qquad &= r_1 \\
\left(b_2 - \frac{a_2}{b_1} c_1 \right) x_2 + c_2 x_3 \qquad\qquad &= r_2 - \frac{a_2}{b_1} r_1 \\
a_3 x_2 + b_3 x_3 + c_3 x_4 \qquad\qquad &= r_3 \\
&\;\;\vdots \\
a_{N-1} x_{N-2} + b_{N-1} x_{N-1} + c_{N-1} x_N &= r_{N-1} \\
a_N x_{N-1} + b_N x_N &= r_N
\end{aligned}
\tag{3.42}
$$

To simplify the notation, define

$$
\beta_1 = b_1, \qquad \rho_1 = r_1,
\tag{3.43}
$$

and

$$
\beta_2 = b_2 - \frac{a_2}{\beta_1} c_1, \qquad \rho_2 = r_2 - \frac{a_2}{\beta_1} \rho_1,
\tag{3.44}
$$

thus obtaining

$$
\begin{aligned}
\beta_1 x_1 + c_1 x_2 \qquad\qquad\qquad\qquad\qquad &= \rho_1 \\
\beta_2 x_2 + c_2 x_3 \qquad\qquad\qquad &= \rho_2 \\
a_3 x_2 + b_3 x_3 + c_3 x_4 \qquad &= r_3 \\
&\vdots \\
a_{N-1} x_{N-2} + b_{N-1} x_{N-1} + c_{N-1} x_N &= r_{N-1} \\
a_N x_{N-1} + b_N x_N &= r_N
\end{aligned}
\qquad (3.45)
$$

We can now proceed to eliminate x_2—multiplying the second equation by a_3/β_2 and subtracting it from the third yields

$$
\begin{aligned}
\beta_1 x_1 + c_1 x_2 \qquad\qquad\qquad\qquad\qquad &= \rho_1 \\
\beta_2 x_2 + c_2 x_3 \qquad\qquad\qquad &= \rho_2 \\
+\beta_3 x_3 + c_3 x_4 \qquad &= \rho_3 \\
&\vdots \\
a_{N-1} x_{N-2} + b_{N-1} x_{N-1} + c_{N-1} x_N &= r_{N-1} \\
a_N x_{N-1} + b_N x_N &= r_N
\end{aligned}
\qquad (3.46)
$$

where we've defined

$$
\beta_3 = b_3 - \frac{a_3}{\beta_2} c_2, \qquad \rho_3 = r_3 - \frac{a_3}{\beta_2} \rho_2. \qquad (3.47)
$$

Clearly, there's a pattern developing here. After $N-1$ such steps, we arrive at the set of equations

$$
\begin{aligned}
\beta_1 x_1 + c_1 x_2 \qquad\qquad\qquad\qquad\qquad &= \rho_1 \\
\beta_2 x_2 + c_2 x_3 \qquad\qquad\qquad &= \rho_2 \\
+\beta_3 x_3 + c_3 x_4 \qquad &= \rho_3 \\
&\vdots \\
\beta_{N-1} x_{N-1} + c_{N-1} x_N &= \rho_{N-1} \\
\beta_N x_N &= \rho_N
\end{aligned}
\qquad (3.48)
$$

where we've defined

$$
\beta_j = b_j - \frac{a_j}{\beta_{j-1}} c_{j-1} \quad \text{and} \quad \rho_j = r_j - \frac{a_j}{\beta_{j-1}} \rho_{j-1}, \qquad j = 2, \ldots, N. \qquad (3.49)
$$

This set of equations can now be solved by "back substitution." From the last of the equations, we have

$$
x_N = \rho_N / \beta_N, \qquad (3.50)
$$

which can then be substituted into the previous equation to yield

$$
x_{N-1} = (\rho_{N-1} - c_{N-1} x_N)/\beta_{N-1}, \qquad (3.51)
$$

and so on. Since all the previous equations have the same form, we are led to the general result

$$x_{N-j} = (\rho_{N-j} - c_{N-j}x_{N-j+1})/\beta_{N-j}, \quad j = 1, \ldots, N-1, \qquad (3.52)$$

the solution to our original problem!

A function to implement the solution we've developed can easily be written. In fact, all that needs to be done is to determine the β_j's and ρ_j's from Equations 3.43 and 3.49, and then back substitute according to Equations 3.50 and 3.52 to determine the x_j's. A suitable code might look like

```
% trisolve.m
% Code fragment for solving a tridiagonal set of equations.
%
function [x] = trisolve(a,b,c,r,N)
% This function solves the tridiagonal set of equations
%
%   / b(1) c(1)                             \  / x(1) \    / r(1) \
%   | a(2) b(2) c(2)                         |  | x(2) |    | r(2) |
%   |      a(3) b(3) c(3)                     |  | x(3) |    | r(3) |
%   |              ...                        |  | ...  | =  | ...  |
%   |              a(N-1) b(N-1) c(N-1)       |  | x(N-1)|    | r(N-1)|
%   \                    a(N)  b(N)          /  \ x(N) /    \ r(N) /
%
% The diagonals A, B, and C, and the right-hand sides
% of the equations R, are provided as input to the function
% and the solution X is returned.
%
if (b(1) == 0) error('Zero diagonal element in TRISOLVE');  end
beta(1) = b(1);
rho(1)  = r(1);
for j=2:N
    beta(j) = b(j) - a(j) *  c (j-1) / beta(j-1);
    rho(j)  = r(j) - a(j) * rho(j-1) / beta(j-1);
    if (b(j) == 0)
        error('Zero diagonal element in TRISOLVE');
    end
end
% Now, for the back substitution...
x(N) = rho(N) / beta(N);
for j = 1:N-1
    x(N-j) = ( rho(N-j)-c(N-j)*x(N-j+1) )/beta(N-j);
end
```

There is one further modification that we should make before we use this code. While "efficiency" is not of overwhelming importance to us, neither should we be carelessly inefficient. Do you see where we have erred? As it stands, an entire array is being wasted—there is no need for both X and RHO! In the elimination phase, the X array is never used, while in the back substitution phase, it is equated to the elements of RHO. Defining two distinct variables was necessary when we were developing the method of solution, and it was entirely appropriate that we used them. At that point, we didn't know what the relationship between ρ_j and x_j was going to be. But *as a result* of our analysis we know, and we should use our understanding of that relationship as best we can. With respect to the computer code, one of the arrays is unnecessary—you should remove all references to RHO in the function, in favor of the array X.

EXERCISE 3.5

After suitably modifying TriSolve, use it to solve the set of equations

$$
\begin{bmatrix}
2 & -1 & 0 & 0 & 0 \\
-1 & 2 & -1 & 0 & 0 \\
0 & -1 & 2 & -1 & 0 \\
0 & 0 & -1 & 2 & -1 \\
0 & 0 & 0 & -1 & 2
\end{bmatrix}
\begin{bmatrix}
x_1 \\ x_2 \\ x_3 \\ x_4 \\ x_5
\end{bmatrix}
=
\begin{bmatrix}
0 \\ 1 \\ 2 \\ 3 \\ 4
\end{bmatrix}.
\tag{3.53}
$$

You can check your result by verifying that your solution satisfies the original equations.

3.6 Cubic Spline Interpolation

Now that we see what's involved, the solution to the cubic spline problem is fairly clear, at least in principle. From the given table of x_j's and $f(x_j)$'s, the tridiagonal set of equations of Equation 3.38 (or Equation 3.39, for the natural spline) is determined. Those equations are then solved, by a function such as TriSolve, for the p_j''. Knowing these, all other quantities can be determined. In pseudocode, the function might look something like

```
function [second] = SplineInit(x,f,fp1,fpN,N)
%
% This function is called with the first derivatives at x=x(1),
% FP1, and at x=x(N), FPN, specified, as well as the X's and F's.
%
% It returns the second derivatives in SECOND.
%
% < Initialize A, B, C---the subdiagonal, main diagonal,
%       and superdiagonal. >
% < Initialize R---the right hand side. >
%
```

```
% < Call TRISOLVE to solve for SECOND, the second derivatives.
% This requires the additional array BETA. >
%
        . . .
```

This function will certainly work. But. . . are all those arrays *really* necessary? If we leave the solution of the tridiagonal system to a separate routine, they probably are. However, it would be just as useful to have a specialized version of TRISOLVE within the spline code. This would make the spline function self-contained, which can be a valuable characteristic in itself. As we think about this, we realize that TRISOLVE will be the *major* portion of the spline routine—what we *really* need to do is to *start* with TRISOLVE, and add the particular features of spline interpolation to it. This new point-of-view is considerably different from what we began with, and not obvious from the beginning. The process exemplifies an important component of good programming and successful computational physics—don't get "locked in" to one way of doing things, always look to see if there is a better way. Sometimes, there isn't. And sometimes, a new point-of-view can lead to dramatic progress.

So, let's start with TRISOLVE. To begin, we should immediately change the name of the array X to SECOND, to avoid confusion with the coordinates that we'll want to use. Then we should realize that we don't need both A and C, since the particular tridiagonal matrix used in the cubic spline problem is symmetric. In fact, we recognize that it's not necessary to have arrays for the diagonals of the matrix at all—we can evaluate them as we go! That is, instead of having a for loop to evaluate the components of A, for example, we can evaluate the specific element we need within the Gauss elimination loop. The arrays A, B, C, and R are not needed! The revised code looks like

```
% Code fragment to initialize the cubic spline by
% providing the second derivative

function [second] = SplineInit(x,f,fp1,fpN,N)
%
% This function performs the initialization of second
% derivatives necessary for CUBIC SPLINE interpolation.
% The arrays x and f contain N values of function and the
% position at which it was evaluated, and fp1 and fpN
% are the first derivatives at x = x(1) and x = x(N).
% The function returns the second derivatives in SECOND.
%
% In a cubic spline, the approximation to the function and
% its first two derivatives are required to be continuous.
% The primary purpose of this function is to solve the
% set of tridiagonal linear equations resulting from this
% requirement for the (unknown) second derivatives and
% knowledge of the first derivatives at the ends of the
% interpolating region. The equations are solved by
```

```
% Gaussian elimination, restricted to tridiagonal systems,
% with A, B, and C being sub, main, and super diagonals,
% and R the right hand side of the equations.

b1 = 2.0 * (x(2)-x(1));
beta(1) = b1;
if(beta(1)==0), error('Zero diagonal element in SplineInit');
end
r1 = 6.0*( (f(2)-f(1))/(x(2)-x(1)) - fp1 );
second(1) = r1;
for j=2:N
    if (j==N)
        bj =  2.0 * ( x(N)-x(N-1));
        rj = -6.0 * ( (f(N)-f(N-1))/(x(N)-x(N-1))-fpN);
        % for j=2:N-1, do the following
    else
        bj = 2.0 * ( x(j+1) - x(j-1) );
        rj = 6.0 * ( (f(j+1)-f( j ))/(x(j+1)-x(j ))...
              -(f( j )-f(j-1))/(x( j )-x(j-1)));
    end
    % Evaluate the off-diagonal elements. Since the
    % matrix is symmetric, A and C are equivalent.
    aj       = x( j ) - x(j-1);
    c        = aj;
    beta(j)  = bj - aj * c / beta(j-1);
    second(j) = rj - aj* second(j-1) / beta(j-1);
    if(beta(j)==0), error('Zero diagonal element in SplineInit');
    end
end
% Now, for the back substitution...
second(N) = second(N) / beta(N);
for j = 1:N-1
    c = x(N-j+1)-x(N-j);
    second(N-j) = (second(N-j)-c*second(N-j+1))/beta(N-j);
end
```

This code could be made more "compact"—that is, we don't really need to use intermediate variables like aj and c, and they could be eliminated—but the clarity might be diminished in the process. It's far better to have a clear, reliable code than one that is marginally more "efficient" but is difficult to comprehend.

Of course, we haven't interpolated anything yet! SplineInit yields the second derivatives, which we need for interpolation, but doesn't do the interpolation itself. SplineInit needs to be called, once, before any interpolation is done.

The interpolation itself, the embodiment of Equation 3.31, is done in the function Spline,

```
% Code fragment for the cubic spline. The second
% derivative is provided by the function SplineInit
```

```
function [y] = Spline(xvalue,x,f,second,N)
%
% This function performs the CUBIC SPLINE interpolation,
% after SECOND has been initialized by SplineInit.
% The arrays F, SECOND, and X contain N values of function,
% its second derivative, and the positions at which they
% were evaluated.
%
% The function returns the cubic spline approximation
% to the function at XVALUE.
%
% Verify that XVALUE is between x(1) and x(N).
if (xvalue < x(1))
    error('xvalue is less than x(1) in Spline');
end
if (xvalue > x(N))
    error('xvalue is greater than x(N) in Spline');
end
% Determine the interval containing xvalue.
j = 1;
while (xvalue > x(j+1))
    j = j + 1;
end
% xvalue is between x(j) and x(j+1).
% Now, for the interpolation...
...
spline = ...
```

Some of the code has been left for you to fill in.

EXERCISE 3.6

Use the cubic spline approximation to the Bessel function $J_1(\rho)$ to find the location of its first zero. From inspection of Table 3.1, it must be between $\rho = 3$ and $\rho = 4$.

In this spline approximation, we need to know the derivatives of the function at the endpoints. But how much do they matter? If we had simply "guessed" at the derivatives, how much would it affect the approximation? One of the advantages of a computational approach is that we answer these questions almost as easily as we can ask them.

EXERCISE 3.7

Investigate the influence of the derivatives on the approximation to J_1, by entering false values for FP1. Instead of the correct derivative, use $J_1'(0) = -3, -2.5,$

$-2, \ldots, 2.5$, and 3, and plot your bogus approximations against the valid one. How much of a difference does the derivative make?

Earlier, we noted that in addition to the "clamped" spline approximation in which the derivatives at the endpoints are specified, there is the "natural" spline for which derivative information is not required.

EXERCISE 3.8
Change `SplineInit` into `NaturalSplineInit`, a function that initializes the natural spline. Plot the "clamped" and natural spline approximations to $J_1(\rho)$, and compare them. (Are changes needed in the function `Spline`?)

Occasionally, we find the derivative capability of the spline approximation to be particularly valuable. Based upon Equation 3.32, it's easy to develop a function analogous to `Spline` that evaluates the derivative.

EXERCISE 3.9
Develop the function `SplinePrime`, which evaluates the derivative of the function, and consider the intensity of light passing through a circular aperture. We previously investigated the location of the dark fringe—past that fringe, the intensity builds toward a maximum—the location of the first light fringe. Where is it, and how bright is it? (Note that you need to approximate I/I_o, not J_1. Extrema of the intensity correspond to zero's of the derivative of the intensity.)

● 3.7 MATLAB's Interpolation Routines

Once again, we find that MATLAB has anticipated our needs and has supplied an interpolator. If a data set of x and y values is available, then the interpolated value at v is found with the command

```
interp1(x, y, v);
```

and a plot of the interpolated values at coordinates xx can be generated with

```
plot(xx, interp1(x, y, xx));
```

Used in this way, `interp1` does linear interpolation, although it's capable of performing other kinds. As always, use the command

```
help interp1
```

to learn more.

3.8 Approximation of Derivatives

If a function, and all its derivatives, are known at some point, then Taylor's series would seem to be an excellent way to approximate the function. As a practical matter, however, the method leaves quite a lot to be desired—how often are a function and all its derivative known? This situation is somewhat complementary to that of Lagrange interpolation—instead of knowing the function at many points, and having "global" information about the function, the Taylor series approximation relies upon having unlimited information about the function "local" to the point of interest. In practice, such information is usually not available. However, Taylor's series plays a crucial role in the numerical calculation of derivatives.

There are several ways to discuss numerical differentiation. For example, we could simply take the definition of the derivative from differential calculus,

$$f'(x) = \frac{df(x)}{dx} = \lim_{h \to 0} \frac{f(x+h) - f(x)}{h}, \qquad (3.54)$$

and suggest that an adequate approximation is

$$f'_h(x) = \frac{f(x+h) - f(x)}{h}. \qquad (3.55)$$

Certainly, $f'_h(x)$ approaches $f'(x)$ in the limit as $h \to 0$, but how does it compare if h is other than zero? What we need is a method that will yield good approximations *of known quality* using *finite* differences; that is, the approximation should not require that the limit to zero be taken, and an estimate of the accuracy of the approximation should be provided. It's in situations like these that the power and usefulness of the Taylor series is most obvious. Making a Taylor series expansion of $f(x+h)$ about the point $f(x)$,

$$f(x+h) = f(x) + hf'(x) + \frac{h^2}{2!}f''(x) + \cdots, \qquad (3.56)$$

we can solve for $f'(x)$ to find

$$f'(x) = \frac{1}{h}\left[f(x+h) - f(x) - \frac{h^2}{2!}f''(x) + \cdots\right]. \qquad (3.57)$$

This is not an approximation—it is an expression for $f'(x)$ that has exactly the same validity as the original Taylor series from which it was derived. And the terms that appear in the expression involve the actual function of interest, $f(x)$, not some approximation to it (quadratic or otherwise). On the other hand, Equation 3.57 certainly *suggests* the approximation,

$$f'(x) \approx \frac{f(x+h) - f(x)}{h}. \qquad (3.58)$$

By referring to Equation 3.57 we see that the error incurred in using this approximation is

$$E(h) = \frac{h}{2} f''(x) + \cdots,$$ (3.59)

where we've written only the leading term of the error expression—the next term will contain h^2 and for small h will be correspondingly smaller than the term exhibited. Another way of indicating the specific approximation being made is to write

$$f'(x) = \frac{f(x+h) - f(x)}{h} + \mathcal{O}(h),$$ (3.60)

where $\mathcal{O}(h)$ indicates the *order* of the approximation being made by neglecting all other terms in the total expansion.

Equation 3.60 is a *forward difference* approximation to the derivative. We can derive a different expression for $f'(x)$, starting with a Taylor series expansion of $f(x - h)$. This leads to an expression analogous to Equation 3.57,

$$f'(x) = \frac{1}{h}\left[f(x) - f(x-h) + \frac{h^2}{2!} f''(x) + \cdots \right],$$ (3.61)

and the *backward difference* approximation,

$$f'(x) = \frac{f(x) - f(x-h)}{h} + \mathcal{O}(h).$$ (3.62)

Since the forward and backward difference formulas are obtained in similar ways, it's not surprising that their error terms are of the same order. Thus neither has a particular advantage over the other, in general. (An exception occurs at the limits of an interval however. If the function is only known on the interval $a < x < b$, then the backward difference formula cannot be used at $x = a$. Likewise, the forward difference formula cannot be used at $x = b$.) However, the two formulas have an interesting relation to one another. In particular, the leading term in the error in one formula is of *opposite sign* compared to the other. If we *add* the two expressions, the leading term will *cancel*! Let's return to the Taylor series expansions, and include some higher-order terms,

$$f(x+h) = f(x) + hf'(x) + \frac{h^2}{2!} f''(x) + \frac{h^3}{3!} f'''(x) + \frac{h^4}{4!} f^{iv}(x) + \cdots$$ (3.63)

and

$$f(x-h) = f(x) - hf'(x) + \frac{h^2}{2!} f''(x) - \frac{h^3}{3!} f'''(x) + \frac{h^4}{4!} f^{iv}(x) + \cdots.$$ (3.64)

Wanting an expression for $f'(x)$, we subtract these expressions to find the *central difference* formula for the derivative,

$$f'(x) = \frac{f(x+h) - f(x-h)}{2h} + \mathcal{O}(h^2),$$ (3.65)

in which the error term is

$$E(h) = -\frac{h^2}{3!}f'''(x) - \frac{h^4}{5!}f^v(x) + \cdots.$$ (3.66)

Not only has the error been reduced to $\mathcal{O}(h^2)$, but all the terms involving odd powers of h have been eliminated.

> As a general rule, symmetric expressions are more accurate than non symmetric ones.

EXERCISE 3.10

Consider the function $f(x) = xe^x$. (You might want to code this as an "inline" function, e.g., `f = inline('x*exp(x)','x')`.) Obtain approximations to $f'(2)$, with $h = 0.5, 0.45, \ldots, 0.05$, using the forward, backward, and central difference formulas. To visualize how the approximation improves with decreasing stepsize, plot the differences between the approximations and the exact result, as a function of h.

In the present instance, we know the correct result and so can also plot the difference between the calculated and the true value of the derivative, the "error." For any function, such as this error, that is written as

$$E(h) \approx h^n,$$ (3.67)

the natural logarithm is simply

$$\ln E(h) \approx n \ln h.$$ (3.68)

Thus, if $\ln E(h)$ is plotted versus $\ln h$, the value of n is just the slope of the line!

EXERCISE 3.11

Verify the order of the error in the backward, forward, and central difference formulas by plotting the natural log of the error versus the natural log of h in your approximation of the derivative of $f = xe^x$ at $x = 2$.

These methods can be used to evaluate higher derivatives. For example, Equations 3.63 and 3.64 can be added to eliminate $f'(x)$ from the expression, yielding

$$f''(x) = \frac{f(x+h) - 2f(x) + f(x-h)}{h^2} + \mathcal{O}(h^2) \qquad (3.69)$$

with an error of

$$E(h) = -\frac{h^2}{12}f^{iv}(x) - \frac{h^4}{360}f^{vi}(x) + \cdots. \qquad (3.70)$$

Again, we note that terms with odd powers of h are absent, a consequence of the symmetry of the expression. To develop a forward difference formula, we need to know that

$$f(x+2h) = f(x) + 2hf'(x) + \frac{4h^2}{2!}f''(x) + \frac{8h^3}{3!}f'''(x) + \frac{16h^4}{4!}f^{iv}(x) + \cdots. \qquad (3.71)$$

Combining this with Equation 3.63 yields

$$f''(x) = \frac{f(x) - 2f(x+h) + f(x+2h)}{h^2} + \mathcal{O}(h). \qquad (3.72)$$

While this expression uses three function evaluations, just as the central difference formula, Equation 3.69, it's not nearly as accurate—in this approximation, the error is

$$E(h) = -hf'''(x) - \frac{7h^2}{12}f^{iv}(x) + \cdots. \qquad (3.73)$$

The reason, of course, is that with the central difference formula the function is evaluated at points surrounding the point of interest, while with the forward difference they're all off to one side. This is entirely consistent with our previous observation concerning the interpolation of functions.

EXERCISE 3.12

Consider the function $f(x) = xe^x$. Obtain approximations to $f''(2)$, with $h = 0.5$, 0.45, ..., 0.05, using the forward and central difference formulas. Verify the order of the error by plotting the log error versus log h.

MATLAB has some very nice plotting capabilities. You could, for example, have two plots in a single window using its subplot function,

```
subplot(1,2,1)    % This indicates that plots will be organized in a
                  %   1x2 array, with the next plot being the first.
plot(x1,y1)
subplot(1,2,2)    % The next plot will be the second.
plot(x2,y2)
```

EXERCISE 3.13
Combine the previous two exercises, and generate both plots in a single window.

We should note that two separate figures could also be produced, if desired, using the code

```
plot(x1,y1)      % Draw the first plot.
figure           % Begin a new figure.
plot(x2,y2)      % Draw another plot.
```

3.9 Richardson Extrapolation

We have seen how *two different* expressions can be combined to eliminate the leading error term and thus yield a more accurate expression. It is also possible to use a *single* expression to achieve the same goal. This general technique is due to L. F. Richardson, a meteorologist who pioneered numerical weather prediction in the 1920s. (His *Weather Prediction by Numerical Process,* written in 1922, is a classic in the field.) Although we will demonstrate the method with regard to numerical differentiation, the general technique is applicable, and very useful, whenever the order of the error is known.

Let's start with the central difference formula, and imagine that we have obtained the usual approximation for the derivative,

$$f'(x) = \frac{f(x+h) - f(x-h)}{2h} - \frac{h^2}{6} f'''(x) + \cdots . \qquad (3.74)$$

Using a *different* stepsize we can obtain a second approximation to the derivative. Then using these two expressions, we can eliminate the leading term of the error. In practice, the second expression is usually obtained by using an h twice as large as the first, so that

$$f'(x) = \frac{f(x+2h) - f(x-2h)}{4h} - \frac{4h^2}{6} f'''(x) + \cdots . \qquad (3.75)$$

While the stepsize is twice as large, the error is four times as large. Dividing this expression by 4 and subtracting it from the previous one eliminates the error! Well, actually only the leading term of the error is eliminated, but it still sounds great! Solving for f', we obtain

$$f'(x) = \frac{f(x-2h) - 8f(x-h) + 8f(x+h) - f(x+2h)}{12h} + \mathcal{O}(h^4), \qquad (3.76)$$

a 5-point central difference formula with error given by

$$E(h) = \frac{h^4}{30}f^v(x) + \cdots.$$
(3.77)

(Yes, we know there are only 4 points used in this expression. The coefficient of the fifth point, $f(x)$, happens to be zero.)

Of course, we can do the same thing with other derivatives: using the 3-point expression of Equation 3.69, we can easily derive the 5-point expression

$$f''(x) = \frac{-f(x-2h) + 16f(x-h) - 30f(x) + 16f(x+h) - f(x+2h)}{12h^2} + \mathcal{O}(h^4),$$
(3.78)

with

$$E(h) = \frac{h^4}{90}f^{vi}(x) + \cdots.$$
(3.79)

Now, there are two different ways that Richardson extrapolation can be used. The first is to obtain "new" expressions, as we've just done, and to use these expressions directly. Be forewarned, however, that these expressions can become rather cumbersome.

Richardson extrapolation can also be used in an indirect computational scheme. We'll carry out exactly the same steps as before, but we'll perform them *numerically* rather than *symbolically*. Let $D_1(h)$ be the approximation to the first derivative obtained from the central difference formula with stepsize h, Equation 3.74, and assume that both $D_1(2h)$ and $D_1(h)$ have been calculated. Clearly, the second approximation will be better than the first. But since the order of the error in this approximation is known, we can do even better. Since the error goes as the square of the stepsize, $D_1(2h)$ must contain four times the error contained in $D_1(h)$! The difference between these two approximations is then three times the error of the second. But the difference is something we can easily calculate, so in fact we can calculate the error! (Or at least, its leading term.) The "correct" answer, $D_2(h)$, is then obtained by simply subtracting this calculated error from the second approximation,

$$D_2(h) = D_1(h) - \left[\frac{D_1(2h) - D_1(h)}{2^2 - 1}\right]$$

$$= \frac{4D_1(h) - D_1(2h)}{3}.$$
(3.80)

Of course, $D_2(h)$ is not the *exact* answer, since we've only accounted for the leading term in the error. Since the central difference formulas have error terms involving only even powers of h, the error in $D_2(h)$ must be $O(h^4)$. Thus $D_2(2h)$

contains 2^4 times as much error as $D_2(h)$, and so this error can be removed to yield an even better estimate of the derivative,

$$D_3(h) = D_2(h) - \left[\frac{D_2(2h) - D_2(h)}{2^4 - 1} \right]$$

$$= \frac{16D_2(h) - D_2(2h)}{15}. \tag{3.81}$$

This processes can be continued indefinitely, with each improved estimate given by

$$D_{i+1}(h) = D_i(h) - \left[\frac{D_i(2h) - D_i(h)}{2^{2i} - 1} \right]$$

$$= \frac{2^{2i} D_i(h) - D_i(2h)}{2^{2i} - 1}. \tag{3.82}$$

To see how this works, consider the function $f(x) = x e^x$ and calculate $D_1(h)$ at $x = 2$ for different values of the stepsize h. It's convenient to arrange these in a column, with each succeeding stepsize half the previous one. The entries in this column are then used to evaluate $D_2(h)$, which can be listed in an adjoining column. In turn, these entries are combined to yield D_3, and so on. We thus build a table of extrapolations, with the most accurate approximation being the bottom rightmost entry:

$$f'(2)$$

h	D_1	D_2	D_3	D_4
0.4	23.1634642931			
0.2	22.4141606570	22.1643927783		
0.1	22.2287868803	22.1669956214	22.1671691443	
0.05	22.1825648578	22.1671575170	22.1671683100	22.1671682968

While we've suggested that this table was created a column at a time, that's not the way it would be done in practice, of course. Rather, it would be built a *row* at a time, as the necessary constituents of the various approximations became available. For example, the first entry in the table is $D_1(0.4)$ and the second entry is $D_1(0.2)$. This is enough information to evaluate $D_2(0.2)$, which fills out that row. (Note that this entry is already more accurate than the last 3-point central difference approximation in the table, $D_1(0.05)$.) If we wanted to obtain the derivative to a specific accuracy, we would compare this last approximation, $D_2(0.2)$, to the best previous approximation, $D_1(0.2)$. In this case, we only have two-digit accuracy, so we would half h and evaluate $D_1(0.1)$. That would enable $D_2(0.1)$ to be evaluated, which would then be used to evaluate $D_3(0.1)$, completing that row. We now have four significant digit agreement between $D_2(0.1)$ and $D_3(0.1)$. Halving h one more time, the fourth row of the table can be generated. The last entries, $D_3(0.05)$ and $D_4(0.05)$, agree to 9 significant digits; $D_4(0.05)$ is actually accurate to all 12 digits displayed.

The coding of this extrapolation scheme can initially be a little intimidating, although (as we shall see) it isn't really all that difficult. As often happens, we will start with a general outline and build upon it—there's no reason to believe that people ever write a complicated computer code off the top of their heads. In fact, quite the opposite is true: the more complicated the code, the more methodical its development should be. From reflection upon the extrapolation table we created, we realize that the "next" row is generated with one newly evaluated derivative and the entries of the "previous" row. So, we'll have an "old" row, and a "new" one, each expressed as an array. An outline of the code might look something like

```
% richardson.m
% This illustrates the RICHARDSON EXTRAPOLATION scheme for the
% calculation of the 2nd derivative.
clear;
...
x = < point where derivative is to be evaluated >
h = < initial stepsize >
iteration = 0; % keep track of number of iterations
while (iteration < 5)
    iteration = iteration + 1;
    for i = 1:4
        old(i) = new(i);
    end
    % <evaluate the derivative DF using the 3-pt formula>
    % using the central difference formular for the 2nd derivative
    new(1) = < DF >
    % The following if-statement structure calculates the
    % appropriate extrapolations.
    if (iteration >= 2), new(2)=(4*new(1) - old(1) )/ 3; end
    if (iteration >= 3), new(3)=(16*new(2) - old(2) )/15; end
    if (iteration ...
        ...
    h = h/2.0;
    ...
```

This is a start. We've dimensioned the arrays to be 4, although we may need to change this later. We've established the basic loop in which the derivative will be evaluated and extrapolations are made, and we've redefined the stepsize at the *end* of the loop. However, we haven't provided any way for the program to STOP! The first thing to do to this code, then, is to provide a way to terminate execution once a specified tolerance for the accuracy of the derivative has been met. You will also want to provide a graceful exit if the tolerance isn't met, after a "reasonable" number of iterations. You might think that more entries should be allowed in the rows—however, experience suggests that the extrapolations don't improve indefinitely, so that the fourth or fifth column is about as far as one really wants to extrapolate. By the way, this general extrapolation procedure can be used any time that the order of the error is known—later, we will use Richardson extrapolation to calculate integrals. In the general case, however, odd powers of h will be present in the error terms and so the coefficients used here would not be appropriate.

EXERCISE 3.14

Modify the code fragment to calculate the *second derivative* of $f(x) = xe^x$, using the 3-point expression of Equation 3.69 and Richardson extrapolation, and generate a table of extrapolates in the same way that the first derivative was evaluated earlier.

3.10 Curve Fitting by Least Squares

To this point, we have discussed *interpolation* in which the approximating function passes through the given points. But what if there is some "scatter" to the points, such as will be the case with actual experimental data? A standard problem is to find the "best" fit to the data, without requiring that the approximation actually coincides with *any* of the specific data points. As an example, consider an experiment in which a ball is dropped, and its velocity is recorded as a function of time. From this data, we might be able to obtain the acceleration due to gravity. (See Figure 3.3.)

Of course, we have to define what we mean by "best fit." We'll take a very simple definition, requiring a certain estimate of the error to be a minimum. Let's make a *guess* at the functional form of the data—in our example, the guess will be

$$v(t) = a + bt \tag{3.83}$$

—and evaluate the *difference* between this guess, evaluated at t_i, and the velocity measured at $t = t_i$, v_i. Because the difference can be positive or negative, we'll square this difference to obtain a non-negative number. Then, we'll add this to the estimate from all other points. We thus use

$$S = \sum_{i=1}^{N} (v(t_i) - v_i)^2 \tag{3.84}$$

as an estimate of the error. Our approximation will be obtained by making this error as small as possible, hence the terminology "least squares fit."

In general, $v(t)$ will be written in terms of unknown parameters, such as the a and b in Equation 3.83. Let's think of varying a, for example, so as to minimize S—a

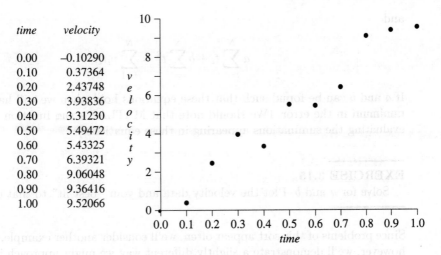

time	velocity
0.00	−0.10290
0.10	0.37364
0.20	2.43748
0.30	3.93836
0.40	3.31230
0.50	5.49472
0.60	5.43325
0.70	6.39321
0.80	9.06048
0.90	9.36416
1.00	9.52066

Figure 3.3   The measured velocity of a particle at various times.

minimum will occur whenever $\partial S/\partial a$ is zero and the second derivative is positive. That is, the error will be an extremum when

$$\frac{\partial S}{\partial a} = \sum_{i=1}^{N} 2(v(t_i) - v_i)\frac{\partial v}{\partial a}\bigg|_{t=t_i} = \sum_{i=1}^{N} 2(a + bt_i - v_i) = 0. \tag{3.85}$$

And since

$$\frac{\partial^2 S}{\partial a^2} = \sum_{i=1}^{N} 2 > 0, \tag{3.86}$$

we will have found a minimum. Of course, we'll have similar equations for b,

$$\frac{\partial S}{\partial b} = \sum_{i=1}^{N} 2(v(t_i) - v_i)\frac{\partial v}{\partial b}\bigg|_{t=t_i} = \sum_{i=1}^{N} 2(a + bt_i - v_i)t_i = 0 \tag{3.87}$$

and

$$\frac{\partial^2 S}{\partial b^2} = \sum_{i=1}^{N} 2t_i^2 > 0, \tag{3.88}$$

so that the error is minimized with respect to b as well. We thus arrive at the equations

$$aN + b\sum_{i=1}^{N} t_i = \sum_{i=1}^{N} v_i, \tag{3.89}$$

and

$$a \sum_{i=1}^{N} t_i + b \sum_{i=1}^{N} t_i^2 = \sum_{i=1}^{N} v_i t_i. \tag{3.90}$$

If a and b can be found such that these equations hold, then we will have found a minimum in the error. (We should note that MATLAB's sum function is ideal for evaluating the summations appearing in these equations.)

EXERCISE 3.15

Solve for a and b. Plot the velocity data and your "best fit" to that data.

Since problems of this sort appear often, we'll consider another example. This time, however, we'll demonstrate a slightly different way we might approach it.

3.11 Kepler's *Harmony of the World*

Working with Tycho Brahe's accurate and extensive observations, Johannes Kepler (1571–1630) was able to deduce what we now know as his Three Laws of Planetary Motion:

1. The orbit of each planet about the Sun is an ellipse with the Sun at one focus.

2. As a planet moves around its orbit, it sweeps out equal areas in equal times.

3. All planets obey the relationship

$$P^2 = a^3$$

where P is the orbital period of the planet and a is the semimajor axis of its elliptical orbit.

The first two laws were described in his *New Astronomy* (1609). These laws describe the motion of a planet about the Sun, and were largely the result of his work with the planet Mars. Subsequently, he attempted to apply his methods to the other planets and, with great effort and despite several distractions (such as developing some early ideas regarding calculus), produced the *Harmony of the World* in 1619. In it, he expresses the third law that all the planets obey, hence truly uniting the solar system into a single, coherent *system*. We will rediscover Kepler's Third Law, using a computational approach.

Let's work with the data in Table 3.2, and assume that there is a simple relationship between the orbital period of a planet, P, and the semimajor axis of its

Table 3.2   Kepler's Planetary Data

	Period P (years)	Relative distance a (AU)
Mercury	0.242	0.388
Venus	0.616	0.724
Earth	1.000	1.000
Mars	1.881	1.524
Jupiter	11.86	5.200
Saturn	29.33	9.510

(This data is taken from C.M. Linton's *From Eudoxus to Einstein: A History of Mathematical Astronomy,* Cambridge University Press, Cambridge, 2004.)

elliptical orbit, a. That is, we'll assume that

$$P = a^n. \tag{3.91}$$

Then

$$\ln(P) = n \ln(a), \tag{3.92}$$

so that $\ln(P)$ and $\ln(a)$ have a simple linear relationship between them. If we plotted these two variables, we'd find that they would lie on a line, with n being the slope of that line. Of course, observational data being what it is, its unlikely that the relationship would be *exact*.

EXERCISE 3.16
Using the least squares program you've developed, find the "best" linear fit to the logarithmic data. What is n, and is your result consistent with Kepler's Third Law?

Of course, finding a relationship from the data in this way doesn't *prove* anything, but it can certainly suggest that there's some interesting physics to be discovered.

In a different situation, we might want to fit the data to a higher-order polynomial, or to a different function altogether. In that case, we'd be led to a system of equations like Equations 3.89 and 3.90, but perhaps larger in number and correspondingly more difficult to solve. That is, most of us have little difficulty with solving two equations for two unknowns. But 5 equations, or 25 equations, is a different matter. Before we go on, we really need to discuss the solution to an arbitrary linear set of simultaneous solutions, a standard topic of linear algebra.

3.12 Gaussian Elimination

Consider the set of equations

$$a_{11}x_1 + a_{12}x_2 + \cdots a_{1N}x_N = b_1$$
$$a_{21}x_1 + a_{22}x_2 + \cdots a_{2N}x_N = b_2$$
$$\vdots$$
$$a_{N1}x_1 + a_{N2}x_2 + \cdots a_{NN}x_N = b_N. \tag{3.93}$$

We'll solve this set via Gauss elimination. In discussing tridiagonal systems, we hit upon the main idea of the process: combine two of the equations in such a way as to eliminate one of the variables, and replace one of the original equations by the reduced one. Although the system of equations confronting us now is not as simple as the tridiagonal one, the process is exactly the same.

We'll start by eliminating x_1 in all but the first equation. Consider the i-th equation,

$$a_{i1}x_1 + a_{i2}x_2 + \cdots a_{iN}x_N = b_i. \tag{3.94}$$

Multiplying the first equation by a_{i1}/a_{11} and subtracting it from the i-th equation gives us

$$\left(a_{i2} - \frac{a_{i1}}{a_{11}}a_{12}\right)x_2 + \left(a_{i3} - \frac{a_{i1}}{a_{11}}a_{13}\right)x_3 + \cdots + \left(a_{iN} - \frac{a_{i1}}{a_{11}}a_{1N}\right)x_N$$
$$= b_i - \frac{a_{i1}}{a_{11}}b_1, \quad i = 2, \ldots, N. \tag{3.95}$$

After x_1 has been eliminated in equations 2 through N, we repeat the process to eliminate x_2 from equations 3 through N. Eventually, we arrive at an upper triangular set of equations that is easily solved by back substitution.

Now, let's repeat some of what we just said, but in matrix notation. We start with the set of equations (3.93), written as a matrix:

$$\begin{bmatrix} a_{11} & a_{12} & a_{13} & \ldots & a_{1N} \\ a_{21} & a_{22} & a_{23} & \ldots & a_{2N} \\ a_{31} & a_{32} & a_{33} & \ldots & a_{3N} \\ \vdots & \vdots & \vdots & \ddots & \vdots \\ a_{N1} & a_{N2} & a_{N3} & \ldots & a_{NN} \end{bmatrix} \begin{bmatrix} x_1 \\ x_2 \\ x_3 \\ \vdots \\ x_N \end{bmatrix} = \begin{bmatrix} b_1 \\ b_2 \\ b_3 \\ \vdots \\ b_N \end{bmatrix}. \tag{3.96}$$

To eliminate x_1, we combined equations in a particular way. That process can be expressed as a matrix multiplication—starting with

$$\mathbf{Ax} = \mathbf{b}, \tag{3.97}$$

we multiplied by the matrix $\mathbf{M}_1$, where

$$\mathbf{M}_1 = \begin{bmatrix} 1 & 0 & 0 & \ldots & 0 \\ -a_{21}/a_{11} & 1 & 0 & \ldots & 0 \\ -a_{31}/a_{11} & 0 & 1 & \ldots & 0 \\ \vdots & \vdots & \vdots & \ddots & \vdots \\ -a_{N1}/a_{11} & 0 & 0 & \ldots & 1 \end{bmatrix}, \tag{3.98}$$

yielding the equation $\mathbf{M}_1\mathbf{A}\mathbf{x} = \mathbf{M}_1\mathbf{b}$ where

$$\mathbf{M}_1\mathbf{A} = \begin{bmatrix} a_{11} & a_{12} & a_{13} & \cdots & a_{1N} \\ 0 & a_{22} - \dfrac{a_{21}}{a_{11}}a_{12} & a_{23} - \dfrac{a_{21}}{a_{11}}a_{13} & \cdots & a_{2N} - \dfrac{a_{21}}{a_{11}}a_{1N} \\ 0 & a_{32} - \dfrac{a_{31}}{a_{11}}a_{12} & a_{33} - \dfrac{a_{31}}{a_{11}}a_{13} & \cdots & a_{3N} - \dfrac{a_{31}}{a_{11}}a_{1N} \\ \vdots & \vdots & \vdots & \ddots & \vdots \\ 0 & a_{N2} - \dfrac{a_{N1}}{a_{11}}a_{12} & a_{N3} - \dfrac{a_{N1}}{a_{11}}a_{13} & \cdots & a_{NN} - \dfrac{a_{N1}}{a_{11}}a_{1N} \end{bmatrix} \tag{3.99}$$

and

$$\mathbf{M}_1\mathbf{b} = \begin{bmatrix} b_1 \\ b_2 - \dfrac{a_{21}}{a_{11}}b_1 \\ b_3 - \dfrac{a_{31}}{a_{11}}b_1 \\ \vdots \\ b_N - \dfrac{a_{N1}}{a_{11}}b_1 \end{bmatrix}, \tag{3.100}$$

which is just what we would expect from Equation 3.95. The next step, to eliminate x_2 from equations 3 through N, is accomplished by multiplying by $\mathbf{M}_2$, and so on.

A particularly useful variation of this method is due to Crout. In it, we write $\mathbf{A}$ as a product of a lower triangular matrix $\mathbf{L}$ and an upper triangular matrix $\mathbf{U}$,

$$\mathbf{A} = \mathbf{LU}, \tag{3.101}$$

or

$$\begin{bmatrix} a_{11} & a_{12} & a_{13} & \dots & a_{1N} \\ a_{21} & a_{22} & a_{23} & \dots & a_{2N} \\ a_{31} & a_{32} & a_{33} & \dots & a_{3N} \\ \vdots & \vdots & \vdots & \ddots & \vdots \\ a_{N1} & a_{N2} & a_{N3} & \dots & a_{NN} \end{bmatrix}$$

$$= \begin{bmatrix} l_{11} & 0 & 0 & \dots & 0 \\ l_{21} & l_{22} & 0 & \dots & 0 \\ l_{31} & l_{32} & l_{33} & \dots & 0 \\ \vdots & \vdots & \vdots & \ddots & \vdots \\ l_{N1} & l_{N2} & l_{N3} & \dots & l_{NN} \end{bmatrix} \begin{bmatrix} 1 & u_{12} & u_{13} & \dots & u_{1N} \\ 0 & 1 & u_{23} & \dots & u_{2N} \\ 0 & 0 & 1 & \dots & u_{3N} \\ \vdots & \vdots & \vdots & \ddots & \vdots \\ 0 & 0 & 0 & \dots & 1 \end{bmatrix}. \tag{3.102}$$

Written out like this, the meaning of "lower" and "upper" triangular matrix is pretty clear. It might seem that finding $\mathbf{L}$ and $\mathbf{U}$ would be difficult, but actually it's not. Consider an element in the first column of $\mathbf{A}$, and compare it to the corresponding element of the matrix product on the right side. We find that $a_{11} = l_{11}$, $a_{21} = l_{21}$, $a_{31} = l_{31}$, and so on, giving us the first column of $\mathbf{L}$. From the first row of $\mathbf{A}$ we find

$$a_{12} = l_{11}u_{12}$$
$$a_{13} = l_{11}u_{13}$$
$$\vdots$$
$$a_{1N} = l_{11}u_{1N}. \tag{3.103}$$

But we already know l_{11}, and so we can solve these equations for the first row of $\mathbf{U}$,

$$u_{1j} = a_{1j}/l_{11}, \qquad j = 2, \dots, N. \tag{3.104}$$

We now move to the second column of $\mathbf{A}$, which gives us

$$a_{22} = l_{21}u_{12} + l_{22}$$
$$a_{32} = l_{31}u_{12} + l_{32}$$
$$\vdots$$
$$a_{N2} = l_{N1}u_{12} + l_{N2}. \tag{3.105}$$

Again, we know u_{12} and all the l_{i1} appearing in these equations, so we can solve them for the second column of $\mathbf{L}$,

$$l_{i2} = a_{i2} - l_{i1}u_{12}, \qquad i = 2, \dots, N. \tag{3.106}$$

We then consider the second row of $\mathbf{A}$, and so on. In general, from the k-th column of $\mathbf{A}$ we find that

$$l_{ik} = a_{ik} - \sum_{j=1}^{k-1} l_{ij} u_{jk}, \quad i = k, k+1, \ldots, N, \tag{3.107}$$

while from the k-th row of $\mathbf{A}$ we find that

$$u_{kj} = \frac{a_{kj} - \sum_{i=1}^{k-1} l_{ki} u_{ij}}{l_{kk}}, \quad j = k+1, k+2, \ldots, N. \tag{3.108}$$

By alternating between the columns and rows, we can solve for all the elements of $\mathbf{L}$ and $\mathbf{U}$.

Recall that the original problem is to find $\mathbf{x}$ in the matrix equation

$$\mathbf{Ax} = \mathbf{b}, \tag{3.109}$$

or, equivalently, in

$$\mathbf{LUx} = \mathbf{b}, \tag{3.110}$$

where we've replaced $\mathbf{A}$ by $\mathbf{LU}$. Defining $\mathbf{z} = \mathbf{Ux}$, this is the same as

$$\mathbf{Lz} = \mathbf{b}, \tag{3.111}$$

an equation for the unknown $\mathbf{z}$. But this is "easy" to solve! In terms of the component equations, we have

$$
\begin{aligned}
l_{11}z_1 &&&= b_1 \\
l_{21}z_1 &+ l_{22}z_2 &&= b_2 \\
l_{31}z_1 &+ l_{32}z_2 &+ l_{33}z_3 &= b_3. \\
\vdots &&& \vdots \\
l_{N1}z_1 &+ l_{N2}z_2 &+ l_{N3} \cdots + l_{NN}z_N &= b_N
\end{aligned}
\tag{3.112}
$$

From the first of these we find $z_1 = b_1/l_{11}$, and from subsequent equations we find

$$
\begin{aligned}
z_i &= \frac{b_i - l_{i1}z_1 - l_{i2}z_2 \cdots - l_{i,i-1}z_{i-1}}{l_{ii}} \\
&= \frac{b_i - \sum_{k=1}^{i-1} l_{ik} z_k}{l_{ii}}, \quad i = 2, \ldots, N,
\end{aligned}
\tag{3.113}
$$

by *forward substitution*. Having found $\mathbf{z}$, we then solve

$$\mathbf{Ux} = \mathbf{z} \tag{3.114}$$

for $\mathbf{x}$. Since $\mathbf{U}$ is upper diagonal, this equation is also easily solved—it's already in the form required for *backward substitution*. We have

$$
\begin{aligned}
x_1 + u_{12}x_2 + u_{13}x_3 \ldots + u_{1N}x_N &= z_1 \\
x_2 + u_{23}x_3 \ldots + u_{2N}x_N &= z_2 \\
x_3 \ldots + u_{3N}x_N &= z_3\,, \\
&\vdots \\
x_N &= z_N
\end{aligned}
\tag{3.115}
$$

from which we find

$$
x_{N-i} = z_{N-i} - \sum_{k=N-i+1}^{N} u_{N-i,k}\,x_k, \qquad i = 1, \ldots, N-1.
\tag{3.116}
$$

In some problems we might be required to solve $\mathbf{Ax} = \mathbf{b}$ for many different $\mathbf{b}$. In that situation we would perform the decomposition only once, storing $\mathbf{L}$ and $\mathbf{U}$ and using them in the substitution step to find $\mathbf{x}$.

Superficially, this process looks much different from Gaussian elimination. However, as you move through it, you find that you're performing exactly the same arithmetic steps as with Gaussian elimination—actually, the Crout decomposition is nothing more than an efficient bookkeeping scheme. It has the additional advantage of not requiring $\mathbf{b}$ until the substitution phase. Thus the decomposition is independent of $\mathbf{b}$, and once the decomposition has been accomplished, only the substitution phases need to be performed to solve for $\mathbf{x}$ with a different $\mathbf{b}$. The LU decomposition is also efficient in terms of storage, in that the original array $\mathbf{A}$ can be used to store its LU equivalent. That is, the array $\mathbf{A}$ will initially contain the elements of $\mathbf{A}$, but can be overwritten so as to store $\mathbf{L}$ and $\mathbf{U}$ in the scheme

$$
[A] = \begin{bmatrix}
\mathtt{L(1,1)} & \mathtt{U(1,2)} & \mathtt{U(1,3)} & \ldots & \mathtt{U(1,N)} \\
\mathtt{L(2,1)} & \mathtt{L(2,2)} & \mathtt{U(2,3)} & \ldots & \mathtt{U(2,N)} \\
\mathtt{L(3,1)} & \mathtt{L(3,2)} & \mathtt{L(3,3)} & \ldots & \mathtt{U(3,N)} \\
\vdots & \vdots & \vdots & \ddots & \vdots \\
\mathtt{L(N,1)} & \mathtt{L(1,2)} & \mathtt{L(1,3)} & \ldots & \mathtt{L(N,N)}
\end{bmatrix}.
\tag{3.117}
$$

There is a problem with the algorithm, however, as it's been presented. If any l_{qq} is zero, the computer will attempt to divide by zero. This could happen, for example, in trying to solve the set of equations

$$
\begin{aligned}
x_2 &= 2 \\
x_1 &= 1.
\end{aligned}
\tag{3.118}
$$

These equations clearly have a trivial solution, but in determining the first row of **U** from Equation 3.104 the algorithm will attempt to evaluate u_{12} as $1/0$. The remedy is to simply interchange the order of the two equations. In general, we'll search for the largest element of the k-th column of **L**, and interchange the rows to move that element onto the diagonal. If the largest element is zero, then the system of equations has no unique solution! In some cases it can also happen that the coefficients vary by orders of magnitude. This makes determining the "largest" difficult. To make the comparison of the coefficients meaningful, the equations should be scaled so that the largest coefficient is made to be unity. (We note that this scaling is done for comparison purposes only, and need not be included as a step in the actual computation.) The swapping of rows and scaling makes the coding a little involved, and so we'll provide a working function, LUsolve, that incorporates these complications.

```
function [x,det] = LUsolve(a,b,N)
% This function solves the linear set of equations
%
%       A x = b
%
% by the method of LU decomposition.
%
% INPUT:   N the actual size of the arrays for this problem
%          A an N by N array of coefficients, altered on output
%          b a vector of length N
%
% OUTPUT: x the 'solution' vector
%          det the determinant of A. If the determinant is zero,
%              A is SINGULAR.
%
det = 1.0;
% First, determine a scaling factor for each row. (We
% could "normalize" the equation by multiplying by this
% factor. However, since we only want it for comparison
% purposes, we don't need to actually perform the
% multiplication.)
for i = 1:N
    order(i) = i;
    max = 0.;
    for j = 1:N
        if(abs(a(i,j)) > max), max = abs(a(i,j)); end
    end
    scale(i) = 1./max;
end
% Start the LU decomposition. The original matrix A
% will be overwritten by the elements of L and U as
% they are determined. The first row and column
```

```
% are specially treated, as is L(N,N).
for k = 1:N-1
    % Do a column of L
    if( k == 1 )
        % No work is necessary.
    else
        % Compute elements of L from Eq. 3.107
        for i = k:N
            sum = a(i,k);
            for j = 1: k-1
                sum = sum - a(i,j)*a(j,k);
            end
            a(i,k) = sum;            % Put L(i,k) into A.
        end
    end
    % Do we need to interchange rows? We want the largest
    % (scaled) element of the recently computed column of L
    % moved to the diagonal (k,k) location.
    max = 0.;
    for i = k:N
        if(scale(i)*a(i,k) >= max)
            max = scale(i)*a(i,k);
            imax=i;
        end
    end
    % Largest element is L(imax,k). If imax=k, the largest
    % (scaled) element is already on the diagonal.
    if(imax == k)
                            % No need to exchange rows.
    else
                            % Exchange rows...
        det = -det;
        for j = 1:N
            temporary = a(imax,j);
            a(imax,j) = a(k,j);
            a(k,j)    = temporary;
        end
                            % scale factors...
        temporary   = scale(imax);
        scale(imax) = scale(k);
        scale(k)    = temporary;
                            % and record changes in the ordering
        itemp       = order(imax) ;
        order(imax) = order(k);
        order(k)    = itemp;
    end
    det = det * a(k,k);
```

```
        % Now compute a row of U.
        if(k==1)
        %  The first row is treated special, see Eq. 3.104.
        for j = 2:N
            a(1,j) = a(1,j) / a(1,1);
        end
    else
        % Compute U(k,j) from Eq. 3.108.
        for j = k+1:N
        sum = a(k,j);
        for i = 1:k-1
            sum = sum - a(k,i)*a(i,j);
        end
        % Put the element U(k,j) into A.
        a(k,j) = sum / a(k,k);
        end
    end
end
% Now, for the last element of L
sum = a(N,N);
for j = 1:N-1
    sum = sum - a(N,j)*a(j,N);
end
a(N,N) = sum;
det = det * a(N,N);

% LU decomposition is now complete.

% We now start the solution phase. Since the equations
% have been interchanged, we interchange the elements of
% B the same way, putting the result into X.
for i = 1:N
    x(i) = b(order(i));
end
                            % Forward substitution...
x(1) = x(1) / a(1,1);
for i = 2:N
    sum = x(i);
    for k = 1:i-1
        sum = sum - a(i,k)*x(k);
    end
    x(i) = sum / a(i,i);
end
                            % and backward substitution...
for i = 1:N-1
    sum = x(N-i);
    for k = N-i+1:N
```

```
            sum = sum - a(N-i,k)*x(k);
        end
        x(N-i) = sum;
    end
                                    % We're done!
```

A calculation of the determinant of the matrix has been included. The determinant of a product of matrices is just the product of the determinants of the matrices. For triangular matrices, the determinant is just the product of the diagonal elements, as you'll find if you try to expand it according to Cramer's rule. So after the matrix **A** has been written as **LU**, the evaluation of the determinant is straightforward. Except, of course, that permuting the rows introduces an overall sign change that must be accounted for. If the determinant is zero, no unique, nontrivial solution exists; small determinants are an indication of an ill-conditioned set of equations whose solution might be very difficult.

EXERCISE 3.17

You might want to test the function by solving the equations

$$
\begin{bmatrix}
2 & -1 & 0 & 0 & 0 \\
-1 & 2 & -1 & 0 & 0 \\
0 & -1 & 2 & -1 & 0 \\
0 & 0 & -1 & 2 & -1 \\
0 & 0 & 0 & -1 & 2
\end{bmatrix}
\begin{bmatrix}
x_1 \\ x_2 \\ x_3 \\ x_4 \\ x_5
\end{bmatrix}
=
\begin{bmatrix}
0 \\ 1 \\ 2 \\ 3 \\ 4
\end{bmatrix},
\tag{3.119}
$$

which you've seen before.

EXERCISE 3.18

As an example of a system that might be difficult to solve, consider

$$
\begin{bmatrix}
1 & 1/2 & 1/3 & 1/4 & 1/5 \\
1/2 & 1/3 & 1/4 & 1/5 & 1/6 \\
1/3 & 1/4 & 1/5 & 1/6 & 1/7 \\
1/4 & 1/5 & 1/6 & 1/7 & 1/8 \\
1/5 & 1/6 & 1/7 & 1/8 & 1/9
\end{bmatrix}
\begin{bmatrix}
x_1 \\ x_2 \\ x_3 \\ x_4 \\ x_5
\end{bmatrix}
=
\begin{bmatrix}
1 \\ 2 \\ 3 \\ 4 \\ 5
\end{bmatrix}.
\tag{3.120}
$$

The matrix with elements $H_{ij} = 1/(i+j-1)$ is called the Hilbert matrix, and is a classic example of an ill-conditioned matrix. With double precision arithmetic, you are equipped to solve this particular problem. However, as the dimension of the array increases it becomes futile to attempt a solution. Even for this 5×5 matrix, the determinant is surprisingly small—be sure to print the determinant, as well as find the solutions.

Before returning to the problem of curve fitting by least squares, we need to emphasize the universality of systems of linear equations, and hence the importance of Gauss elimination in their solution. You've probably seen this problem arise many times already, and you will surely see it many more times. For example, consider a typical University Physics problem: electrical networks, such as in Figure 3.4.

Let's arbitrarily define the potential at reference point i to be zero; the potential at a is then V. Knowing the resistances and the applied voltage, the problem is to determine the potential at each of the other points $b, c, \ldots, h$. Current enters the resistance grid at a, passes through the resistors, and returns to the battery through point i. Since there is no accumulation of charge at any point, any current flowing into a node must also flow out—this is simply a statement of the conservation of electrical charge. As an example, the current flowing through R_1 to the point b must equal the sum of the currents flowing through resistors R_3 and R_4 away from the point b. And from Ohm's Law we know that the voltage drop across a resistor is the product of the resistance and the current, or that the current is simply the voltage drop divided by the resistance. For point b we can then write

$$\frac{V - V_b}{R_1} = \frac{V_b - V_d}{R_3} + \frac{V_b - V_e}{R_4}, \qquad (3.121)$$

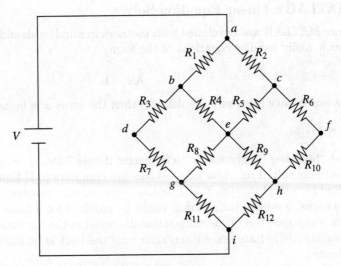

Figure 3.4   An electrical network requiring the solution of a set of simultaneous linear equations.

and similar equations for all the other points in the network. Consider a specific network in which $R_1 = R_3 = R_4 = R_9 = R_{10} = R_{12} = 1$ ohm, $R_2 = R_5 = R_6 = R_7 = R_8 = R_{11} = 2$ ohm, and $V = 10$ volts. We easily find the following set of 7 equations describing the system,

$$
\begin{aligned}
3V_b & & -V_d & & -V_e & & & & & = & 10 \\
& 3V_c & & & -V_e & & -V_f & & & = & 10 \\
2V_b & & & -3V_d & & & & +V_g & & = & 0 \\
2V_b & +V_c & & & -6V_e & & & +V_g & +2V_h & = & 0 \\
& V_c & & & & -3V_f & & & +2V_h & = & 0 \\
& & & V_d & +V_e & & -3V_g & & & = & 0 \\
& & & & V_e & +V_f & & & -3V_h & = & 0
\end{aligned}
\tag{3.122}
$$

EXERCISE 3.19
Use LUsolve to find the voltages in the described electrical network.

Much more complicated networks can also be considered. Any network involving simply batteries and resistors will lead to a set of simultaneous linear equations such as these. Incorporation of capacitors and inductors, which depend upon the time rate of change of the voltage, give rise to linear differential equations. Including transistors and diodes further complicates the problem by adding nonlinearity to the network.

3.13 MATLAB's Linear Equation Solver

Since MATLAB was developed with matrices in mind, it should come as no surprise that it easily handles equations of the form

$$
\mathbf{Ax} = \mathbf{b}.
\tag{3.123}
$$

If A and b have been suitably defined, then the array x is found as

```
x = A \ b;
```

The "backslash" indicates a "left matrix divide," i.e., $x = A^{-1}b$. The equation is actually solved by—how else?—Gaussian elimination. If Equation 3.123 is to be solved for a single b, then this is undoubtedly the way to solve the problem. In some situations, however, the solution might be required for a large number of different b, in which case the LU decomposition discussed in the previous sections could lead to substantially faster execution, since only the back substitution step needs to be executed.

3.14 General Least Squares Fitting

We can now turn our attention to least squares fitting with an arbitrary polynomial of degree m. We'll write the polynomial as

$$p(x) = c_0 + c_1 x + c_2 x^2 + \cdots + c_m x^m. \tag{3.124}$$

The sum of the square of the errors is then

$$S = \sum_{j=1}^{N} \left(p(x_i) - y_i \right)^2, \tag{3.125}$$

where $p(x)$ is our assumed functional form for the data known at the N points (x_i, y_i). This error is to be minimized by an appropriate choice of the coefficients c_i; in particular, we require

$$\frac{\partial S}{\partial c_0} = \sum_{j=1}^{N} 2 \left(c_0 + c_1 x_j + c_2 x_j^2 + \cdots + c_m x_j^m - y_j \right) = 0,$$

$$\frac{\partial S}{\partial c_1} = \sum_{j=1}^{N} 2 x_j \left(c_0 + c_1 x_j + c_2 x_j^2 + \cdots + c_m x_j^m - y_j \right) = 0,$$

$$\vdots$$

$$\frac{\partial S}{\partial c_m} = \sum_{j=1}^{N} 2 x_j^m \left(c_0 + c_1 x_j + c_2 x_j^2 + \cdots + c_m x_j^m - y_j \right) = 0. \tag{3.126}$$

This gives us $m + 1$ equations for the $m + 1$ unknown coefficients c_j,

$$
\begin{aligned}
c_0 N & + c_1 \sum x_j & + c_2 \sum x_j^2 & + \cdots & + c_m \sum x_j^m - \sum y_j & = 0, \\
c_0 \sum x_j & + c_1 \sum x_j^2 & + c_2 \sum x_j^3 & + \cdots & + c_m \sum x_j^{m+1} - \sum x_j y_j & = 0, \\
\vdots \quad & \qquad \vdots & \qquad \vdots & & & = 0, \\
c_0 \sum x_j^m & + c_1 \sum x_j^{m+1} & + c_2 \sum x_j^{m+2} & + \cdots & + c_m \sum x_j^{m+m} - \sum x_j^m y_j & = 0.
\end{aligned}
\tag{3.127}
$$

These simultaneous linear equations, also known as *normal equations,* can be solved by LUsolve for the coefficients.

Alternatively, we can use MATLAB's built-in function **polyfit** to do the job. With data stored in the x and y arrays, the command

```
p = polyfit(x,y,N)
```

returns the coefficients of the best N-th order polynomial fitting the data, in the least squares sense. The value of this polynomial at the point v can then be obtained using `polyval`,

`polyval(p,v)`

or a plot can be generated using the points in the array xx with

`plot(xx,polyval(p,xx))`

Consider an experiment in which an object has been hurled into the air and its position measured as a function of time. The data obtained in this hypothetical experiment is contained in Figure 3.5. From our studies of mechanics we know that the height should vary as the square of the time, so instead of a linear fit to the data we should use a quadratic one.

EXERCISE 3.20

Fit a quadratic to the position data, using least squares, and determine g, the acceleration due to gravity.

For some problems, particularly if the functional dependence of the data isn't known, there's a temptation to use a high order least squares fit. This approach didn't work earlier when we were interpolating data, and for the same reasons it won't work here either. Simply using a curve with more parameters doesn't guarantee a *better* fit. To illustrate, let's return to the position data and fit a linear, a quadratic, and a cubic polynomial to the data. For the linear fit, the least squares error is computed to be 2.84, which seems rather large given the magnitudes of

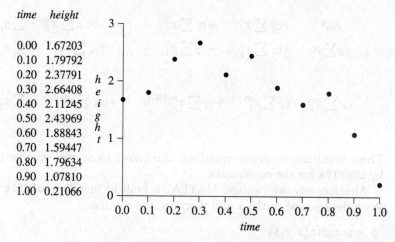

time	height
0.00	1.67203
0.10	1.79792
0.20	2.37791
0.30	2.66408
0.40	2.11245
0.50	2.43969
0.60	1.88843
0.70	1.59447
0.80	1.79634
0.90	1.07810
1.00	0.21066

Figure 3.5 The measured height of a particle at various times.

our data. Even more revealing is the residual error, $y_i - p(x_i)$, which is plotted in Figure 3.6. The magnitudes of the error tell us the fit is not very good. Note that the residual error is almost systematic—at first, it's negative, and then it's positive, and then it's negative again. If we had a good fit, we would expect that the sign of the error would be virtually random. In particular, we would expect that the sign of the error at one point would be independent of the sign at the previous point, so that we would expect the sign of the error to change about half the time. But in these residuals, the error only changes sign twice. This *strongly* suggests a functional dependence in the data that we have not included in our polynomial approximation.

But in Exercise 3.20 you have already determined the best quadratic fit and found that the least squares error, as determined from Equation 3.125, was about 0.52. The quadratic fit is thus a considerable improvement over the linear one. Moreover, the residual error is smaller in magnitude and more scattered than for the linear fit. In fact, there are 7 sign changes in the error, much more consistent with the picture of the approximation "fitting" through the scatter in the data than was the linear fit.

So we have found a good fit to the data, having both a small magnitude in the error and a healthy scatter in the signs of the residual errors. The prudent course of action is to quit! And what if we were to consider a higher degree polynomial? If there were no scatter in the data, then trying to fit a cubic would yield a c_3 coefficient that was zero. Of course, there's always some scatter in the data, so this rarely happens. But the fit is no better than we already have—we find that $S = 0.52$ again. The unmistakable conclusion is that there is no advantage in going to higher degree approximations.

To summarize: The primary factor in determining a good least squares fit is the validity of the functional form to which you're fitting. Certainly, theoretical or

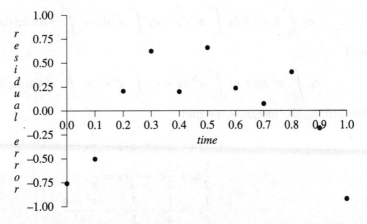

Figure 3.6   The residual error from the linear least squares fit to the data of Figure 3.5.

analytic information about the physical problem should be incorporated whenever it's available. The residual error, the difference between the determined "best fit" and the actual data, is a good indicator of the quality of the fit, and can suggest instances when a systematic functional dependence has been overlooked.

3.15 Least Squares and Orthogonal Polynomials

Although fitting data is a primary application of the method of least squares, the method can also be applied to the approximation of functions. Consider, for example, a known function $f(x)$ that we want to approximate by the polynomial $p(x)$. Instead of a Taylor series expansion, we'll try to find the *best* polynomial approximation, in the least squares sense, to the function $f(x)$. To this end we replace the sum over data points by an integral, and define the error as being

$$S = \int_a^b \left(f(x) - p(x) \right)^2 \, dx. \tag{3.128}$$

We'll obtain normal equations just as before, by minimizing S with respect to the coefficients in the approximating polynomial.

Consider a specific example: What quadratic polynomial best approximates $\sin \pi x$ between 0 and 1? We define the least squares error as

$$S = \int_0^1 \left(\sin \pi x - (c_0 + c_1 x + c_2 x^2) \right)^2 \, dx, \tag{3.129}$$

and take the partial derivatives of S with respect to the coefficients to determine the normal equations

$$c_0 \int_0^1 dx + c_1 \int_0^1 x \, dx + c_2 \int_0^1 x^2 \, dx = \int_0^1 \sin \pi x \, dx, \tag{3.130}$$

$$c_0 \int_0^1 x \, dx + c_1 \int_0^1 x^2 \, dx + c_2 \int_0^1 x^3 \, dx = \int_0^1 x \sin \pi x \, dx, \tag{3.131}$$

and

$$c_0 \int_0^1 x^2 \, dx + c_1 \int_0^1 x^3 \, dx + c_2 \int_0^1 x^4 \, dx = \int_0^1 x^2 \sin \pi x \, dx. \tag{3.132}$$

Performing the integrals, we find

$$c_0 + \frac{1}{2}c_1 + \frac{1}{3}c_2 = \frac{2}{\pi},$$

$$\frac{1}{2}c_0 + \frac{1}{3}c_1 + \frac{1}{4}c_2 = \frac{1}{\pi},$$

$$\frac{1}{3}c_0 + \frac{1}{4}c_1 + \frac{1}{5}c_2 = \frac{\pi^2 - 4}{\pi^3}. \tag{3.133}$$

We can solve this set of equations for the coefficients, and thus determine the "best" quadratic approximation to be

$$p(x) = -0.0505 + 4.1225x - 4.1225x^2, \qquad 0 < x < 1. \tag{3.134}$$

This expression certainly would not have been found by a Taylor's series expansion. It is, in fact, fundamentally different. Whereas the Taylor series is an expansion about a point, the least squares fit results from consideration of the function over a specific region.

In principle, we could find higher degree polynomials giving an even better approximation to the function. But Equation 3.133 seems familiar—writing it in matrix form we have

$$\begin{bmatrix} 1 & 1/2 & 1/3 \\ 1/2 & 1/3 & 1/4 \\ 1/3 & 1/4 & 1/5 \end{bmatrix} \begin{bmatrix} c_0 \\ c_1 \\ c_2 \end{bmatrix} = \begin{bmatrix} 2/\pi \\ 1/\pi \\ (\pi^2 - 4)/\pi^3 \end{bmatrix}, \tag{3.135}$$

and we recognize the square array as a Hilbert matrix. If we were to consider higher degree approximations, the dimension of the Hilbert matrix would increase and its determinant would become exceedingly small, making it very difficult to solve this problem. We should stress that *any* polynomial approximation by least squares leads to this form, not just the particular example we've treated. (Actually, the function being approximated only appears on the right-hand side, and so doesn't influence the array at all. Only the limits of the integration affect the numerical entries in the array.)

Instead of expanding in the function as

$$f(x) \approx p(x) = c_0 + c_1 x + c_2 x^2, \tag{3.136}$$

let's expand it in a more general fashion as

$$f(x) \approx p(x) = \alpha_0 p_0(x) + \alpha_1 p_1(x) + \alpha_2 p_2(x), \tag{3.137}$$

where α_i are coefficients and the $p_i(x)$ are i-th degree polynomials. Let's see what conditions we might put on these polynomials to make the normal equations easier to solve. We'll consider the general problem of fitting over the region $[-1, 1]$, and write the error as

$$S = \int_{-1}^{1} \left(f(x) - \alpha_0 p_0(x) - \alpha_1 p_1(x) - \alpha_2 p_2(x) \right)^2 dx, \tag{3.138}$$

partial differentiation with respect to the α_i lead to the normal equations

$$\alpha_0 \int_{-1}^{1} p_0^2(x)\,dx + \alpha_1 \int_{-1}^{1} p_0(x)p_1(x)\,dx + \alpha_2 \int_{-1}^{1} p_0(x)p_2(x)\,dx$$

$$= \int_{-1}^{1} p_0(x)f(x)\,dx, \tag{3.139}$$

$$\alpha_0 \int_{-1}^{1} p_0(x)p_1(x)\,dx + \alpha_1 \int_{-1}^{1} p_1^2(x)\,dx + \alpha_2 \int_{-1}^{1} p_1(x)p_2(x)\,dx$$

$$= \int_{-1}^{1} p_1(x)f(x)\,dx, \tag{3.140}$$

and

$$\alpha_0 \int_{-1}^{1} p_0 p_2(x)\,dx + \alpha_1 \int_{-1}^{1} p_1(x)p_2(x)\,dx + \alpha_2 \int_{-1}^{1} p_2^2(x)\,dx$$

$$= \int_{-1}^{1} p_2(x)f(x)\,dx. \tag{3.141}$$

Now, these equations for α_i would be easier to solve if we could choose the $p_i(x)$ to make some of these integrals vanish. That is, if

$$\int_{i1}^{1} p_i(x)p_j(x)\,dx = 0, \qquad i \neq j, \tag{3.142}$$

then we could immediately solve the normal equations and find that the "best fit" in the least squares sense is obtained when the expansion coefficients are simply

$$\alpha_i = \frac{\int_{-1}^{1} p_i(x)f(x)\,dx}{\int_{-1}^{1} p_i^2(x)\,dx}. \tag{3.143}$$

We should also note that the determination of one coefficient is independent from all the others—once α_1 has been found, it doesn't change as the expansion is extended to include higher degree polynomials. These are remarkable properties, well worth having.

Functions that satisfy Equation 3.142 are called *orthogonal polynomials*, and play several important roles in computational physics. We might define them in a more general fashion, as satisfying

$$\int_{a}^{b} w(x)\phi_i(x)\phi_j(x)\,dx = 0, \qquad i \neq j, \tag{3.144}$$

where $[a, b]$ is the region of interest and $w(x)$ is a weighting function. Several well-known functions are actually orthogonal functions, some of which are listed in Table 3.3. Of these, the Legendre, Laguerre, and Hermite polynomials are all of direct physical significance, and so we often find instances in which the physical solution is expanded in terms of these functions. The Chebyshev polynomials have no direct physical significance, but are particularly convenient for approximating functions.

Table 3.3   Orthogonal Polynomials

$[a, b]$	$w(x)$	Symbol	Name
$[-1, 1]$	1	$P_n(x)$	Legendre
$[-1, 1]$	$(1 - x^2)^{-1/2}$	$T_n(x)$	Chebyshev I
$[-1, 1]$	$(1 - x^2)^{+1/2}$	$U_n(x)$	Chebyshev II
$[0, \infty)$	e^{-x}	$L_n(x)$	Laguerre
$(-\infty, \infty)$	e^{-x^2}	$H_n(x)$	Hermite

3.16 Nonlinear Least Squares

Not all the problems that confront us are linear. Imagine that you have some experimental data that you believe should fit a particular theoretical model. For example, atoms in a gas emit light in a range of wavelengths described by the Lorentzian lineshape function

$$I(\lambda) = I_0 \frac{1}{1 + 4(\lambda - \lambda_0)^2/\Gamma^2}, \qquad (3.145)$$

where λ is the wavelength of the light emitted, λ_0 is the resonant wavelength, Γ is the width of the curve (full width at half maximum), and I_0 is the intensity of the light at $\lambda = \lambda_0$. From measurements of $I(\lambda)$, which necessarily contain experimental noise, we're to determine λ_0, Γ, and I_0. (Actually, the intensity is often measured in arbitrary units, and so is unimportant. The position and width of the curve, however, are both significant quantities. The position depends upon the atom emitting the light and hence serves to identify the atom, while the width conveys information concerning the atom's environment, e.g., the pressure of the gas.)

Sample data of ambient room light, obtained by an optical multichannel analyzer, is presented in Figure 3.7. A diffraction grating is used to spread the light, which then falls upon a linear array of very sensitive electro-optical elements, so that each element is exposed to some (small) range of wavelengths. Each element then responds according to the intensity of the light falling upon it, yielding an entire spectrum at one time. Note that the data is not falling to zero away from the peak as would be suggested by our theoretical lineshape. This is typical of experimental data—a baseline must also be established. We thus define our error as

$$S = \sum_{j=1}^{N} \left(I_j - B - I(\lambda_j)\right)^2, \qquad (3.146)$$

where I_j are the measured intensities. To obtain the normal equations, we minimize S with respect to B, the baseline, and the lineshape parameters λ_0, Γ, and I_0, as before. However, $I(\lambda)$ is not a linear function of λ_0 and Γ, so that the normal equations we derive will be *nonlinear* equations, much more difficult than the linear ones we had earlier.

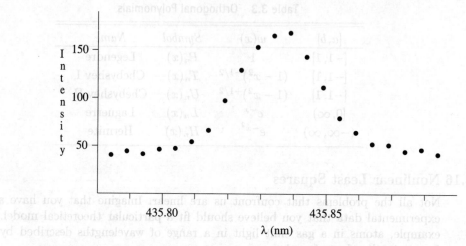

Figure 3.7   A spectrum of ambient room light, in arbitrary units of intensity. *(Data courtesy L. W. Downes, Miami University.)*

Rather than pursue this approach, let's look at the problem from a different perspective. First, let's write the least squares error as

$$S(a_1, a_2, \ldots, a_m) = \sum_{k=1}^{N} \left(y_k - Y(x_k; a_1, a_2, \ldots, a_m)\right)^2, \qquad (3.147)$$

where y_k are the data at x_k and $Y(x_k; a_1, a_2, \ldots a_m)$ is the proposed function evaluated at x_k and parameterized by the coefficients a_1, a_2, ..., a_m. Our goal is to minimize S—why don't we simply vary the parameters a_i until we find a minimum? If we already have initial guesses $a_1^0, a_2^0, \ldots, a_m^0$ that lie near a minimum, then S will be approximately quadratic. Let's evaluate S at $a_1^0 + h_1$, a_1^0, and $a_1^0 - h_1$, holding all the other parameters fixed. The minimum of a quadratic interpolating polynomial through these points then gives us a better approximation to the minimum of S,

$$a_1^1 = a_1^0 - \frac{h_1}{2} \frac{S(a_1^0 + h_1, \ldots) - S(a_1^0 - h_1, \ldots)}{S(a_1^0 + h_1, \ldots) - 2S(a_1^0, \ldots) + S(a_1^0 - h_1, \ldots)}. \qquad (3.148)$$

The process is then repeated for a_2, a_3, ..., a_m. Admittedly, this is a crude procedure, but it works! (Sort of.)

We want to keep the programming as general as possible, so that we don't have to rewrite the routine to solve a different problem. Crucial portions of the code might look something like the following:

```
function minimize
clear;
% Initial guesses for the parameters:
```

```
a(1) = 435.84; % resonant wavelength
a(2) =    .03; % linewidth
a(3) =  120.0; % intensity
a(4) =   40.0; % Baseline
% Initial values for the step sizes
h(1) = 0.01;
h(2) = 0.005;
h(3) = 4.0;
h(4) = 2.0;
%
disp('                                        Least Squares');
disp('    wavelength   linewidth  intensity  baseline    Error');
fprintf(' %12.6f %10.6f %9.2f  %8.2f  %8.2f\n',a(1),a(2),a(3),a(4),LSE(a));
%
[a,h] = crude(a,h);
fprintf(' %12.6f %10.6f %9.2f  %8.2f  %8.2f\n',a(1),a(2),a(3),a(4),LSE(a));
end


function [a,h] = crude(a,h)
% Cycle through each parameter
for i = 1:length(a)
    % The SUM will be evaluated with the parameters
    % A_PLUS, A, and A_MINUS:
    for k = 1:length(a)
        if(k == i)
            a_plus(i) = a(i) + h(i);
            a_minus(i)= a(i) - h(i);
        else
            a_plus(k) = a(k);
            a_minus(k)= a(k);
        end
    end
    sp = LSE(a_plus); % Evaluate the sums.
    s0 = LSE( a );
    sm = LSE(a_minus);

    a(i) = a(i) - 0.5*h(i)*(sp-sm)/(sp-2.*s0+sm);
    % As we move toward a minimum, we should decrease
    % step size used in calculating the derivative.
    h(i) = 0.5 * h(i);
end
end

function [ss] = LSE(a)
% All the information about the Least Squares Error,
% including the proposed functional form of the data
% --- and the data itself --- is located in this
```

```
% function, and NOWHERE ELSE.
x = [ 435.784, 435.789, 435.794, 435.799, 435.804, 435.809, 435.814,...
      435.819, 435.824, 435.829, 435.834, 435.839, 435.844, 435.849,...
      435.854, 435.859, 435.864, 435.869, 435.874, 435.879, 435.884];
y = [  40.0,    44.0,    41.0,    46.0,    47.0,    54.0,    66.0,...
       97.0,   129.0,   153.0,   165.0,   168.0,   143.0,   111.0,...
       79.0,    64.0,    52.0,    51.0,    44.0,    46.0,    41.0];
%
% The theoretical curve TC is given as
%
%                                      intensity
% TC(lambda) = baseline + --------------------------------
%                          1+4(lambda-lambda_0)**2/gamma**2
% where
                  lambda_0 = a(1); % the resonance wavelength
                     gamma = a(2); % the linewidth
                 intensity = a(3);
                  baseline = a(4);
ss = 0.;
for i = 1:21
    lambda = x(i);
    % evaluate the theoretical curve:
    TC=baseline+intensity/(1.+4.*(lambda-lambda_0)^2/gamma^2);
    % add the square of the difference to the sum:
    ss=ss+(y(i)-TC )^2;
end
```

As presented, the code will vary each of the parameters once. But of course, this doesn't assure us of finding a true minimum. In general, we'll need to repeat the process many times, adjusting the parameters each time so that the sum of the errors is decreased. S can be reduced to zero only if the proposed curve fits every data point. Since we assume there is random scatter in the experimental data, this cannot occur. Rather, the error will be reduced to some minimum, determined by the validity of the proposed curve and the "noise" in the data. Modify the code to make repeated calls to CRUDE. As with the root-finder, exercise caution—terminate the process if the error hasn't decreased sufficiently, and provide a graceful exit after some maximum number, say fifteen, iterations.

EXERCISE 3.21
With these modifications, perform a least squares fit to the lineshape data. By the way, can you identify the atom?

Although this crude method works, it can be rather slow to converge. In essence, it's possible for the routine to "walk around" a minimum, getting closer at each step but not moving directly toward it. This happens because the method does not use any information about the (multidimensional) shape of S to decide in which direction to move—it simply cycles through each parameter in turn. Let's reexamine our approach and see if we can develop a method that is more robust in moving toward the minimum.

Our goal is to determine the point at which

$$\frac{\partial S(a_1, a_2, \ldots, a_m)}{\partial a_i} = 0, \tag{3.149}$$

for $i = 1, \ldots, m$. (These are just the normal equations we had before.) Let's expand $\partial S / \partial a_i$ about $(a_1^0, a_2^0, \ldots, a_m^0)$, keeping only the linear terms,

$$\frac{\partial S(a_1, a_2, \ldots, a_m)}{\partial a_i} = \frac{\partial S(a_1^0, a_2^0, \ldots, a_m^0)}{\partial a_i}$$
$$+ (a_1 - a_1^0) \frac{\partial}{\partial a_1} \frac{\partial S(a_1^0, a_2^0, \ldots, a_m^0)}{\partial a_i}$$
$$+ (a_2 - a_2^0) \frac{\partial}{\partial a_2} \frac{\partial S(a_1^0, a_2^0, \ldots, a_m^0)}{\partial a_i}$$
$$+ \cdots$$
$$+ (a_m - a_m^0) \frac{\partial}{\partial a_m} \frac{\partial S(a_1^0, a_2^0, \ldots, a_m^0)}{\partial a_i}. \tag{3.150}$$

Defining $\delta_i^0 = a_i - a_i^0$,

$$S_i = \frac{\partial S(a_1^0, a_2^0, \ldots, a_m^0)}{\partial a_i}, \tag{3.151}$$

and

$$S_{ij} = \frac{\partial^2 S(a_1^0, a_2^0, \ldots, a_m^0)}{\partial a_i \partial a_j}, \tag{3.152}$$

we arrive at the set of *linear* equations

$$S_{11}\delta_1^0 + S_{12}\delta_2^0 + \cdots S_{1m}\delta_m^0 = -S_1$$
$$S_{21}\delta_1^0 + S_{22}\delta_2^0 + \cdots S_{2m}\delta_m^0 = -S_2$$
$$\vdots$$
$$S_{m1}\delta_1^0 + S_{m2}\delta_2^0 + \cdots S_{mm}\delta_m^0 = -S_m. \tag{3.153}$$

These equations are linear, of course, because we kept only linear terms in the expansion of the partial derivative, Equation 3.150. We can write them in matrix form as

$$
\begin{bmatrix}
S_{11} & S_{12} & \dots & S_{1m} \\
S_{21} & S_{22} & \dots & S_{2m} \\
\vdots & \vdots & \ddots & \vdots \\
S_{m1} & S_{m2} & \dots & S_{mm}
\end{bmatrix}
\begin{bmatrix}
\delta_1^0 \\
\delta_2^0 \\
\vdots \\
\delta_m^0
\end{bmatrix}
= -
\begin{bmatrix}
S_1 \\
S_2 \\
\vdots \\
S_m
\end{bmatrix} . \tag{3.154}
$$

The square array whose elements are the second partial derivatives of S is known as the *Hessian* of S.

Being a linear matrix equation, we can use the function `LUsolve` to solve for the δ^0's in Equation 3.154. A better approximation to the location of the minimum will then be

$$
a_i^1 = a_i^0 + \delta_i^0, \qquad i = 1, \dots, m. \tag{3.155}
$$

This is virtually the same process we used in finding the roots of equations, except that we now have a set of simultaneous equations to solve. As with root finding, this process is executed repeatedly, so that after the k-th iteration we would write

$$
a_j^k = a_j^{k-1} + \delta_j^{k-1}. \tag{3.156}
$$

The process continues until the δ's are all sufficiently small, or until the iterations fail to significantly reduce S.

This method is nothing more than *Newton's method*, extended to several functions in several independent variables. When close to a minimum, it converges quite rapidly. But if it's started far from the minimum, Newton's method can be slow to converge, and in fact move to a totally different region of parameter space. In one dimension we placed restrictions on the method so that would not happen, but in multiple dimensions such bounds are not easily placed. (In one dimension, bounds are simply two points on the coordinate, but to bound a region in two dimensions requires a curve, which is much harder to specify.) To increase the likelihood of Newton's method being successful—unfortunately, we can't guarantee it!—we need a good initial guess to the minimum, which is most easily obtained by using one or two cycles of the `CRUDE` method before we begin applying Newton's method to the problem. Fundamentally, we're trying to solve a nonlinear problem, a notoriously difficult task full of hidden and disguised subtleties. Nonlinear equations should be approached with a considerable degree of respect and solved with caution.

In Newton's method we need to evaluate the Hessian, the array of second derivatives. This can be done analytically by explicit differentiation of S. However, it's often more convenient—and less prone to error—to use approximations to these derivatives. From our previous discussion of central difference equations, we can easily find that

$$S_{ii} = \frac{\partial^2 S(\ldots, a_i^0, \ldots)}{\partial a_i^2}$$

$$\approx \frac{S(\ldots, a_i^0 + h_i, \ldots) - 2S(\ldots, a_i^0, \ldots,) + S(\ldots, a_i^0 - h_i, \ldots)}{h_i^2} \quad (3.157)$$

and

$$S_{ij} = \frac{\partial^2 S(\ldots, a_i^0, \ldots, a_j^0, \ldots)}{\partial a_i^0 \partial a_j^0}$$

$$\approx \frac{1}{2h_i} \left[\frac{S(\ldots, a_i^0 + h_i, \ldots, a_j^0 + h_j, \ldots) - S(\ldots, a_i^0 + h_i, \ldots, a_j^0 - h_j, \ldots)}{2h_j} \right.$$

$$\left. - \frac{S(\ldots, a_i^0 - h_i, \ldots, a_j^0 + h_j, \ldots) - S(\ldots, a_i^0 - h_i, \ldots, a_j^0 - h_j, \ldots)}{2h_j} \right]. \quad (3.158)$$

In coding these derivatives, one might consider writing separate expressions for each of them. But this runs counter to our programing philosophy of writing general code, rather than specific examples. Having once written the function, we shouldn't have to change it just because some new problem has 6 parameters instead of 4. With a little thought, we can write a very general routine. The code to calculate the Hessian might look like

```
function [a] = newton(a,h)
m = length (a)
% Inputs:
%    a Starting values of the problem parameters
%    h Starting values of the stepsizes whose values are changed
% Outputs:
%    a The new parameters
%
% Function in use
% LSE   contains the information about the data's functional form
%
% The arrays used by NEWTON have the following contents:
% a    a(1), ...,      a(i)    , ..., a(m)
% ap   a(1), ...,   a(i)+h(i), ..., a(m)
% am   a(1), ...,   a(i)-h(i), ..., a(m)
%
% app  a(1), .., a(i)+h(i),  ..., a(j)+h(j), ..., a(m)
% apm  a(1), .., a(i)+h(i),  ..., a(j)-h(j), ..., a(m)
% amp  a(1), .., a(i)-h(i),  ..., a(j)+h(j), ..., a(m)
% amm  a(1), .., a(i)-h(i),  ..., a(j)-h(j), ..., a(m)
```

```
%
...
% Compute the Hessian:
for i = 1:m
    for j = i:m
        if (i ==j)
            for k =1:m
                ap(k) = a(k);
                am(k) = a(k);
            end
            ap(i) = a(i) + h(i);
            am(i) = a(i) - h(i);
            hessian(i,i)=(LSE(ap)-2.0*LSE(a)+LSE(am))/(h(i)*h(i));
        else
            for k = 1:m
                app(k) = a(k);
                apm(k) = a(k);
                amp(k) = a(k);
                amm(k) = a(k);
            end
            app(i) = a(i) + h(i);
            app(j) = a(j) + h(j);
            apm(i) = a(i) + h(i);
            apm(j) = a(j) - h(j);
            amp(i) = a(i) - h(i);
            amp(j) = a(j) + h(j);
            amm(i) = a(i) - h(i);
            amm(j) = a(j) - h(j);
            hessian(i,j) =( (LSE(app)-LSE(apm))/(2.0*h(j))-...
                    (LSE(amp)-LSE(amm))/(2.0*h(j)) )/(2.0*h(i));
            hessian(j,i) = hessian(i,j);
        end
    end
end
...
```

We've used the array **Apm**, for example, to store the parameters $a_1, \ldots, a_i + h_i, \ldots,$ $a_j - h_j, \ldots, a_m$. By introducing these auxiliary arrays, the second derivatives S_{ijg}, having any number of parameters, are easily evaluated.

EXERCISE 3.22
Complete the development of the function **NEWTON**, and apply it to the line shape problem of the previous exercise.

3.17 References

Interpolation is a standard topic of many numerical analysis texts, and is discussed in several of those listed at the conclusion of Chapter 2. Gaussian elimination and Crout decomposition are topics from linear algebra, and are also discussed in those texts.

There are many "special functions" of physics, such as gamma functions, Bessel functions, and Legendre, Laguerre, Chebyshev, and Hermite polynomials. These are discussed in many mathematical physics textbooks. We've found the following few to be particularly helpful.

George Arfken and Hans J. Weber, *Mathematical Methods for Physicists*, Elsevier Science & Technology Books, New York, NY, 2005.

Mary L. Boas, *Mathematical Methods in the Physical Sciences, 3rd Edition*, John Wiley & Sons, Hoboken, NJ, 2005.

Sadri Hassani, *Foundations of Mathematical Physics*, Allyn and Bacon, Needham Heights, MA, 1991.

Numerical
Integration

Perhaps the most common elementary task of computational physics is the evaluation of integrals. You undoubtedly know many techniques for integrating, and numerical integration should be looked upon as merely another useful method. Certainly, a numerical integration should never be performed if the integral has an analytic solution, except perhaps as a check. You should note, however, that such a check might be used to verify an analytic result, rather than checking the accuracy of the numerical algorithm. It is thus important that we have some brute force numerical methods to evaluate integrals. Initially, we will consider well-behaved integrals over a finite range, such as

$$I = \int_a^b f(x)\,dx. \tag{4.1}$$

Eventually we will also treat infinite ranges of integration, and integrands that are not particularly well-behaved. But first, a little Greek history....

4.1 Anaxagoras of Clazomenae

The Age of Pericles, the fifth century B.C., was the zenith of the Athenian era, marked by substantial accomplishments in literature and the arts, and attracting scholars from all of Greece and beyond. From Ionia came Anaxagoras, a proponent of rational inquiry, and a teacher of Pericles. Anaxagoras asserted that the Sun was not a deity, but simply a red-hot glowing stone. Despite the enlightenment of the era, such heresy could not be left unrewarded, and he was thrown in prison. (Pericles was eventually able to gain his release.) Plutarch tells us that while Anaxagoras was imprisoned, he occupied himself by attempting to square the circle. This is the first record of this problem, one of the three "classic problems of antiquity": to square the circle, to double a cube, and to trisect an angle. As now understood, the problem is to construct a square, exactly equal in area to the circle, using only compass and straightedge. This problem was not finally "solved" until 1882, when it was proved to be impossible!

The fundamental goal, of course, is to determine the area of the circle. For over two thousand years this problem occupied the minds of the great scholars of the world. In partial payment of those efforts, we refer to the numerical methods of integration, and hence finding the area bounded by curves, as integration by *quadrature*. That is, integration can be thought of as finding the edge length of the square, i.e., four-sided regular polygon *ergo quad*, having the same area as bounded by the original curve.

4.2 Primitive Integration Formulas

It is instructive, and not very difficult, to derive many of the commonly used integration formulas. The basic idea is to evaluate the function at specific locations, and to use those function evaluations to approximate the integral. We thus seek a *quadrature* formula of the form

$$I \approx \sum_{i=0}^{N} W_i f_i, \tag{4.2}$$

where x_i are the evaluation points, $f_i = f(x_i)$, W_i is the weight given the i-th point, and $N + 1$ is the number of points evaluated. To keep things simple, we will use equally spaced evaluation points separated by a distance h. Let's begin by deriving a *closed* formula, one that uses function evaluations at the endpoints of the integration region. The simplest formula is thus

$$I \approx W_0 f_0 + W_1 f_1, \tag{4.3}$$

where $x_0 = a$ and $x_1 = b$, the limits of the integration. We want this approximation to be useful for a variety of integrals, and so we'll require that it be *exact* for the simplest integrands, $f(x) = 1$ and $f(x) = x$. Since these are the first two terms in a Taylor series expansion of any function, this approximation will converge to the exact result as the integration region is made smaller, for any $f(x)$ that has a Taylor series expansion. Demanding the equalities, we have

$$\int_{x_0}^{x_1} 1 \, dx = x_1 - x_0 = W_0 + W_1,$$

and

$$\int_{x_0}^{x_1} x \, dx = \frac{x_1^2 - x_0^2}{2} = W_0 x_0 + W_1 x_1. \tag{4.4}$$

This is simply a set of two simultaneous equations in two unknowns, W_0 and W_1, easily solved by the methods of linear algebra to give

$$W_0 = W_1 = \frac{x_1 - x_0}{2}. \tag{4.5}$$

Writing $h = b - a$, the approximation is then

$$\int_{x_0}^{x_1} f(x)\,dx \approx \frac{h}{2}(f_0 + f_1), \qquad (4.6)$$

the so-called trapezoid rule. For the sake of completeness we'll exhibit these formulas as equalities, using Lagrange's expression for the remainder term in the Taylor series expansion, Equation 2.7, so that we have

$$\int_{x_0}^{x_1} f(x)\,dx = \frac{h}{2}(f_0 + f_1) - \frac{h^3}{12}f^{[2]}(\xi), \qquad (4.7)$$

where ξ is some point within the region of integration. Of course, we're not limited to $N = 1$; for three points, we find the equations

$$\int_{x_0}^{x_2} 1\,dx = x_2 - x_0 = W_0 + W_1 + W_2,$$

$$\int_{x_0}^{x_2} x\,dx = \frac{x_2^2 - x_0^2}{2} = W_0 x_0 + W_1 x_1 + W_2 x_2,$$

and

$$\int_{x_0}^{x_2} x^2\,dx = \frac{x_2^3 - x_0^3}{3} = W_0 x_0^2 + W_1 x_1^2 + W_2 x_2^2. \qquad (4.8)$$

Solving for the weights, we are led to Simpson's rule,

$$\int_{x_0}^{x_2} f(x)\,dx = \frac{h}{3}(f_0 + 4f_1 + f_2) - \frac{h^5}{90}f^{[4]}(\xi). \qquad (4.9)$$

Continuing in this fashion, with 4 points we are led to Simpson's three-eighths rule,

$$\int_{x_0}^{x_3} f(x)\,dx = \frac{3h}{8}(f_0 + 3f_1 + 3f_2 + f_3) - \frac{3h^5}{80}f^{[4]}(\xi), \qquad (4.10)$$

while with five points we find Boole's rule

$$\int_{x_0}^{x_4} f(x)\,dx = \frac{2h}{45}(7f_0 + 32f_1 + 12f_2 + 32f_3 + 7f_4) - \frac{8h^7}{945}f^{[6]}(\xi). \qquad (4.11)$$

These integration formulas all require that $f(x)$ be expressed as a polynomial, and could have been derived by fitting $f(x)$ to an approximating polynomial and integrating that function exactly. As more points are incorporated in the integration formula, the quadrature is exact for higher-degree polynomials. This process could be continued indefinitely, although the quadratures become increasingly more complicated.

4.3 Composite Formulas

As an alternative to higher-order approximations, we can divide the total integration region into many segments, and use a low order, relatively simple quadrature over each segment. Probably the most common approach is to use the trapezoid rule, one of the simplest quadratures available. Dividing the region from x_0 to x_N into N segments of width h, we can apply the trapezoid rule to each segment to obtain the composite trapezoid rule as illustrated in Figure 4.1.

$$
\int_{x_0}^{x_N} f(x)\,dx \approx \frac{h}{2}(f_0 + f_1) + \frac{h}{2}(f_1 + f_2) + \cdots + \frac{h}{2}(f_{N-1} + f_N)
$$

$$
= h\left(\frac{f_0}{2} + f_1 + f_2 + \cdots + f_{N-1} + \frac{f_N}{2}\right). \tag{4.12}
$$

This is equivalent to approximating the actual integrand by a series of straight line segments, and integrating; such a fit is said to be piecewise linear. A similar procedure yields a composite Simpson's rule,

$$
\int_{x_0}^{x_N} f(x)\,dx \approx \frac{h}{3}(f_0 + 4f_1 + 2f_2 + \cdots + 2f_{N-2} + 4f_{N-1} + f_N), \tag{4.13}
$$

where h is again the distance between successive function evaluations. This is equivalent to a piecewise quadratic approximation to the function, and hence is more accurate than the composite trapezoid rule using the same number of function evaluations. Piecewise cubic and quartic approximations are obviously available by making composite versions of the primitive integration formulas in Equations 4.10 and 4.11.

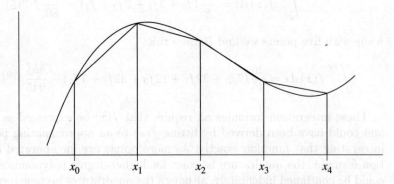

Figure 4.1   Constructing a composite formula from the trapezoid rule.

EXERCISE 4.1
Evaluate the integral $\int_0^\pi \sin x\, dx$ using approximations to the integrand that are piecewise linear, quadratic, and quartic. With N intervals, and hence $N+1$ points, evaluate the integral for $N = 4, 8, 16, \ldots, 1024$, and compare the accuracy of the methods.

4.4 Errors... and Corrections

Let's rederive the Trapezoid rule. Earlier, we noted that we can derive quadrature formulas by expanding the integrand in a Taylor series and integrating. Let's try that: consider the integral of Equation 4.1, and expand the function $f(x)$ in a Taylor series about $x = a$:

$$\int_a^b f(x)\, dx = \int_a^b \left[f(a) + (x-a)f'(a) + \frac{(x-a)^2}{2!}f''(a) \right.$$
$$\left. + \frac{(x-a)^3}{3!}f'''(a) + \frac{(x-a)^4}{4!}f^{[4]}(a) + \cdots \right] dx$$
$$= hf(a) + \frac{h^2}{2!}f'(a) + \frac{h^3}{3!}f''(a) + \frac{h^4}{4!}f'''(a) + \frac{h^5}{5!}f^{[4]}(a) + \cdots . \quad (4.14)$$

But we could just as easily have expanded about $x = b$, and would have found

$$\int_a^b f(x)\, dx = \int_a^b \left[f(b) + (x-b)f'(b) + \frac{(x-b)^2}{2!}f''(b) \right.$$
$$\left. + \frac{(x-b)^3}{3!}f'''(b) + \frac{(x-b)^4}{4!}f^{[4]}(b) + \cdots \right] dx$$
$$= hf(b) - \frac{h^2}{2!}f'(b) + \frac{h^3}{3!}f''(b) - \frac{h^4}{4!}f'''(b) + \frac{h^5}{5!}f^{[4]}(b) + \cdots . \quad (4.15)$$

The symmetry between these two expressions is quite evident. A new expression for the integral can be obtained by simply combining these two equations,

$$\int_a^b f(x)\, dx = \frac{h}{2}\left[f(a) + f(b)\right] + \frac{h^2}{4}\left[f'(a) - f'(b)\right] + \frac{h^3}{12}\left[f''(a) + f''(b)\right]$$
$$+ \frac{h^4}{48}\left[f'''(a) - f'''(b)\right] + \frac{h^5}{240}\left[f^{[4]}(a) + f^{[4]}(b)\right] + \cdots . \quad (4.16)$$

As it stands, this expression is no better or worse than the previous two, but it's leading us to an interesting and useful result. We see that the odd- and even-order derivatives enter this expression somewhat differently, as either a difference or sum of derivatives at the endpoints. Let's see if we can eliminate the even order ones—the motivation will be clear in just a bit. Making a Taylor series expansion of $f'(x)$ about the point $x = a$, we have

$$f'(x) = f'(a) + (x - a)f''(a) + \frac{(x-a)^2}{2}f'''(a) + \frac{(x-a)^3}{6}f^{[4]}(a) + \cdots . \quad (4.17)$$

In particular, at $x = b$,

$$f'(b) = f'(a) + hf''(a) + \frac{h^2}{2}f'''(a) + \frac{h^3}{6}f^{[4]}(a) + \cdots . \quad (4.18)$$

And of course, we could have expanded about $x = b$, and have found

$$f'(a) = f'(b) - hf''(b) + \frac{h^2}{2}f'''(b) - \frac{h^3}{6}f^{[4]}(b) + \cdots . \quad (4.19)$$

These expressions can be combined to yield

$$f'''(a) + f'''(b) = \frac{2}{h}[f'(b) - f'(a)] - \frac{h}{2}[f'''(a) - f'''(b)]$$
$$- \frac{h^2}{6}\left[f^{[4]}(a) + f^{[4]}(b)\right] + \cdots . \quad (4.20)$$

We could also expand the $f'''(x)$ about $x = a$ and $x = b$ to find

$$f^{[4]}(a) + f^{[4]}(b) = \frac{2}{h}[f'''(b) - f'''(a)] + \cdots . \quad (4.21)$$

Equations 4.20 and 4.21 can now be used to eliminate the even-order derivatives from Equation 4.16, obtaining

$$\int_a^b f(x)\,dx = \frac{h}{2}[f(a) + f(b)] + \frac{h^2}{12}[f'(a) - f'(b)] - \frac{h^4}{720}[f'''(a) - f'''(b)] + \cdots . $$
$$(4.22)$$

The importance of Equation 4.22 is not that the even derivatives are missing, but that the derivatives that are present appear in differences. A new composite formula can now be developed by dividing the integration region from a to b into many smaller segments, and applying Equation 4.22 to each of these segments. Except at the points a and b, the odd-order derivatives contribute to two adjacent segments, once as the left endpoint and once as the right. But they contribute *with different signs,* so that their contributions to the total integral cancel! We thus find the *Euler-McClaurin* integration rule,

$$\int_{x_0}^{x_N} f(x)\,dx = h\left(\frac{f_0}{2} + f_1 + f_2 + \cdots + f_{N-1} + \frac{f_N}{2}\right)$$
$$+ \frac{h^2}{12}[f_0' - f_N'] - \frac{h^4}{720}[f_0''' - f_N'''] + \cdots . \quad (4.23)$$

This is simply the Trapezoid rule, Equation 4.12, with correction terms, and so gives us the error incurred when using the standard composite trapezoid rule. When the integrand is easily differentiated, the Euler-McClaurin integration formula is far superior to other numerical integration schemes. A particularly attractive situation arises when the derivatives vanish at the limits of the integration, so that the "simple" trapezoid rule can yield surprisingly accurate results.

___

EXERCISE 4.2
Reevaluate the integral $\int_0^\pi \sin x \, dx$ using the trapezoid rule with first one and then two correction terms, and compare to the previous calculations for $N = 4, 8, \ldots$, 1024 points. Since the integrand is relatively simple, analytic expressions for the correction terms should be used.

___

4.5 Romberg Integration

Although the Euler-McClaurin formula is very powerful when it can be used, the more common situation is that the derivatives are not so pleasant to evaluate. However, from Euler-McClaurin we know how the error behaves, and so we can apply Richardson extrapolation to obtain an improved approximation to the integral.

Let's denote the result obtained by the trapezoid rule with $n = 2^m$ intervals as $T_{m,0}$, which is known to have an error proportional to h^2. Then $T_{m+1,0}$, obtained with an interval half as large, will have one-fourth the error of the previous approximation. We can thus combine these two approximations to eliminate this leading error term, and obtain

$$T_{m+1,1} = \frac{4T_{m+1,0} - T_{m,0}}{3}. \tag{4.24}$$

(Though not at all obvious, you might want to convince yourself that this is simply Simpson's rule.) Of course, we only eliminated the *leading* term—$T_{m+1,1}$ is still in error, but proportional to h^4. If we then compared this Simpson's rule approximation $T_{m+1,1}$ to the next one, $T_{m+2,1}$, with half the interval size, the error in $T_{m+2,1}$ would be one-sixteenth as large. But this error can then be eliminated to yield

$$T_{m+2,2} = \frac{16T_{m+2,1} - T_{m+1,1}}{15}. \tag{4.25}$$

(Again not obvious, this is Boole's rule.) In this way, a triangular array of increasingly accurate results can be obtained, with the general entry in the array given by

$$T_{m+k,k} = \frac{4^k T_{m+k,k-1} - T_{m+k-1,k-1}}{4^k - 1}. \tag{4.26}$$

For moderately smooth functions, this *Romberg integration scheme* yields very good results. As we found with Richardson extrapolation of derivatives, there are decreasing benefits associated with higher and higher extrapolations, so that k should probably be kept less than 4 or 5.

The code fragment developed earlier for Richardson extrapolation is directly applicable to the present problem, using the trapezoid rule approximation to the integral as the function being extrapolated. The composite trapezoid rule can itself be simplified, since all (interior) function evaluations enter with the same weight and all the points used in calculating $T_{m,0}$ were already used in calculating $T_{m-1,0}$. In fact, it's easy to show that

$$\int_a^b f(x)\,dx \approx T_{m,0} = \frac{1}{2}T_{m-1,0} + h \sum_{\substack{i=1,3,\ldots}}^{2^m-1} f(a+ih),$$

$$h = \frac{b-a}{2^m},$$ (4.27)

where the sum is over the points *not* included in $T_{m-1,0}$. The higher Romberg extrapolants can then be calculated from Equation 4.26, as before.

EXERCISE 4.3
Write a computer code to perform Romberg integration, obtaining 8-figure accuracy in the calculation of the integral, as determined by a relative error check. Your code should include a "graceful exit" if convergence hasn't been obtained after a specified number of halvings, say if $m \geq 15$. The dimensions used in the previous code fragment should be adjusted appropriately. Test your code on the integral

$$\int_0^{\pi/2} \frac{d\theta}{1+\cos\theta}.$$

4.6 MATLAB's Integration Routines

With numerical integration being such an important aspect of scientific programming, it is not at all surprising that MATLAB supplies its own numerical integrators. The first is the trapezoid function, `trapz(y)`. (As with all of MATLAB's features, a brief description of the method is available by typing `help trapz` at the command prompt. More complete documentation is available online, at www.mathworks.com.) In interactive mode, you can enter

```
h = pi/50;
f = inline('sin(x)','x');
y = f(0:h:pi);
h*trapz(y)
```

to calculate the integral

$$\int_0^\pi \sin x \, dx.$$

The result is not particularly accurate, as you would expect from using only 50 intervals for the approximation.

A more powerful method is the `quad` function, which utilizes an adaptive, recursive version of Simpson's rule. Instead of specifying the specific x_i to be used, the interval size is varied to ensure an accuracy of 10^{-6}, although this tolerance can be changed by the user. Suitable code to calculate the same integral would be

```
f = inline('sin(x)','x');
format long;
quad(f, 0, pi)
```

Note that we've added the command `format long` so that 15 digits will be displayed. (Otherwise, the result is rounded to 5 digits for display purposes, `2.0000`, and we wouldn't see the accuracy of the result.) A significantly more accurate answer can be obtained by specifying a smaller tolerance,

```
quad(f, 0, pi, 1.e-8)
```

For complicated expressions, it's best to define the function in a separate M-file, with the name of the function being the same as the file name, of course. For our example, we might write the code

```
% mySine.m
% This function demonstrates the use of a function
%    stored in its own M-file.
function [y] = mySine(x)
y = sin(x);
```

and store it in the file `mySine.m`. The integral could then be evaluated by invoking the command

```
quad('mySine', 0, pi)
```

MATLAB is also capable of performing symbolic integration, which requires the symbolic math toolbox, now part of the standard Student Edition. (Beginning with release R2008b.)

4.7 Diffraction at a Knife's Edge

In optics, we learn that light "bends around" objects, i.e., it exhibits diffraction. Perhaps the simplest case to study is the bending of light around a straightedge.

In this case, we find that the intensity of the light varies as we move away from the edge according to

$$I = 0.5I_o \left\{ [C(v) + 0.5]^2 + [S(v) + 0.5]^2 \right\}, \tag{4.28}$$

where I_o is the intensity of the incident light, v is proportional to the distance moved, and $C(v)$ and $S(v)$ are the Fresnel integrals

$$C(v) = \int_0^v \cos(\pi w^2/2)\, dw \tag{4.29}$$

and

$$S(v) = \int_0^v \sin(\pi w^2/2)\, dw. \tag{4.30}$$

EXERCISE 4.4

Numerically integrate the Fresnel integrals, and thus evaluate I/I_o as a function of v. Plot your results.

4.8 A Change of Variables

Well, now we have a super-duper method of integrating... or do we? Consider the integral

$$I = \int_{-1}^{1} \sqrt{1 - x^2}\, dx, \tag{4.31}$$

as illustrated in Figure 4.2.

This doesn't look like it should give us much trouble, yet when we try to do Romberg integration, we generate the following table:

m	$T_{m,0}$	$T_{m,1}$	$T_{m,2}$	$T_{m,3}$
0	0.0000 0000			
1	1.0000 0000	1.3333 3333		
2	1.3660 2540	1.4880 3387	1.4983 4724	
3	1.4978 5453	1.5417 9758	1.5453 8182	1.5461 2841
4	1.5449 0957	1.5605 9458	1.5618 4772	1.5621 0908
5	1.5616 2652	1.5671 9883	1.5676 3912	1.5677 3104
6	1.5675 5121	1.5695 2611	1.5696 8126	1.5697 1368
7	1.5696 4846	1.5703 4754	1.5704 0230	1.5704 1375
8	1.5703 9040	1.5706 3771	1.5706 5705	1.5706 6110
9	1.5706 5279	1.5707 4026	1.5707 4709	1.5707 4852
10	1.5707 4558	1.5707 7650	1.5707 7892	1.5707 7943

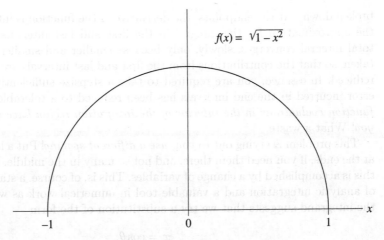

$$f(x) = \sqrt{1-x^2}$$

Figure 4.2   A simple looking integral.

It's clear that *none* of the approximations are converging very rapidly—What went wrong?

Well, let's see. . . . The Euler-McClaurin formula gives us an idea of what the error should be, in terms of the derivatives of the integrand at the endpoints. And for this integrand, these derivatives are *infinite*! No wonder Romberg integration failed!

Before trying to find a "cure," let's see if we can find a diagnostic that will indicate when the integration is failing. Romberg integration works, when it works, because the error in the trapezoid rule is quartered when the step-size is halved— that seems simple enough to check. Using the difference between $T_{m+1,0}$ and $T_{m,0}$ as an indication of the error "at this step," we can evaluate the ratio of errors at consecutive steps. In order for the method to work, this ratio should be about 4:

$$R_m = \frac{T_{m-1,0} - T_{m,0}}{T_{m,0} - T_{m+1,0}} \approx 4. \tag{4.32}$$

Using the trapezoid approximations given in the table, we compute the ratios to be

m	R_m
1	2.73205
2	2.77651
3	2.80159
4	2.81481
5	2.82157

These ratios are obviously not close to 4, and the integration fails. The reason, of course, is that the Taylor series expansion, upon which all this is based, has broken down—at the endpoints, the derivative of the function is infinite! Therefore, the approximation for the integral in the first and last intervals is terrible! The total integral converges, slowly, only because smaller and smaller steps are being taken, so that the contributions from the first and last intervals are correspondingly reduced. In essence, you are required to take a stepsize sufficiently small that the error incurred in the end intervals has been reduced to a tolerable level. *All those function evaluations in the interior of the integration region have done nothing for you!* What a waste.

This problem is crying out to you, *use a different spacing!* Put a lot of evaluations at the ends, if you need them there, and not so many in the middle. Mathematically, this is accomplished by a change of variables. This is, of course, a standard technique of analytic integration and a valuable tool in numerical work as well. The form of the integrand suggests that we try a substitution of the form

$$x = \cos\theta, \tag{4.33}$$

so that the integral becomes

$$I = \int_{-1}^{1} \sqrt{1 - x^2}\, dx = \int_{0}^{\pi} \sin^2\theta\, d\theta. \tag{4.34}$$

Running this through the Romberg integrator, we generate the following results:

m	$T_{m,0}$	$T_{m,1}$	$T_{m,2}$	$T_{m,3}$
0	0.0000 0000			
1	1.5707 9633	2.0943 9510		
2	1.5707 9633	1.5707 9633	1.5358 8974	
3	1.5707 9633	1.5707 9633	1.5707 9633	1.5713 5040
4	1.5707 9633	1.5707 9633	1.5707 9633	1.5707 9633

At first blush, these results are more surprising than the first ones—*only one nonzero function evaluation was required to yield the <u>exact</u> result!* Well, one thing at a time. First, it's only coincidence that the result is exact—in general, you have to do *some* work to get a good result. However, we shouldn't have to work too hard—*look at the derivatives at the endpoints!* For this integrand, all those derivatives are zero, so that Euler-McClaurin tells us that the trapezoid rule is good enough, once h is sufficiently small.

As a practical matter, we need to do two things to the Romberg computer code. First, the ratios R_m should be evaluated, to verify that the method is working correctly. The ratio will not be *exactly* 4, but it should be close, say within 10%. If the ratio doesn't meet this requirement, the program should exit and print the relevant information. (Of course, if the requirement *is* met, there's no reason to print any of this information. However, a message indicating that the test was performed and the requirement met should be printed.) The second thing relates to the last Table we generated. All the results were exact, except the first ones in each column. In general, we should allow the integrator to have a reasonable approximation, one obtained with more that just two function evaluations, before we begin the extrapolation procedure. Delaying the extrapolation a few iterations will either improve the accuracy of the result, by avoiding the spurious approximations generated early in the process, or have no effect at all—let's avoid that top entry by not starting the extrapolations until $m = 2$.

EXERCISE 4.5
Modify your Romberg integrator, and use it to evaluate the elliptic integral

$$I = \int_{-1}^{1} \sqrt{(1 - x^2)(2 - x)}\, dx.$$

First, test your diagnostic by trying to evaluate the integral in its present form. If the diagnostic indicates that Romberg integration is failing, perform a change of variables and integrate again.

4.9 The "Simple" Pendulum

A standard problem of elementary physics is the motion of the simple pendulum, as in Figure 4.3. From Newton's laws, or from either Lagrange's or Hamilton's formulations, the motion is found to be described by the differential equation

$$ml\frac{d^2\theta}{dt^2} = -mg \sin\theta. \tag{4.35}$$

The mass doesn't enter the problem, and the equation can be written as

$$\ddot{\theta} = -\frac{g}{l}\sin\theta \tag{4.36}$$

where we've written the second time derivative as $\ddot{\theta}$. For *small amplitudes*, $\sin\theta \approx \theta$, so that the motion is described approximately by the equation

$$\ddot{\theta} = -\frac{g}{l}\theta, \tag{4.37}$$

which has as its solution

$$\theta(t) = \theta_0 \cos\sqrt{\frac{g}{l}}t, \tag{4.38}$$

for the case of the motion beginning at $t = 0$ with the pendulum motionless at $\theta = \theta_0$.

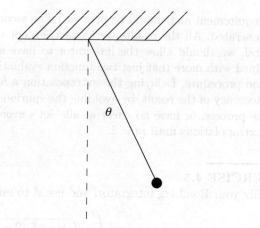

Figure 4.3   The simple pendulum.

But what about the *real* motion? For large amplitude (how large?), we should expect this *linearized* description to fail. In particular, this description tells us that the period of the oscillation is independent of the amplitude, or *isochronous*, which seems unlikely. Let's see if we can do better.

Now, we could attempt an improved description by applying perturbation theory—that is, by starting with the linearized description and finding corrections to it. In the days before computers, this was not only the approach of choice, it was virtually the only approach available! Today, of course, we have computers, and ready access to them. We *could* simply solve the differential equation describing the exact motion, directly. And in Chapter 5, that's exactly what we'll do! But to *always* jump to the numerical solution of the differential equation is to be just as narrow-minded and shortsighted as insisting on applying perturbation theory to every problem that comes along. There are many ways to approach a problem, and we often learn *different things* as we explore different approaches. This lesson, learned when analytic methods were all we had, is just as valuable now that we have new tools to use. The computational approach to physics is most successful when numerical methods are used to complement analytic ones, not simply replace them.

Starting with Equation 4.36, multiply both sides by $\dot{\theta}$ and integrate to obtain

$$\frac{1}{2}\dot{\theta}^2 = \frac{g}{l}\cos\theta + C, \tag{4.39}$$

where C is a constant of integration, to be determined from the initial conditions: for $\dot{\theta} = 0$ at $t = 0$, we have $C = -(g/l)\cos\theta_0$. Solving for $\dot{\theta}$, we find

$$\dot{\theta} = \frac{d\theta}{dt} = \sqrt{\frac{2g}{l}}\sqrt{\cos\theta - \cos\theta_0}, \tag{4.40}$$

or

$$dt = \sqrt{\frac{l}{2g}} \frac{d\theta}{\sqrt{\cos\theta - \cos\theta_0}}. \tag{4.41}$$

Now the total period, T, is just four times the time it takes the pendulum to travel from $\theta = 0$ to $\theta = \theta_0$, so that

$$T = 4\sqrt{\frac{l}{2g}} \int_0^{\theta_0} \frac{d\theta}{\sqrt{\cos\theta - \cos\theta_0}}. \tag{4.42}$$

This is an elliptic integral of the first kind, and is an exact result for the period of the pendulum. But of course, it remains to *evaluate* the integral. In particular, the integrand is a little unpleasant at the upper limit of integration.

Let's convert this integral into the "standard" form, originated by Legendre, using the identity

$$\cos\theta - \cos\theta_0 = 2\left(\sin^2\frac{\theta_0}{2} - \sin^2\frac{\theta}{2}\right) \tag{4.43}$$

and the substitution

$$\sin\xi = \frac{\sin\frac{\theta}{2}}{\sin\frac{\theta_0}{2}}. \tag{4.44}$$

We then find that

$$T = 4\sqrt{\frac{l}{g}}K\left(\sin\frac{\theta_0}{2}\right), \tag{4.45}$$

where

$$K(k) = \int_0^{\pi/2} \frac{d\xi}{\sqrt{1 - k^2\sin^2\xi}} \tag{4.46}$$

is the *complete elliptic integral of the first kind*. Clearly, this integrand is much nicer than the previous one. The most general elliptic integral of the first kind is parametrically dependent upon the upper limit of the integration,

$$F(k, \phi) = \int_0^{\phi} \frac{d\xi}{\sqrt{1 - k^2\sin^2\xi}}. \tag{4.47}$$

From these definitions, we clearly have that $K(k) = F(k, \frac{\pi}{2})$.

The real value of a "standard form" is that you might find values for it tabulated somewhere. You could then check your integration routine by computing the standard integral for the values tabulated, before you solved the particular problem of your interest. For example, the following table is similar to one found in several reference books of mathematical functions.

$$K(k) = \int_0^{\pi/2} \frac{d\xi}{\sqrt{1 - k^2\sin^2\xi}}$$

$\sin^{-1} k$	$K(k)$
0°	1.57079 63270
10°	1.58284 28043
20°	1.62002 58991
30°	1.68575 03548
40°	1.78676 91349
50°	1.93558 10960
60°	2.15651 56475
70°	2.50455 00790
80°	3.15338 52519
90°	∞

You might want to verify these values before returning your attention to the motion of the simple pendulum.

EXERCISE 4.6

Calculate the period of the simple pendulum, using whatever method you feel appropriate to evaluate the integral. Be prepared to justify your choice. Produce a table of results, displaying the calculated period versus the amplitude. For what values of the amplitude does the period differ from $2\pi\sqrt{l/g}$ by more than 1%? Is there a problem at $\theta_0 = 180°$? Why?

Legendre was thoroughly absorbed by these integrals, and developed a second and third standard form. Of some interest to physics is the elliptic integral of the second kind,

$$E(k, \phi) = \int_0^\phi \sqrt{1 - k^2 \sin^2 \xi}\, d\xi, \tag{4.48}$$

which arises in determining the length of an elliptic arc.

4.10 Improper Integrals

Integrals of the form

$$I = \int_0^\infty f(x)\, dx \tag{4.49}$$

are certainly not uncommon in physics. It is possible that this integral diverges; that is, that $I = \infty$. If this is the case, don't ask your numerical integrator for the answer! But often these integrals do exist, and we need to be able to handle them. Many techniques are available to us; however, none of them *actually* try to integrate all the way to infinity numerically. That is, if the integral is

$$I = \int_0^\infty x^2 e^{-x}\, dx, \tag{4.50}$$

it might be tempting to integrate up to some large number A, and then go a little farther to A', and stop if the integrals aren't much different. But "how much farther" is enough?—infinity is a long way off! It's better to use a different approach, one that in some way accounts for the infinite extent of the integration domain.

One such approach is to split the integration region into two segments,

$$\int_0^\infty f(x)\, dx = \int_0^a f(x)\, dx + \int_a^\infty f(x)\, dx. \tag{4.51}$$

The first integral is over a finite region and can be performed by a standard numerical method. The appropriate value for a will depend upon the particular integrand, and how the second integral is to be handled. For example, it can be mapped into a finite region by a change of variables such as

$$x \to 1/y,$$

so that the integral becomes

$$\int_a^\infty f(x)\, dx = \int_0^{1/a} \frac{f(y^{-1})}{y^2}\, dy. \tag{4.52}$$

If the change of variables hasn't introduced an additional singularity into the integrand, this integral can often be evaluated by one of the standard numerical methods.

EXERCISE 4.7

Evaluate the integral $\int_0^\infty \frac{dx}{1+x^2}$ to eight significant digits. (Let $a = 1$, and break the interval into two domains.)

Note that $x \to 1/y$ is not the only substitution that might be used—for a particular $f(x)$ it might be better to choose $x \to e^{-y}$, for example. The substitution

$$x \to \frac{1+y}{1-y} \tag{4.53}$$

is interesting in this regard as it transforms the interval $[0, \infty]$ into $[-1, 1]$, which is particularly convenient for Gauss-Legendre integration, to be discussed later. The goal is to use a transform that maps the semi-infinite region into a finite one while yielding an integrand that we can evaluate.

EXERCISE 4.8

Using the transformation

$$x \to \frac{y}{1-y}, \tag{4.54}$$

transform the integral

$$I = \int_0^\infty \frac{x\,dx}{(1+x)^4} \tag{4.55}$$

into one over a finite domain, and evaluate.

There's another approach we can take to the evaluation of an integral: expand all or part of it in an infinite series. Let's imagine that we need to evaluate the integral

$$I = \int_0^\infty \frac{dx}{(1+x)\sqrt{x}}, \tag{4.56}$$

and have broken it into two domains. We first consider the integral

$$I_2 = \int_a^\infty \frac{dx}{(1+x)\sqrt{x}}, \tag{4.57}$$

where we have chosen a to be much larger than 1. Then we can use the binomial theorem to write

$$\frac{1}{1+x} = \frac{1}{x(1+\frac{1}{x})} = \frac{1}{x}\left(1 - \frac{1}{x} + \frac{1}{x^2} - \cdots\right). \tag{4.58}$$

Substituting this into the integral, we find

$$\int_a^\infty \frac{dx}{(1+x)\sqrt{x}} = \int_a^\infty (x^{-\frac{3}{2}} - x^{-\frac{5}{2}} + x^{-\frac{7}{2}} - \cdots)dx$$

$$= 2a^{\frac{1}{2}} - \frac{2}{3}a^{\frac{3}{2}} + \frac{2}{5}a^{\frac{7}{2}} - \cdots. \tag{4.59}$$

The series will converge, by virtue of the convergence of the binomial expansion, for any $a > 1$, although it clearly converges faster for larger a. Series expansions can be extremely useful in situations such as these, but we must always be certain that we are using the series properly. In particular, the series will only converge if it's being used within its domain of convergence.

So, all we need to do now is to perform the integral from zero to a, but there seems to be a small problem...

$$I_1 = \int_0^a \frac{dx}{(1+x)\sqrt{x}} \tag{4.60}$$

—the integrand is infinite at one end-point. Before proceeding, we should probably convince ourselves that the integral is finite. This can be done by noting that

$$\frac{1}{1+x} \leq 1, \quad x \geq 0,$$

so that

$$\int_0^a \frac{dx}{(1+x)\sqrt{x}} \leq \int_0^a \frac{dx}{\sqrt{x}} = 2\sqrt{a}. \tag{4.61}$$

We thus have a finite upper bound on the integral, so the integral itself must be finite. To evaluate the integral, we might try a power series expansion such as

$$\frac{1}{1+x} = 1 - x + x^2 - x^3 + \cdots. \tag{4.62}$$

However, we must note that this series converges *if and only if* $|x| < 1$. Since we've already specified that $a > 1$, this series cannot be used over the entire integration region. However, we could break the interval again, into one piece near the origin and the other piece containing everything else:

$$\int_0^a \frac{dx}{(1+x)\sqrt{x}} = \int_0^\epsilon \frac{dx}{(1+x)\sqrt{x}} + \int_\epsilon^a \frac{dx}{(1+x)\sqrt{x}}. \tag{4.63}$$

This is a very reasonable approach to take—the idea of isolating the difficult part into one term upon which to concentrate is a very good tactic, one that we often use. In some cases, it might happen that you not even need to do the difficult part. For example, in this case you might evaluate the second integral for increasingly smaller ϵ and extrapolate to the limit of $\epsilon \to 0$.

Let's try something totally different from the power series method—just *subtract* the singularity away! We've already discovered that near zero the integrand behaves as $1/\sqrt{x}$, which we were able to integrate to yield an upper bound. So, let's simply write

$$\int_0^a \frac{dx}{(1+x)\sqrt{x}} = \int_0^a \left[\frac{1}{\sqrt{x}} + \frac{1}{(1+x)\sqrt{x}} - \frac{1}{\sqrt{x}} \right] dx$$

$$= \int_0^a \frac{dx}{\sqrt{x}} + \int_0^a \frac{-x\,dx}{(1+x)\sqrt{x}}$$

$$= 2\sqrt{a} - \int_0^a \frac{\sqrt{x}\,dx}{1+x}. \tag{4.64}$$

The desired integral is thus expressed as an integrated term containing the difficult part, plus a difference expression that can be integrated numerically.

EXERCISE 4.9
Evaluate the integral

$$I = \int_0^2 \frac{dx}{(1+x)\sqrt{x}}$$

by subtracting the singularity away.

If we can add and subtract terms in an integrand, we can also multiply and divide them. In general, we might write

$$\int f(x)\,dx = \int \frac{f(x)}{g(x)}\,g(x)\,dx. \qquad (4.65)$$

This hasn't gained us much, unless $g(x)$ is chosen so that $g(x)\,dx = dy$. If this is so, then we can make the substitution $x \to y$ to arrive at the integral

$$\int \frac{f(y)}{g(y)}\,dy. \qquad (4.66)$$

Since we are free to choose g, we will choose it so that the integrand in this expression is "nicer" than just $f(x)$. This, of course, is nothing more than a rigorous mathematical description of a change of variables, with the function g being the Jacobian of the transformation. In our example, we might choose $g(x) = 1/\sqrt{x}$, so that

$$\int_0^a \frac{dx}{(1+x)\sqrt{x}} = \int_0^a \left(\frac{\sqrt{x}}{(1+x)\sqrt{x}}\right)\left(\frac{dx}{\sqrt{x}}\right). \qquad (4.67)$$

We now have $dy = dx/\sqrt{x}$, or $y = 2\sqrt{x}$. Note that we are choosing g to make the integrand nice, and from that *deriving* what the new variable should be—virtually the reverse of the usual change of variable procedure. Making the substitution, we find

$$\int_0^a \frac{dx}{(1+x)\sqrt{x}} = \int_0^{2\sqrt{a}} \frac{1}{1+y^2/4}\,dy. \qquad (4.68)$$

Once again, we find that the transformed integrand will be easy to integrate, which of course was the motivation for transforming in the first place.

EXERCISE 4.10

Evaluate the integral

$$I = \int_0^2 \frac{dx}{(1+x)\sqrt{x}}$$

by changing the variable of integration.

From time-to-time, you'll have to evaluate a function that superficially appears divergent. An example of such a situation is the integral

$$\int_0^\pi \frac{\sin x}{x}\, dx.$$

The integral exists, and in fact the function is finite at every point. However, if you simply ask the computer to evaluate the integrand at $x = 0$, you'll have problems with "zero divided by zero." Clearly, either a series expansion of $\sin x$ or the use of L'Hôpital's rule will remove the difficulty—but that's your job, not the computer's!

EXERCISE 4.11

Using the integration tools we've discussed, evaluate the integral

$$\int_0^1 \frac{\cos x}{\sqrt{x}}\, dx.$$

4.11 The Mathematical Magic of Gauss

Carl Friedrich Gauss (1777–1855) was the greatest mathematician of his era, and made significant contributions to the field of pure mathematics. He also developed practical methods to solve difficult numerical problems, such as the Gaussian elimination method and the method of least squares discussed in the previous chapter, and a method of integration that's the topic of this section. Although his first love was mathematics, in 1801 he became distracted by a certain astronomical problem. The Italian astronomer Giuseppe Piazzi had discovered the first dwarf planet, Ceres, on New Year's Day, 1801. He had observed the planet for several months as it moved some three degrees through the night sky, until it was lost in the glare of the Sun. It should have reappeared after a few months in the night time sky, but Piazzi was unable to locate it. Gauss heard of the problem, and set about to calculate it's position, relying upon the method of least squares that he had previously developed. After several months' work, he predicted where Ceres would be, and indeed, it was located within half a degree of Gauss' prediction. Thus Gauss, by the age of 24, was well established as both a mathematician and astronomer—in 1807 he was appointed director of the Göttingen Observatory, a post he held for the next forty years, while continuing to make contributions to both mathematics and physics.

Earlier we performed numerical integration by repeated use of the Trapezoid rule, using the composite formula

$$\int_{x_0}^{x_N} f(x)\, dx = h\left[\frac{f_0}{2} + f_1 + \cdots + f_{N-1} + \frac{f_N}{2}\right],\qquad(4.69)$$

where $h = (x_N - x_0)/N$ and the x_m, where the function is being evaluated, are evenly spaced on the interval $[a, b]$. That is, the total integration region has been divided into N equal intervals of width h, and the function is being evaluated $N+1$ times. But there's really no reason to *require* that the intervals be of equal size. We chose this equidistant spacing while developing the primitive integration formulas so as to keep the derived expressions simple—in fact, we can obtain much more accurate formulas if we relax this requirement. We begin as we did before, trying to approximate the integral by a quadrature of the form

$$\int_a^b f(x)\, dx \approx \sum_{m=1}^{N} W_m f(x_m).\qquad(4.70)$$

Note that we are starting the sum at $m = 1$, so that N refers to the number of function evaluations being made. As with the primitive integration quadratures, W_m is an unknown; now, however, the x_m are also unknown! This gives us $2N$ unknowns, so that we need $2N$ equations in order to determine them. And, as before, we obtain these equations by *requiring* that the quadrature be exact for $f(x)$ being the lowest order polynomials, $f(x) = 1,\ x,\ x^2, \ldots,\ x^{2N-1}$. Unfortunately, the equations thus obtained are nonlinear and extremely difficult to solve (by standard algebraic methods). For example, we can take $N = 2$ and require the integration formula to be exact for $f(x) = 1,\ x,\ x^2$, and x^3, yielding the four equations

$$(b - a) = W_1 + W_2,\qquad(4.71a)$$

$$\frac{1}{2}(b^2 - a^2) = W_1 x_1 + W_2 x_2,\qquad(4.71b)$$

$$\frac{1}{3}(b^3 - a^3) = W_1 x_1^2 + W_2 x_2^2,\qquad(4.71c)$$

$$\frac{1}{4}(b^4 - a^4) = W_1 x_1^3 + W_2 x_2^3.\qquad(4.71d)$$

Although they're nonlinear, we can solve this relatively simple set of equations analytically. The first thing is to note that any finite interval $[a, b]$ can be mapped onto the interval $[-1, 1]$ by a simple change of variable:

$$y = -1 + 2\frac{x - a}{b - a}. \tag{4.72}$$

Thus it is sufficient for us to consider only this *normalized* integration region, in terms of which the nonlinear equations can be expressed as

$$2 = W_1 + W_2, \tag{4.73a}$$

$$0 = W_1 x_1 + W_2 x_2, \tag{4.73b}$$

$$2/3 = W_1 x_1^2 + W_2 x_2^2, \tag{4.73c}$$

$$0 = W_1 x_1^3 + W_2 x_2^3. \tag{4.73d}$$

Equations 4.73b and 4.73d can be combined to yield $x_1^2 = x_2^2$; since the points must be distinct (else we wouldn't have 4 independent variables), we have that $x_1 = -x_2$. Then from Equation 4.73b we have $W_1 = W_2$, and from Equation 4.73a we have $W_1 = 1$. Equation 4.73c then gives us

$$2/3 = 2x_1^2,$$

or that $x_1 = 1/\sqrt{3}$. To summarize, we find that the function should be evaluated at $x_m = \pm 1/\sqrt{3}$, and that the evaluations have an equal weighting of 1. If you like, you may try to find the weights and abscissas for $N = 3$, but be forewarned: it gets harder. (*Much* harder!) This is where Professor Gauss steps in to save the day. But first, we need to know about...

4.12 Orthogonal Polynomials

Orthogonal polynomials are one of those "advanced" topics that many of us never quite get to, although they really aren't that difficult to understand. The basic idea is that there exists a set of polynomials $\phi_m(x)$ such that

$$\int_a^b w(x)\phi_m(x)\phi_n(x)\,dx = \delta_{mn}C_m. \tag{4.74}$$

(Actually, we can *construct* such a set, if we don't already have one!) This *orthogonality condition* that orthogonal polynomials obey is simply a mathematical statement that the functions are fundamentally different. Equation 4.74 gives us the way to measure the "sameness" of two functions—if $m \neq n$, then the functions are not the same, and the integral is zero. Let's see what this means in terms of a particular example.

The polynomials we're most comfortable with are the ones x^0, x^1, x^2, and so on. Start with these, and call them $u_m = x^m$. For the moment, let's forget the weighting function, setting $w(x) = 1$, and let $a = -1$ and $b = 1$. The very first integral to think about is

$$\int_{-1}^{1} \phi_0(x)\phi_0(x)\,dx = C_0. \tag{4.75}$$

We could simply choose $\phi_0(x) = u_0(x) = 1$, and satisfy this equation with $C_0 = 2$. Although not *necessary*, it's often convenient to normalize these functions as well, requiring all the $C_m = 1$, so that we actually choose $\phi_0(x) = 1/\sqrt{2}$. The integral of Equation 4.74 will then yield 1, expressing the fact that the functions are identical.

The next integral to consider is

$$\int_{-1}^{1} \phi_0(x)\phi_1(x)\,dx = 0. \tag{4.76}$$

Since the subscripts differ, this integral is required to be zero. In this case, we can choose $\phi_1(x) = u_1$ and find that Equation 4.76 is satisfied. But in general we can't count on being so lucky. What we need is a universal method for choosing ϕ_m, independent of $w(x)$, a, and b, that can be applied to whatever particular case is at hand.

Let's take ϕ_1 to be a linear combination of what we have, u_1 and ϕ_0, and *make* it satisfy Equation 4.76. That is, we choose

$$\phi_1(x) = u_1 + \alpha_{10}\phi_0, \tag{4.77}$$

and require α_{10} to take on whatever value necessary to *force* the integral to vanish. With this expression for ϕ_1, we have

$$\int_{-1}^{1} \phi_0(x)\phi_1(x)\,dx = \int_{-1}^{1} \phi_0(x)\left[u_1 + \alpha_{10}\phi_0(x)\right]\,dx$$

$$= \int_{-1}^{1} \frac{1}{\sqrt{2}}\left[x + \alpha_{10}/\sqrt{2}\right]\,dx$$

$$= 0 + \alpha_{10}. \tag{4.78}$$

Since the integral is zero, we have $\alpha_{10} = 0$ and hence $\phi_1 = x$. Again, we'll normalize this result by considering the integral

$$\int_{-1}^{1} \phi_1(x)\phi_1(x)\,dx = \int_{-1}^{1} x^2\,dx = \frac{2}{3}, \tag{4.79}$$

so that the normalized polynomial is

$$\phi_1(x) = \sqrt{\frac{3}{2}}x. \tag{4.80}$$

The next orthogonal polynomial is found by choosing ϕ_2 to be a linear combination of u_2, ϕ_0, and ϕ_1:

$$\phi_2(x) = u_2 + \alpha_{21}\phi_1(x) + \alpha_{20}\phi_0(x)$$
$$= x^2 + \alpha_{21}\sqrt{3/2}\,x + \alpha_{20}/\sqrt{2}, \tag{4.81}$$

and requiring *both*

$$\int_{-1}^{1} \phi_0(x)\phi_2(x)\,dx = 0 \tag{4.82}$$

and

$$\int_{-1}^{1} \phi_1(x)\phi_2(x)\,dx = 0. \tag{4.83}$$

From the first we find $\alpha_{20} = -\sqrt{2}/3$, and from the second $\alpha_{21} = 0$. After normalization, we find

$$\phi_2(x) = \sqrt{\frac{5}{2}}\,\frac{3x^2 - 1}{2}. \tag{4.84}$$

The astute reader will recognize these as the first three Legendre polynomials, although the unnormalized versions are more popular than these normalized ones. This process, known as *Gram-Schmidt Orthogonalization*, can be used to generate various sets of orthogonal polynomials, depending upon $w(x)$, a, and b.

EXERCISE 4.12

Using this Gram-Schmidt Orthogonalization process, find the next Legendre polynomial, $\phi_3(x)$.

● 4.13 Gaussian Integration

We now return to the evaluation of integrals. We'll consider a slightly larger class of integrals than previously indicated, by considering integrals of the form

$$\int_a^b f(x)\,w(x)\,dx = \sum_{m=1}^{N} W_m f(x_m), \tag{4.85}$$

where $w(x)$ is a positive definite (i.e., never negative) weighting function. (And yes, it's the same weighting function we just discussed.) Since both the weights and abscissas are treated as unknowns, we have $2N$ coefficients to be determined. Our plan will be to *require* that this quadrature be *exact* for polynomials of order $2N - 1$ and less, and use this requirement to *determine* the weights and abscissas of the quadrature!

Let $f(x)$ be a polynomial of degree $2N - 1$ (or less), and $\phi_N(x)$ be a specific orthogonal function of order N. In particular, we let ϕ_N be the orthogonal polynomial appropriate for the particular weighting function $w(x)$ and limits of integration a and b, so that

$$\int_a^b w(x)\, \phi_m(x)\, \phi_n(x)\, dx = \delta_{mn} C_m. \tag{4.74}$$

That is, the particular set of orthogonal polynomials to be used is dictated by the integral to be evaluated. (That's not so surprising, is it?)

Now, consider what happens if $f(x)$ is divided by $\phi_N(x)$: the leading term in the quotient will be of order $N - 1$, and the leading term in the remainder will also be of order $N - 1$. (This is not necessarily obvious, so do the division on an example of your own choosing. The division will probably not come out evenly—the remainder is what you need to *subtract* from $f(x)$ to make it come out even.) In terms of the quotient and the remainder, we can write

$$f(x) = q_{N-1}(x)\, \phi_N(x) + r_{N-1}(x), \tag{4.86}$$

where both $q_{N-1}(x)$ and $r_{N-1}(x)$ are polynomials of order $N - 1$.

With this expression for $f(x)$, the integral of Equation 4.85 becomes

$$\int_a^b f(x)\, w(x)\, dx = \int_a^b q_{N-1}(x)\, \phi_N(x)\, w(x)\, dx + \int_a^b r_{N-1}(x)\, w(x)\, dx. \tag{4.87}$$

Since the functions $\{\phi_m\}$ are a complete set, we can expand the function $q_{N-1}(x)$ as

$$q_{N-1}(x) = \sum_{i=0}^{N-1} q_i\, \phi_i(x), \tag{4.88}$$

where the q_i are constants. Note that the summation ranges up to $N - 1$, since $q_{N-1}(x)$ is an $(N-1)$-th order polynomial. The first integral on the right side of Equation 4.87 is then

$$\int_a^b q_{N-1}(x)\, \phi_N(x)\, w(x)\, dx = \sum_{i=0}^{N-1} q_i \int_a^b \phi_i(x)\, \phi_N(x)\, w(x)\, dx$$

$$= \sum_{i=0}^{N-1} q_i\, \delta_{iN} C_N$$

$$= 0. \tag{4.89}$$

Note that the integrals on the right side are merely the orthogonality integrals of Equation 4.74 and that the total integral is zero since the summation only ranges up to $N - 1$.

We began by requiring that the integration formula of Equation 4.85 be exact for $f(x)$, an arbitrary function of order $2N - 1$. The product $q_{N-1}(x)\phi_N$ is also a polynomial of order $2N - 1$, so it must be true that

$$\int_a^b q_{N-1}(x)\,\phi_N(x)\,w(x)\,dx = \sum_{m=1}^N W_m\,q_{N-1}(x_m)\,\phi_N(x_m). \qquad (4.90)$$

But from Equation 4.89 we know this integral to be zero. Since $f(x)$ is arbitrary, the derived $q_{N-1}(x)$ must also be arbitrary, and so the sum doesn't vanish because of any unique characteristics of the function q_{N-1}. The only way to *guarantee* that this sum will be zero is to require that *all* the $\phi_N(x_m)$ be zero! Now, that's not as difficult as it might seem—the x_m are *chosen* such that the orthogonal polynomial $\phi_N(x)$ is zero at these points; since we need N of these x_m, we're fortunate that $\phi_N(x)$ just happens to be an N-th order polynomial and so possesses N roots. Do *you* believe in coincidence? (In a general sense, these roots might be complex. In cases of practical interest they are always real.) We've thus determined the abscissas x_m.

The integration formula is to be exact for polynomials of order $2N - 1$, so surely it must be exact for a function of lesser order as well. In particular, it must be true for the $(N - 1)$-th order polynomial $l_{i,N}(x)$, defined as

$$l_{i,N}(x) = \frac{(x - x_1)\cdots(x - x_{i-1})(x - x_{i+1})\cdots(x - x_N)}{(x_i - x_1)\cdots(x_i - x_{i-1})(x_i - x_{i+1})\cdots(x_i - x_N)}. \qquad (4.91)$$

This function occurs in connection with Lagrange's interpolating polynomial, and has the interesting property, easily verified, that

$$l_{i,N}(x_j) = \begin{cases} 0, & j \neq i \\ 1, & j = i. \end{cases} \qquad (4.92)$$

We thus have the exact result

$$\int_a^b l_{i,N}(x)\,w(x)\,dx = \sum_{m=1}^N W_m\,l_{i,N}(x_m) = W_i, \qquad (4.93)$$

so that the weights W_i can be obtained by analytically performing the indicated integration.

Let's consider an example of how this works. In particular, let's develop an integration rule for the integral

$$I = \int_{-1}^1 f(x)\,dx, \qquad (4.94)$$

using two function evaluations. Since the limits of the integration are $a = -1$, $b = 1$, and the weighting function is $w(x) = 1$, Legendre functions are the appropriate orthogonal polynomials to use. We already know that

$$\phi_2(x) = \sqrt{\frac{5}{2}} \frac{3x^2 - 1}{2}. \tag{4.95}$$

The abscissas for the *Gauss-Legendre* integration are the zeros of this function,

$$x_1 = -\sqrt{\frac{1}{3}} \quad \text{and} \quad x_2 = +\sqrt{\frac{1}{3}}. \tag{4.96}$$

The weights are then evaluated by performing the integral of Equation 4.93. In this case,

$$W_1 = \int_{-1}^{1} l_{1,N} \, dx = \int_{-1}^{1} \frac{x - x_2}{x_1 - x_2} \, dx$$

$$= \frac{1}{x_1 - x_2} \left[\frac{x^2}{2} - x_2 x \right]_{-1}^{1} = \frac{-2x_2}{x_1 - x_2} = 1 \tag{4.97}$$

and

$$W_2 = \int_{-1}^{1} l_{2,N} \, dx = \int_{-1}^{1} \frac{x - x_1}{x_2 - x_1} \, dx$$

$$= \frac{1}{x_2 - x_1} \left[\frac{x^2}{2} - x_1 x \right]_{-1}^{1} = \frac{-2x_1}{x_2 - x_1} = 1. \tag{4.98}$$

This agrees with our previous result, but was much easier to obtain than solving a set of nonlinear equations.

EXERCISE 4.13
Determine the weights and abscissas for the Gauss-Legendre integration rule for $N = 3$.

Fortunately, we don't actually have to do all this work every time we need to perform numerical integrations by Gaussian quadrature—since they're used so frequently, weights and abscissas for various weighting functions and limits of integration have already been tabulated. For example, weights and abscissas for the Gauss–Legendre quadrature are listed in Table 4.1. Since double precision corresponds to roughly 15 decimal digits, the weights and abscissas are given to one digit more than this precision. Clearly, for highly accurate work even more precision is required—one of the standard references for this work, *Gaussian Quadrature Formulas* by Stroud and Secrest, actually presents the data to 30 digits.

Table 4.1   Gauss–Legendre Quadrature: Weights and Abscissas

$$\int_{-1}^{1} f(x)\,dx = \sum_{m=1}^{N} W_m\,f(x_m)$$

x_m	W_m
	$N = 2$
±.5773 5026 9189 6258	1.0000 0000 0000 0000
	$N = 3$
±.7745 9666 9241 4834	.5555 5555 5555 5556
.0000 0000 0000 0000	.8888 8888 8888 8889
	$N = 4$
±.8611 3631 1594 0526	.3478 5484 5137 4539
±.3399 8104 3584 8563	.6521 4515 4862 5461
	$N = 5$
±.9061 7984 5938 6640	.2369 2688 5056 1891
±.5384 6931 0105 6831	.4786 2867 0499 3665
.0000 0000 0000 0000	.5688 8888 8888 8889
	$N = 6$
±.9324 6951 4203 1520	.1713 2449 2379 1703
±.6612 0938 6466 2645	.3607 6157 3048 1386
±.2386 1918 6083 1969	.4679 1393 4572 6910
	$N = 7$
±.9491 0791 2342 7585	.1294 8496 6168 8697
±.7415 3118 5599 3944	.2797 0539 1489 2767
±.4058 4515 1377 3972	.3818 3005 0505 1189
.0000 0000 0000 0000	.4179 5918 3673 4694
	$N = 8$
±.9602 8985 6497 5362	.1012 2853 6290 3763
±.7966 6647 7413 6267	.2223 8103 4453 3745
±.5255 3240 9916 3290	.3137 0664 5877 8873
±.1834 3464 2495 6498	.3626 8378 3378 3620
	$N = 9$
±.9681 6023 9507 6261	.0812 7438 8361 5744
±.8360 3110 7326 6358	.1806 4816 0694 8574
±.6133 7143 2700 5904	.2606 1069 6402 9355
±.3242 5342 3403 8089	.3123 4707 7040 0028
.0000 0000 0000 0000	.3302 3935 5001 2598

(continued)

Table 4.1   Gauss-Legendre Quadrature: Weights and Abscissas (continued)

$$N = 10$$

±.9739 0652 8517 1717	.0666 7134 4308 6881
±.8650 6336 6688 9845	.1494 5134 9150 5806
±.6794 0956 8299 0244	.2190 8636 2515 9820
±.4333 9539 4129 2472	.2692 6671 9309 9964
±.1488 7433 8981 6312	.2955 2422 4714 7529

$$N = 11$$

±.9782 2865 8146 0570	.0556 6856 7116 1737
±.8870 6259 9768 0953	.1255 8036 9464 9046
±.7301 5200 5574 0493	.1862 9021 0927 7343
±.5190 9612 9206 8118	.2331 9376 4591 9905
±.2695 4315 5952 3450	.2628 0454 4510 2467
.0000 0000 0000 0000	.2729 2508 6777 9006

$$N = 12$$

±.9815 6063 4246 7193	.0471 7533 6386 5118
±.9041 1725 6370 4749	.1069 3932 5995 3184
±.7699 0267 4194 3047	.1600 7832 8543 3462
±.5873 1795 4286 6174	.2031 6742 6723 0659
±.3678 3149 8998 1802	.2334 9253 6538 3548
±.1252 3340 8511 1689	.2491 4704 5813 4028

This need for precision introduces an additional complicating factor—how to ensure that the data is entered in the program correctly, in the first place.

```
% gaussquad.m
% Fragment to evaluate the integral of x^m on [-1,1] using
% Gaussian quadrature formulas.
clear;
%
% T H E R E    A R E    E R R O R S    I N    T H I S    D A T A
%
x = [ -0.9061798459386640, -0.5384963101056831, 0.0,...
      0.5384693101056831,  0.9061798459386640];
w = [  0.2369268550561891,  0.4786286704993665,
       0.5688888888888889,...
       0.4786286704993665,  0.2369268550561891];

% The generic form of the integration loop is:
% integral = sum( w(i) * f(x(i)))
integral = sum(w.*x. ^m);
...
```

This coding is not necessarily the most economical use of space, but that's not the point! By spacing the numbers like this they become relatively easy to read and many "typo" errors will be immediately caught because the columns will be out of alignment. But there still might be an error—a digit can simply be mistyped. But there's an easy way to check: this integration formula should be *exact*, i.e., accurate to about 15 digits, for polynomials through x^9, so do the integral! (You were going to write an integration routine anyway, weren't you?)

EXERCISE 4.14
Evaluate the integral $\int_{-1}^{1} x^m \, dx, m = 0, 1, \ldots, 9$. If the weights and abscissas have been entered correctly, the results should be accurate to about 15 digits. By the way, *there are errors* in the listed code fragment.

This sort of verification is not particularly exciting, but it saves an immense amount of wasted effort in the long run. Assuming that you now have a valid table entered into the program, verify that the statements made concerning the accuracy of the integration are true.

EXERCISE 4.15
Evaluate the integral

$$\int_0^1 x^7 \, dx$$

using quadratures with $N = 2, 3, 4$, and 5. Don't forget to map the given integration interval into the region $[-1, 1]$. You should observe that the error decreases as more points are used in the integration, and that the integral is obtained exactly if four or more points are used.

But polynomials are easy to evaluate!

EXERCISE 4.16
Using quadratures with 2, 3, 4, and 5 points, evaluate the integral

$$\int_0^1 e^{-x^2} \, dx.$$

Since the integrand is not a polynomial, the numerical evaluation is not exact. As the number of points in the quadrature is increased, however, the result becomes more and more accurate.

4.14 Composite Rules

It should be clear from the preceding discussion and from these numerical experiments that Gaussian quadrature will always be better than Romberg integration. However, going to larger quadratures is not necessarily the best thing to do. As was discussed with Romberg integration, the use of higher-order polynomial approximations to the integrand is not a guarantee of obtaining a more accurate result. The alternative is to use a composite rule, in which the total integration region is divided into segments, and to use a relatively simple integration rule on each segment.

An additional advantage of a composite rule, of course, is that the error, as determined by difference in succeeding approximations, can be monitored and the integration continued until a predetermined level of accuracy has been achieved.

EXERCISE 4.17

Evaluate the integral

$$\int_0^1 e^{-x^2}\, dx,$$

by a composite rule, using 4-point Gauss-Legendre integration within each segment. For comparison, repeat the evaluation using the Trapezoid rule and Romberg integration. Compare the effort needed to obtain eight significant digit accuracy with these different methods.

4.15 Gauss-Laguerre Quadrature

To use Gauss-Legendre quadrature the limits of the integration must be finite. But it can happen, and often does, that the integral of interest extends to infinity. That is, a physically significant quantity might be expressed by the integral

$$I = \int_0^\infty g(x)\, dx. \qquad (4.99)$$

For this integral to exist, $g(x)$ must go to zero asymptotically, faster than $1/x$. It might even happen that the particular integral of interest be of the form

$$I = \int_0^\infty e^{-x} f(x)\, dx. \qquad (4.100)$$

In this case, $f(x)$ can be a polynomial, for example, since the factor e^{-x} will cause the integrand to vanish asymptotically.

In order to develop a Gauss-style integration formula, we need a set of functions that are orthogonal over the region $[0, \infty]$ with the weighting function $w(x) = e^{-x}$.

Proceeding as before, we can *construct* a set of polynomials that has precisely this characteristic! Beginning (again) with the set $u_m = x^m$, we first consider the function $\phi_0 = \alpha_{00} u_0$, and the integral

$$\int_0^\infty w(x)\,\phi_0(x)\,\phi_0(x)\,dx = \alpha_{00}^2 \int_0^\infty e^{-x}\,dx = \alpha_{00}^2 = C_0. \tag{4.101}$$

With C_0 set to unity, we find $\phi_0(x) = 1$. We then consider the next polynomial,

$$\phi_1(x) = u_1(x) + \alpha_{10}\phi_0(x), \tag{4.102}$$

and require that

$$\int_0^\infty e^{-x}\phi_0(x)\phi_1(x)\,dx = 0, \tag{4.103}$$

and so on. This process constructs the *Laguerre* polynomials; the zeros of these functions can be found, and the appropriate weights for the integration determined. We have thus found the sought after Gauss-Laguerre integration formulas,

$$\int_0^\infty e^{-x}f(x)\,dx = \sum_{m=1}^N W_m\,f(x_m). \tag{4.104}$$

The weights and abscissas are listed in Table 4.2. Since the upper limit of the integration is infinite, we cannot develop composite formulas with Gauss-Laguerre integration. Of course, we can use Gauss-Legendre integration, using composite formulas if needed, up to some (arbitrary) finite limit, and then use Gauss-Laguerre integration from that finite limit up to infinity (with an appropriate change of variable, of course).

Table 4.2   Gauss-Laguerre Quadrature: Weights and Abscissas

$$\int_0^\infty e^{-x}\,f(x)\,dx = \sum_{m=1}^N W_m\,f(x_m)$$

x_m	W_m
N = 2	
5.8578 6437 6269 0495e−1	8.5355 3390 5932 7376e−1
3.4142 1356 2373 0950	1.4644 6609 4067 2624e−1
N = 4	
3.2254 7689 6193 9231e−1	6.0315 4104 3416 3360e−1
1.7457 6110 1158 3466	3.5741 8692 4377 9969e−1
4.5366 2029 6921 1280	3.8887 9085 1500 5384e−2
9.3950 7091 2301 1331	5.3929 4705 5613 2745e−4

(continued)

Table 4.2   Gauss-Laguerre Quadrature: Weights and Abscissas (continued)

$N = 6$

2.2284 6604 1792 6069e−1	4.5896 4673 9499 6359e−1
1.1889 3210 1672 6230	4.1700 0830 7721 2099e−1
2.9927 3632 6059 3141	1.1337 3382 0740 4498e−1
5.7751 4356 9104 5105	1.0399 1974 5314 9075e−2
9.8374 6741 8382 5899	2.6101 7202 8149 3206e−4
1.5982 8739 8060 1702e+1	8.9854 7906 4296 2124e−7

$N = 8$

1.7027 9632 3051 0100e−1	3.6918 8589 3416 3753e−1
9.0370 1776 7993 7991e−1	4.1878 6780 8143 4296e−1
2.2510 8662 9866 1307	1.7579 4986 6371 7181e−1
4.2667 0017 0287 6588	3.3343 4922 6121 5652e−2
7.0459 0540 2393 4657	2.7945 3623 5225 6725e−3
1.0758 5160 1018 0995e+1	9.0765 0877 3358 2131e−5
1.5740 6786 4127 8005e+1	8.4857 4671 6272 5315e−7
2.2863 1317 3688 9264e+1	1.0480 0117 4871 5104e−9

$N = 10$

1.3779 3470 5404 9243e−1	3.0844 1115 7650 2014e−1
7.2945 4549 5031 7050e−1	4.0111 9929 1552 7355e−1
1.8083 4290 1740 3160	2.1806 8287 6118 0942e−1
3.4014 3369 7854 8995	6.2087 4560 9867 7747e−2
5.5524 9614 0063 8036	9.5015 0697 5181 1006e−3
8.3301 5274 6764 4967	7.5300 8388 5875 3878e−4
1.1843 7858 3790 0066e+1	2.8259 2334 9599 5656e−5
1.6279 2578 3137 8102e+1	4.2493 1398 4962 6864e−7
2.1996 5858 1198 0762e+1	1.8395 6482 3979 6308e−9
2.9920 6970 1227 3892e+1	9.9118 2721 9609 0086e−12

$N = 12$

1.1572 2117 3580 2068e−1	2.6473 1371 0554 4319e−1
6.1175 7484 5151 3067e−1	3.7775 9275 8731 3798e−1
1.5126 1026 9776 4188	2.4408 2011 3198 7756e−1
2.8337 5133 7743 5072	9.0449 2222 1168 0931e−2
4.5992 2763 9418 3485	2.0101 2811 5463 4097e−2
6.8445 2545 3115 1773	2.6639 7354 1865 3159e−3
9.6213 1684 2456 8670	2.0323 1592 6629 9939e−4
1.3006 0549 9330 6348e+1	8.3650 5585 6819 7987e−6
1.7116 8551 8746 2256e+1	1.6684 9387 6540 9103e−7
2.2151 0903 7939 7006e+1	1.3423 9103 0515 0041e−9
2.8487 9672 5098 4000e+1	3.0616 0163 5035 0208e−12
3.7099 1210 4446 6920e+1	8.1480 7746 7426 2419e−16

(continued)

Table 4.2   Gauss-Laguerre Quadrature: Weights and Abscissas (continued)

$$N = 18$$

7.8169 1666 6970 5471e−2	1.8558 8603 1469 1881e−1
4.1249 0085 2591 2929e−1	3.1018 1766 3702 2529e−1
1.0165 2017 9623 5397	2.6786 6567 1485 3635e−1
1.8948 8850 9969 7609	1.5297 9747 4680 7491e−1
3.0543 5311 3202 6598	6.1434 9178 6096 1653e−2
4.5042 0553 8889 8928	1.7687 2130 8077 2931e−2
6.2567 2507 3949 1115	3.6601 7976 7759 9178e−3
8.3278 2515 6605 6300	5.4062 2787 0077 3532e−4
1.0737 9900 4775 7609e+1	5.6169 6505 1214 2311e−5
1.3513 6562 0755 5090e+1	4.0153 0788 3701 1576e−6
1.6689 3062 8193 0106e+1	1.9146 6985 6675 6750e−7
2.0310 7676 2626 7743e+1	5.8360 9526 8631 5941e−9
2.4440 6813 5928 3703e+1	1.0717 1126 6955 3901e−10
2.9168 2086 6257 9616e+1	1.0890 9871 3888 8339e−12
3.4627 9270 6566 0172e+1	5.3866 6474 8378 3089e−15
4.1041 8167 7280 8758e+1	1.0498 6597 8035 7034e−17
4.8833 9227 1608 6522e+1	5.4053 9845 1631 0536e−21
5.9090 5464 3590 1251e+1	2.6916 5326 9201 0286e−25

EXERCISE 4.18

The integral

$$\int_0^\infty \frac{x^3}{e^x - 1}\, dx$$

appears in Planck's treatment of blackbody radiation. Perform the integral numerically, with Gauss-Laguerre integration using 2, 4, 6, and 8 points.

4.16 Multidimensional Numerical Integration

Now that we can integrate in one-dimension, it might seem that the jump to two or more dimensions would not be particularly difficult. But actually it is! First is the issue of the number of function evaluations: if a typical integration requires, say, 100 points in one-dimension, then a typical integration in two-dimensions should take 10,000 points, and in three-dimensions a million points are required. That's a lot of function evaluations! A second difficulty is that instead of simply specifying the limits of integration, as is done in one-dimension, in two-dimensions a *region* of integration is specified, perhaps as bounded by a particular curve. And in three-dimensions it's a volume, as specified by a boundary surface—so simply specifying the region of integration can become difficult. In general, multidimensional integration is *a lot harder* than integration in a single variable.

Let's imagine that we need to evaluate the integral

$$I = \int_a^b \int_c^d f(x, y) \, dx \, dy. \tag{4.105}$$

If a, b, c, and d are constants then the integration region is simply a rectangle in the xy-plane, and the integral is nothing more than

$$I = \int_a^b F(y) \, dy, \tag{4.106}$$

where

$$F(y) = \int_c^d f(x, y) \, dx. \tag{4.107}$$

Figure 4.4 suggests what's happening—the rectangular integration region is broken into strips running in the x-direction: the area under the function $f(x, y)$ along each strip is obtained by integrating in x, and the total area is obtained by adding the contributions from all the strips. Of course, we could equally well have chosen to perform the y integral first, so that

$$I = \int_c^d G(x) \, dx, \tag{4.108}$$

where

$$G(x) = \int_a^b f(x, y) \, dy. \tag{4.109}$$

As indicated in Figure 4.5, this corresponds to running the strips along the y-axis.

The computer code to perform such two-dimensional integrals is easily obtained from the one-dimensional code. Although a single function with nested loops would

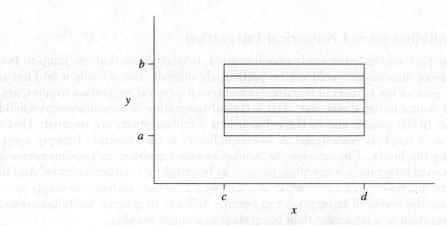

Figure 4.4   Two-dimensional integration, doing the x-integral "first."

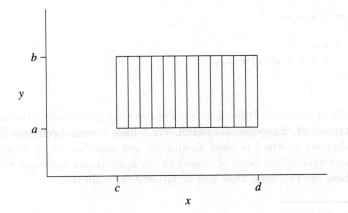

Figure 4.5   Two-dimensional integration, doing the y-integral "first."

certainly do the job, it might be easier to simply have two functions, one that does the x integral and one that does the y integral. Of course, what goes into each will depend upon the order in which you choose to perform the integrations. Let's say that you've decided to do the x-integral "first," so that the integral is to be evaluated according to Equations 4.106 and 4.107, and as depicted in Figure 4.4. Then the code might look something like:

```
% int2dim.m
% This code does two-dimensional numerical integration,
% using the function FofY to perform the integration in
% the x-dimension.
...
% Do all necessary setup...
global c d;
...
% This loop does the integral of F(y)dy on [a,b]
total = 0.0
for i = 1:ny
    ...
    y = ...
    total = total + w(i) * FofY(y)
end
...

%
function [I] = FofY(y)
% This function evaluates the integral of f(x,y) dx
% between the limits of x=c and x=d. With regard to this
% x-integration, y is a constant.
...
% This loop does the x-integral.
I = 0.0;
```

```
for i = 1:nx
    ...
    x = ...
    I = I + ww(i)*f(x,y);
end
...
```

This is only an outline of the appropriate computer code—the method of integration (trapezoid, Simpson, Gaussian, etc.) hasn't even been specified. And of course, whatever method is used should be put together so as to guarantee that either convergence has been obtained or an appropriate message will be displayed. But these are problems that you've already encountered.

EXERCISE 4.19
Numerically integrate

$$\iint e^{-xy} \, dx \, dy$$

on the rectangular domain defined by $0 \le x \le 2$ and $0 \le y \le 1$. Use your personal preference for the method of integration, but be sure that your result is accurate to eight significant digits.

Needless to say(?), MATLAB has its own two-dimensional integration routine, dblquad, that can be used in place of your own.

4.17 Other Integration Domains

Integration on a rectangular domain is a rather straightforward task, but we often need to perform the integration over different regions of interest. For example, perhaps we need the integral evaluated in the first quadrant, bounded by a circle of radius 1, as indicated in Figure 4.6. The y variable still varies from 0 to 1, but

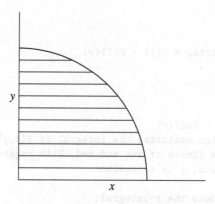

Figure 4.6   A two-dimensional integration region divided into Cartesian strips.

the limits of the x integration vary from 0 to $\sqrt{1 - y^2}$. In general, the limits of the integration are a function of all variables yet to be integrated. The computer code just discussed is still appropriate for this problem except that d, the upper limit of the x-integration, is not a constant and is different for each evaluation of the function FofY, i.e., for each x-integration. The function FofY itself would remain unchanged.

EXERCISE 4.20

Modify your program so that the calling routine adjusts the limits of the integration. (No changes are needed in the *called* function, however.) Then evaluate the integral

$$I = \int_0^1 \left(\int_0^{\sqrt{1-y^2}} e^{-xy} dx \right) dy.$$

over the quarter circle of unit radius lying in the first quadrant.

It should be noted that a change of variables can sometimes be used to simplify the specification of the bounding region. For example, if the integration region is bounded by a circle, then it might be advantageous to change from Cartesian to polar coordinates. This would yield integration domains as indicated in Figure 4.7.

EXERCISE 4.21

Evaluate the integral

$$I = \int_0^1 \left(\int_0^{\sqrt{1-y^2}} e^{-xy} dx \right) dy$$

over the quarter circle of radius 1 lying in the first quadrant, by first changing to polar coordinates. Note that in these coordinates, the limits of integration are constant.

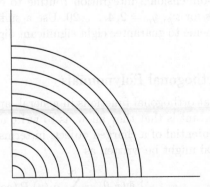

Figure 4.7   A two-dimensional integration region divided into Polar strips.

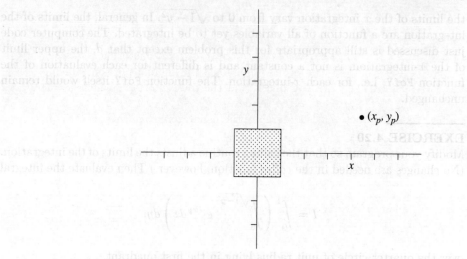

(x_p, y_p)

Figure 4.8   A uniformly charged square region in Cartesian coordinates.

4.18 A Little Physics Problem

Consider a square region in the xy-plane, such that $-1 \leq x \leq 1$ and $-1 \leq y \leq 1$, containing a uniform charge distribution ρ, as depicted in Figure 4.8. The electrostatic potential at the point (x_p, y_p) due to this charge distribution is obtained by integrating over the charged region,

$$\Phi(x_p, y_p) = \frac{\rho}{4\pi\varepsilon_0} \int_{-1}^{1} \int_{-1}^{1} \frac{dx\,dy}{\sqrt{(x - x_p)^2 + (y - y_p)^2}}. \qquad (4.110)$$

For simplicity, take $\rho/4\pi\varepsilon_0$ to be one.

EXERCISE 4.22

Use your two-dimensional integration routine to evaluate $\Phi(x_p, y_p)$, and create a table of values for $x_p, y_p = 2, 4, \ldots, 20$. Use a sufficient number of points in your integration scheme to guarantee eight significant digit accuracy in your final results.

4.19 More on Orthogonal Polynomials

One reason that orthogonal functions in general, and Legendre functions in particular, are important is that they allow us to write a complicated thing, such as the electrostatic potential of a charged object, in terms of just a few coefficients. That is, the potential might be written as

$$\Phi(r, \theta) = \sum_{i=0}^{\infty} a_i(r)\, P_i(\cos\theta). \qquad (4.111)$$

A relatively few coefficients are then sufficient to describe the potential to high accuracy, rather than requiring a table of values. Note that the coefficients $a_i(r)$ are functions of r, but are *constants with respect to* θ. Factoring the potential in this way divides the problem into two portions: the angular portion, which is often geometric in nature and easily solved, and the radial portion, which is where the real difficulty of the problem often resides.

The Legendre functions used here are the usual, *unnormalized* ones, the first few of which are

$$P_0(x) = 1$$
$$P_1(x) = x$$
$$P_2(x) = (3x^2 - 1)/2$$
$$P_3(x) = (5x^3 - 3x)/2$$
$$P_4(x) = (35x^4 - 30x^2 + 3)/8$$
$$P_5(x) = (63x^5 - 70x^3 + 15x)/8 \tag{4.112}$$

The orthogonality condition for these unnormalized functions is

$$\int_0^\pi P_m(\cos\theta) P_n(\cos\theta) \sin\theta \, d\theta = \frac{2}{2m+1}\delta_{mn}. \tag{4.113}$$

Equation 4.111 can then be multiplied by $P_j(\cos\theta)$ and integrated to yield

$$a_j(r) = \frac{2j+1}{2} \int_0^\pi \Phi(r,\theta) \, P_j(\cos\theta) \sin\theta \, d\theta. \tag{4.114}$$

Due to the nature of the integrand, Gaussian quadrature is well suited to evaluate this integral, although a change of variables is necessary since the specified integration is on the interval $[0, \pi]$.

Let's reconsider the problem of the uniformly charged square. If you have not already done so, you should write a function that performs the two-dimensional integral of Equation 4.110, returning the value of the potential at the point (x_p, y_p). This function evaluation will be needed to evaluate the integral for $a_i(r_p)$, as given in Equation 4.114. Of course, the points at which the function is to be evaluated are determined by r_p and the abscissas at which the θ_p integral is to be performed. That is, measuring θ counterclockwise from the positive x-axis, we have

$$x_p = r_p \cos\theta_p$$
$$\text{and} \quad y_p = r_p \sin\theta_p, \tag{4.115}$$

as illustrated in Figure 4.9.

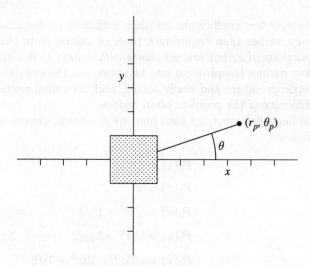

Figure 4.9   A uniformly charged square region in polar coordinates.

EXERCISE 4.23

Expand the potential in a series of Legendre functions through P_5. That is, evaluate the r_p-dependent coefficients $a_i(r_p)$ for $i = 0, \ldots, 5$ at $r_p = 2, 4, \ldots, 20$. Perform the required integrations by Gaussian quadrature, using an appropriate number of points N in the integration. (MATLAB's `legendre(N,x)` function can be used.) *Justify your choice of N.*

4.20 Monte Carlo Integration

The integration methods discussed so far are all based upon making a polynomial approximation to the integrand. But there are other ways of calculating an integral, some of which are *very* different. One class of these methods rely upon random numbers, and have come to be known under the general rubric of *Monte Carlo* methods, after the famous casino.

Consider a function to be integrated, as in Figure 4.10—the integral is just the area under the curve. If we knew the area, we could divide by the width of the interval, $(b - a)$, and define the *average* value of the function, $\langle f \rangle$. Conversely, the width times the average value of the function is the integral,

$$\int_a^b f(x)\, dx = (b - a) \langle f \rangle. \tag{4.116}$$

So if we just had some way of calculating the average....

And that's where the need for random numbers arises. Let's imagine that we have a "list" of random numbers, the x_i, uniformly distributed between a and b.

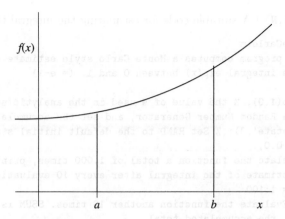

Figure 4.10   The integral of $f(x)$ between a and b.

To calculate the function average, we simply evaluate $f(x)$ at each of the randomly selected points, and divide by the number of points:

$$\langle f \rangle_N = \frac{1}{N} \sum_{i=1}^{N} f(x_i). \tag{4.117}$$

As the number of points used in calculating the average increases, $\langle f \rangle_N$ tends toward the "real" average, $\langle f \rangle$, and so we write the Monte Carlo estimate of the integral as

$$\int_a^b f(x)\, dx \approx (b-a) \frac{1}{N} \sum_{i=1}^{N} f(x_i). \tag{4.118}$$

Finding a "list" of random numbers could be a real problem, of course. Fortunately for us, it's a problem that has already been tackled by others, and as a result *random number generators* are fairly common. Unfortunately, there is a wide range in the quality of these generators, with some of them being quite unacceptable. For a number of years a rather poor random number generator was widely distributed in the scientific community, and more recently algorithms now described as "mediocre" were circulated. For our purposes, which are not particularly demanding, the `rand` command supplied by MATLAB, which returns a number between 0 and 1, will suffice. As our needs became more stringent, however, verifying the quality of the generator, and replacing it if warranted, would take a high priority. In any event, we should note that these numbers are generated by a computer algorithm, and hence are not truly random—they are in fact *pseudo-random*—but they'll serve our purpose. To make the sequence of random numbers reproducible, we'll reset the random number generator using the command `rand('state',0)`. (It's also possible to create a whole N×N array of random numbers with the single command rand(N,N).) A suitable code for estimating the integral then would be

```
% MonteCarlo.m
% This program computes a Monte Carlo style estimate of
%   the integral exp(x) between 0 and 1. (= e-1)
clear;
e = exp(1.0); % the value of e used in the analytic solution
% Use a Random Number Generator, and set the accumulated SSUM to zero.
rand('state',0); % Set RAND to the default initial state
ssum = 0.0;
% Calculate the function a total of 1,000 times, printing
% an estimate of the integral after every 10 evaluations.
for i = 1:100
    % Evaluate the function another 10 times. SSUM is
    %   the accumulated total.
    for j = 1:10
        x = rand;
        ssum = ssum + exp(x);
    end
    % The function has now been evaluated a total of (10*i) times.
    N = i*10;
    monte = ssum/N;
    % Calculate the relative error, from the known value of the integral.
    error = abs(monte-(e-1.0) )/(e-1.0);
    fprintf('N=%6.0f, monte=%15.12f, error=%15.12f\n',N, monte, error)
end
```

As discussed above, we must first initialize the random number generator to its default initial state. The generator will then provide the same sequence of random numbers every time it's called. This is essential to obtaining reproducible results and in debugging complicated programs.

This code prints the estimate of the integral after every 10 function evaluations; typical results (which is to say, the ones we found) are presented in Figure 4.11. With 1,000 function evaluations the Monte Carlo estimate of the integral is 1.7219184, compared to $e - 1 \approx 1.7182818$, for an accuracy of about three significant digits. The figure suggests that the estimate of the integral has stabilized, if not converged, to this value. This is an illusion, however; as the number of accumulated points grows, the influence of the last few points diminishes, so that the variation from one estimate to the next is necessarily reduced.

The accuracy of the Monte Carlo method can be enhanced by using information about the function. For example, if $g(x) \approx f(x)$, and if we can integrate g, then we can write

$$\int_a^b f(x)\,dx = \int_a^b \frac{f(x)}{g(x)} g(x)\,dx = \int_{y^{-1}(a)}^{y^{-1}(b)} \frac{f(x)}{g(x)}\,dy, \qquad (4.119)$$

where

$$y(x) = \int^x g(t)\,dt. \qquad (4.120)$$

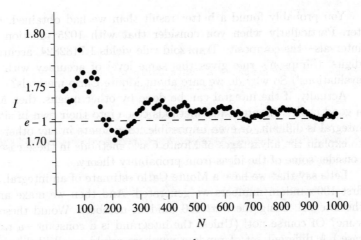

Figure 4.11   Monte Carlo estimates of the integral $\int_0^1 e^x \, dx$ using various numbers of sampling points. The correct result is indicated by the dashed line.

Instead of uniformly sampling x to integrate $f(x)$, we uniformly sample y and integrate $f(x)/g(x)$! To the extent that g is a good approximation to f, the integrand will be unity, and easy to evaluate. This technique, known as *importance sampling*, has the effect of placing a larger number of sample points where the function is large, thus obtaining a better estimate of the integral.

EXERCISE 4.24

Consider the integral

$$I = \int_0^1 e^x \, dx. \tag{4.121}$$

Since $e^x \approx 1 + x$, the integral can be rewritten as

$$I = \int_0^1 \frac{e^x}{1+x}\,(1+x)\,dx = \int_0^{3/2} \frac{e^{\sqrt{1+2y}-1}}{\sqrt{1+2y}}\,dy, \tag{4.122}$$

where

$$y = \int^x (1+t)\,dt = x + \frac{x^2}{2} \tag{4.123}$$

and

$$x = -1 + \sqrt{1+2y}. \tag{4.124}$$

This change of variables modifies the limits of integration and the form of the integrand, of course. To evaluate the integral in its new form, y is to be uniformly sampled on the interval $[0, 3/2]$. Modify the previous Monte Carlo program to evaluate this integral.

You probably found a better result than we had obtained, but not much better. Particularly when you consider that with 1025 function evaluations—1024 intervals—the composite Trapezoid rule yields 1.7182824, accurate to 7 significant digits. (Simpson's rule gives this same level of accuracy with only 129 function evaluations!) So why do we care about Monte Carlo methods?

Actually, if the integral can be done by other means, then Monte Carlo *is not* a good choice. Monte Carlo methods come into their own in situations where the integral is difficult, or even impossible, to evaluate in any other way. And in order to explain the advantages of Monte Carlo methods in these cases, we need first to consider some of the ideas from probability theory.

Let's say that we have a Monte Carlo estimate of an integral, obtained with the first 100 random numbers we generated. And then we make another estimate of the integral, using the *next* 100 random numbers. Would these estimates be the same? Of course not! (Unless the integrand is a constant—a rather uninteresting case.) A different set of random numbers would in all likelihood yield a different estimate, although perhaps not too different. And as a larger and larger number of estimates are considered, we would expect a smooth distribution of estimates to be observed—most of them near the true value of the integral, with the number of estimates decreasing as we moved away from that true value.

And that's exactly what we see! In Figure 4.12, two distributions of 10,000 estimates of the integral are displayed. The distribution on the left was obtained by using 100 points in the estimate of the integral. The plot should look (at least vaguely) familiar to you—something like a bell shape. In fact, the Central Limit Theorem of probability theory states that, if N is sufficiently large, the distribution of sums will be a normal distribution, e.g., described by a Gaussian function.

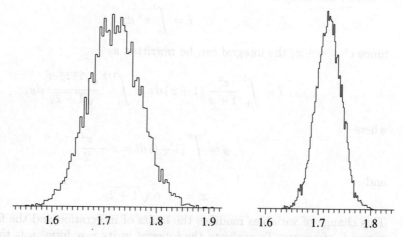

Figure 4.12 Distributions of 10,000 Monte Carlo estimates of the integral $\int_0^1 e^x\,dx$. On the left, each integral was evaluated with $N = 100$ points; on the right, with $N = 400$ points.

Now, what would happen if we used more points N to estimate the integral? It would seem reasonable to expect to get a "better" answer, in the sense that if a large number of estimates of the integral were made, the distribution of estimates would be narrower about the true answer. And indeed, this is what's seen on the right side of Figure 4.12, where another 10,000 estimates of the integral are plotted. This time, each estimate of the integral was obtained using $N = 400$ points.

(To generate these histograms, we kept track of how many Monte Carlo estimates fell within each narrow "bin." The plot is simply the number of estimates in each bin. For $N = 100$, the bin was 0.004 wide; for the $N = 400$ example, it was reduced to 0.002. Alternatively, MATLAB's `hist` function could be used.)

Comparing the two distributions in the figure, we immediately see that the second distribution is much narrower than the first. We can take a ruler and measure the width of the distributions, say at half their maximum values, and find that the second distribution is very nearly one half the width of the first. This is another fundamental result from probability theory—that the width of the distribution of estimates of an integral is proportional to $1/\sqrt{N}$, so that when we quadrupled the number of points, we halved the width of the distribution.

Probability theory also tells us how to estimate the standard deviation of the mean, a measure of the width of the distribution of estimates. Since 68.3% of all estimates lie within one standard deviation of the mean, we can also say that there is a 68.3% probability that our particular estimate $\langle f \rangle_N$ lies within one standard deviation of the exact average $\langle f \rangle$! (There's also a 95.4% probability of being within 2 standard deviations, a 99.7% probability of being within three standard deviations, and so on.) The standard deviation can be estimated from the points sampled in evaluating the integral:

$$\sigma_N = \sqrt{\frac{\frac{1}{N}\sum f(x_i)^2 - \left(\frac{1}{N}\sum f(x_i)\right)^2}{N-1}}. \tag{4.125}$$

It's important to note that σ_N is accumulated as more points are sampled. That is, the two sums appearing in Equation 4.125 are updated with every additional point, and σ_N can be evaluated whenever it's needed or desired. Thus

$$\int_a^b f(x)\, dx \approx (b-a)\left(\langle f \rangle_N \pm \sigma_N\right), \tag{4.126}$$

with 68.3% confidence. Implicit in this is one of the strengths of the Monte Carlo method—if a more accurate estimate of the integral is desired, you need only to sample the integrand at more randomly selected points. As N increases, σ_N decreases, and the probability of your result lying within some specified vicinity of the correct result increases. But also contained is its weakness—the improvement goes only as the square root of N.

EXERCISE 4.25
Modify the Monte Carlo code to include the calculation of the standard deviation.
Use your code to estimate the integral

$$I = \int_0^\pi \sin x \, dx \tag{4.127}$$

and its standard deviation. In general, the addition of importance sampling will
greatly increase the accuracy of the integration. Noting that

$$\sin x \approx \frac{4}{\pi^2} x (\pi - x), \quad 0 \le x \le \pi, \tag{4.128}$$

reevaluate the integral using importance sampling, and compare the estimated
standard deviations.

The "error" in a Monte Carlo calculation is fundamentally different from that in
the other methods of integration that we've discussed. With the Trapezoid Rule,
for example, the error represents the inadequacy of the linear approximation in
fitting the actual integrand being integrated—by making the stepsize smaller, the
fit is made better, and the error decreases. Since the error $\sim h^2$, the error can be
halved if h is decreased by $\sqrt{2}$, which is to say that N would be increased by $\sqrt{2}$.
In a two-dimensional integral, the stepsizes in both dimensions would have to be
decreased, so that N would need to be increased by a factor of 2. In a general,
multidimensional integral of dimension d, N must be increased by a factor of $2^{d/2}$
in order to decrease the error by a factor of two.

In a Monte Carlo calculation, the "error" is of a probabilistic nature—68.3% of
the time, the estimate is within one standard deviation of the "correct" answer.
As more points are included, the average gets better, in that sense. To perform a
multidimensional integration, the random number generator will be called d times
to get each of d coordinate values. Then the function is evaluated, and the sums
updated. Although the Monte Carlo method converges slowly—only the square root
of N—this convergence is dependent upon the probabilistic nature of the averaging
process, and not the dimensionality of the integral! That is, to reduce the error
by two, N must be increased by four, *independent of the dimensionality of the
integral!* Thus the convergence of the Monte Carlo method is comparable to the
trapezoid rule in four-dimensions, and faster if $d > 4$. For integrals of sufficiently
high dimensionality, Monte Carlo methods actually converge *faster* than any of the
other methods we've discussed!

In some areas of physics, such multidimensional integrals occur frequently. In
statistical mechanics, for example, a standard problem goes like this: Given a microscopic variable u, which is defined at every point in phase space, The equilibrium

thermodynamic value $\bar{u}$ is given as

$$\bar{u} = \frac{\int u \exp\left[-E/kT\right] dx^{3N} dv^{3N}}{\int \exp\left[-E/kT\right] dx^{3N} dv^{3N}},$$

(4.129)

where the notation $dx^{3N} dv^{3N}$ means to integrate over the three components of position and velocity for each of N particles. N doesn't need to be very large for the integral to become intractable to all but Monte Carlo methods of attack.

And even in situations where the standard methods are applicable, Monte Carlo might still be preferred, purely on the number of function evaluations required. For example, to evaluate a 10-dimensional integral, using only 10 points per coordinate, requires 10 billion function evaluations. That might take a while. It's not unusual for symmetry considerations to substantially reduce the complexity of the problem, but still—we're not going to evaluate an integral like that by direct methods! With Monte Carlo methods we can at least obtain *some* estimate, and a reasonable idea of the error, with however many points we have. And to improve the result, we need only to add more function evaluations to the approximation. Clearly, this process is not likely to yield a highly precise result—but it can give valid estimates of one or two significant digit accuracy where other methods totally fail.

EXERCISE 4.26

Evaluate the nine-dimensional integral

$$I = \int_0^1 \cdots \int_0^1 \frac{da_x \, da_y \, da_z \, db_x \, db_y \, db_z \, dc_x \, dc_y \, dc_z}{|(\vec{a} + \vec{b}) \cdot \vec{c}|}.$$

Use a sufficient number of points in the integration so that the estimated standard deviation is less than 10% of the estimated integral.

Can you find some other way to evaluate the integral? An additional feature of Monte Carlo integration is that singularities don't bother it too much—this can't be said of other integration schemes. Integrals similar to the one in the exercise appear in the study of electron plasmas, but they are more complicated in that the integration extends over all of space. By an appropriate change of variable and the use of importance sampling, Monte Carlo methods can be used to give (crude) estimates of these integrals, where no other methods can even be applied.

• 4.21 Monte Carlo Simulations

In addition to evaluating multidimensional integrals, Monte Carlo methods are widely used to mimic, or simulate, "random" processes. In fact, one of the first uses of Monte Carlo methods was in designing nuclear reactors; in particular, how much shielding is necessary to stop neutrons. One could imagine following the path of a neutron as it moved through the shielding material, encountering various nuclei and being scattered. But after a few such collisions, any "memory" the neutron had of its initial conditions would be lost. That is, the specific result of a particular collision would have no correlation with the initial conditions, i.e., it would be "random." Such processes are said to be *stochastic*. Such stochastic problems, or physical problems that are treatable by stochastic methods, abound in physics. And in many cases, the use of simulations is the only practical tool for their investigation.

As a rather trivial example, consider the drunken sailor problem. A young seaman, after many months at sea, is given shore leave in a foreign port. He and his buddies explore the town, find an interesting little bistro and proceed to partake of the local brew. In excess, unfortunately. When it's time to return to the ship, he can hardly stand. As the sailor leaves the bistro, a physicist sitting at the end of the bar observes that the sailor is equally likely to step in any direction. In his condition, how far will he travel after taking N steps?

We can *simulate* this walk by using random numbers. Let's imagine a square grid, with an equal probability of moving on this grid in any of four directions. A random number generator will be called upon to generate the direction: if between 0 and 0.25, move North; between 0.25 and 0.50, move East; and so on. A typical path is shown in Figure 4.13. Of course, we don't learn much from a single path—we need to take a large number of paths, and build up a distribution. Then we can state, in a probabilistic sense, how far the sailor is likely to travel.

EXERCISE 4.27

Write a computer code to investigate the random walk problem. Plot the mean distance traveled versus the number of steps taken. For large N, can you make a statement concerning the functional relationship between these quantities?

It might seem that this exercise is pure fancy, having little to do with physics. But what if we were investigating the mobility of an atom attached to the surface of a crystal? With the atom playing the role of the sailor, and the grid points corresponding to lattice points of the crystal, we have a description of a real physical situation. And we can use the simulation to ask *real* physical questions: How far will the atom travel in a given period of time? What percentage of the surface needs to be covered to ensure that two atoms will be at adjoining sites 50% of the time? As the percentage of coverage increases, will patterns of atoms develop on the surface?

In the example, only steps taken in the cardinal directions were permitted. This restriction can be relaxed, of course, and we can also consider motion in three-dimensions. For example, consider the problem of diffusion. At room temperature, molecules in the air are travelling at hundreds of meters per second. Yet, when a

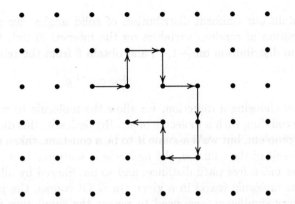

Figure 4.13   A "typical" random walk on a two-dimensional square grid.

bottle of perfume is opened at the far end of the classroom, it takes several minutes for the aroma to be perceived at the other end. Why?

The explanation is that while the velocity of the molecules is great, there are a large number of collisions with other molecules. Each such collision changes the direction of the aromatic molecule, so that it wanders about, much like our drunken sailor, making many collisions while achieving only modest displacement from its origin. Let's model this process with our Monte Carlo approach.

We begin with a single molecule, and allow it to travel in a random direction. The first problem, then, is determining the direction. We want a uniform distribution of directions, but an element of solid angle is

$$d\Omega = \sin\theta \, d\theta \, d\phi. \tag{4.130}$$

If we were simply to take a uniform distribution in θ and in ϕ, there would be a "bunching" of chosen directions about the poles. What we really want is a $\sin\theta$ distribution so that the directions are uniformly distributed throughout space, i.e., uniformly distributed on the unit sphere. (This is very similar to what we encountered with importance sampling—changing the variables in such a way as to put points where we want them. This similarity is not mere coincidence: ultimately we will take a large number of events and average over them, and hence *are* performing an integration.) In this case, let's introduce the variable g such that

$$d\Omega = dg \, d\phi, \tag{4.131}$$

so that g and ϕ should be uniformly sampled. But that means that

$$dg = \sin\theta \, d\theta \tag{4.132}$$

or that

$$g(\theta) = \cos\theta. \tag{4.133}$$

To obtain our uniform distribution of solid angles, we select ϕ from a uniform distribution of random variables on the interval $[0, 2\pi]$. We then select g from a uniform distribution on $[-1, 1]$, and obtain θ from the relation

$$\theta = \cos^{-1} g. \qquad (4.134)$$

After choosing a direction, we allow the molecule to move some given distance before colliding with a molecule of air. Realistically, this distance is another variable of the problem, but we'll assume it to be a constant, taken to be the mean free path. As a result of the collision, the molecule is scattered in a random direction, travels another mean free path distance, and so on. Slowed by all these collisions, how far will the molecule travel in a given time? Of course, the path of a single molecule isn't very significant—we need to repeat the simulation for many molecules, and average the results.

EXERCISE 4.28

Consider the diffusion of an aromatic molecule in air, having a velocity of 500 meters per second and a mean free path λ of 1 meter. Calculate the distance $\langle d \rangle$ a molecule moves in one second, averaging over 100 different molecules.

You probably found that the net displacement is much less than the 500 meters a free molecule would have traveled. We argued that this would be the case, as a consequence of the many collisions, but we have now successfully modeled that phenomena on the computer. The importance of Monte Carlo simulation is not the precision of the result, but the fact that it can yield qualitatively valid results in situations where any result is difficult to obtain.

Just how valid are the results? Certainly, the average displacement can be monitored as more molecular paths are considered, and some feel for the convergence of the results can be acquired, but perhaps a better approach is to monitor the *distribution* of displacements obtained. Physically, this distribution is akin to the density of aromatic molecules in the air at different distances from the perfume bottle, a distribution we clearly expect to be continuous. In our simulation, we have started all the molecules at the same instant, as if the perfume bottle were opened, many molecules allowed to escape, and then the bottle closed. After 1 second, and 500 collisions, we would expect very few molecules to still be in the vicinity of the origin. We would also expect few molecules to be found at large displacements since insufficient time has elapsed for them to travel very far. The distribution is thus expected to be small (or even zero) at the origin, to smoothly increase to a maximum, and then to smoothly decrease to zero at large displacements. If the Monte Carlo sampling is sufficiently large, then the distribution we obtain should mimic this physically expected one. Conversely, if the distribution is not realistic, then a larger sampling is needed.

EXERCISE 4.29

Investigate the distribution of net displacements as described. Plot a histogram indicating the number of paths yielding displacements between 0 and 1 m, between 1 and 2 m, and so on, using 100 different paths. Repeat the exercise, plotting histograms with 200, 300, 400, and 500 different paths, and compare the histograms obtained with what is expected on physical grounds.

Once we're satisfied that the method is working properly and that the results are statistically valid, we must ask ourselves if the results are *physically* valid. (Actually, this is a question we ask ourselves at every opportunity!) That the displacement is considerably less than the free displacement would have been is certainly expected, but what about the magnitude of the result itself? If you found, as we did, that after one second the net displacement is between 10 and 20 meters, then the aroma of the perfume reaches the front of a 30-foot room in less than a second! That seems much too rapid. Our own recollection of similar events is that it takes several minutes for the aroma to travel that far.

We're forced to conclude that the actual diffusion is slower than what we've found, which in turn means that the mean free path we've adopted is too large. We could repeat our simulation with a different value for the mean free path, but there might be a better way. Consider: Does the value of the mean free path really enter the calculation? Or have we actually evaluated something more universal than we thought: the net displacement, in units of the mean free path length, after 500 collisions? This is an example of a scaling relation, and is very important. If we can determine a fundamental relationship between the magnitude of the displacement, in units of the mean free path, and the number of collisions, then we can apply that relation to many different physical situations.

EXERCISE 4.30

Re-examine the simulation. Instead of monitoring the displacement after 1 second, monitor it after every collision, and average over a sufficiently large number of molecular paths to yield valid results. Plot the average net displacement as a function of the number of collisions.

Averaging over 1000 molecular paths, the results presented in Figure 4.14 were obtained. The curve is remarkably smooth, and appears vaguely familiar, which suggests that further investigation might be worthwhile. Recall that if the displacement is proportional to a power of the number of collisions, N,

$$\frac{\langle d \rangle}{\lambda} \approx N^q, \tag{4.135}$$

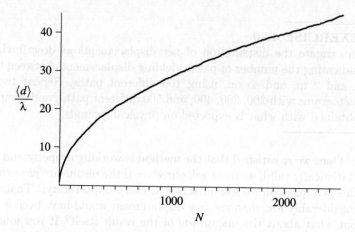

Figure 4.14   The average displacement $\langle d \rangle$ (in units of the mean free path λ) is plotted versus the number of steps taken. These data were obtained by averaging over 1000 different paths.

then

$$\ln \frac{\langle d \rangle}{\lambda} \approx q \ln N. \tag{4.136}$$

That is, a log–log plot of the data will be linear, and the slope of the line will be the power q. Such a plot is presented in Figure 4.15. Clearly, the plot is a linear one, with a slope close to 0.5.

There are certain numbers of which we should always be mindful: π, e, integers, and their reciprocals and powers. The slope we've determined is very close to 1/2— close enough to suspect that it's not accidental. We seem to have stumbled upon

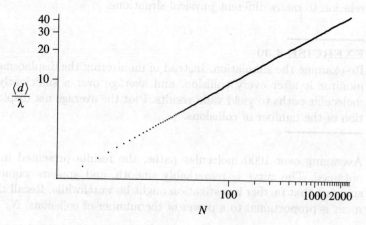

Figure 4.15   This is the same data as plotted in Figure 4.14, but plotted on a log–log scale. The apparent linearity of the curve suggests a simple power-law dependence.

a fundamental truism, that the displacement is proportional to the square root of N,

$$\frac{\langle d \rangle}{\lambda} \approx \sqrt{N}. \tag{4.137}$$

While we should always use analytic results to guide our computations, we should also be open to the possibility that our computations can lead us to new analytic results. Our results *do not prove* this relationship, of course, but strongly suggest that the relationship exists. At this juncture, we should set aside the computer and our computations, and research the availability of analytic derivations of this result. As Hamming, a pioneer in modern computing, has said, "The purpose of computing is insight, not numbers." It appears that we have gained significant insight from this simulation.

EXERCISE 4.31
Plot your data on a log–log scale, and verify the power dependence.

4.22 References

Since numerical integration is fundamental to many applications, accurate weights and abscissas for Gaussian integration were developed at nearly the same time as large-scale computers were becoming available to the scientific community. To avoid duplication of this effort, Stroud and Secrest published their results for all to use.

A. H. Stroud and Don Secrest, *Gaussian Quadrature Formulas.* Prentice-Hall, Englewood Cliffs, 1966.

An indispensable source of information regarding mathematical functions is the reference

Handbook of Mathematical Functions, edited by Milton Abramowitz and Irene A. Stegun, Dover Publications, New York, 1965.

Monte Carlo methods are becoming more widely used every day. A good introduction is provided by

Malvin H. Kalos and Paula A. Whitlock, *Monte Carlo Methods,* John Wiley & Sons, New York, 1986.

Some insight into the quality of random number generators can be discerned from the article

William H. Press and Saul A. Teukolsky, "Portable Random Number Generators," *Computers in Physics* **6**, 522 (1992).

Obtaining a Gaussian distribution of random numbers, rather than a uniform distribution, is discussed in

G. E. P. Box and M. E. Muller, "A note on the generation of random normal deviates," *Ann. Math. Statist.* **29**, 610 (1958).

Ordinary Differential Equations

To a large extent, the study of Physics is the study of differential equations, so it's no surprise that the numerical solution of differential equations is a central issue in computational physics. The surprise is that so few traditional courses in physics, and even mathematics courses in differential equations, provide tools that are of practical use in solving real problems. The number of physically relevant "linear second-order homogeneous differential equations with constant coefficients" is not large; experience has led us to the conclusion that *all the interesting equations are either trivial, or impossibly difficult to solve analytically.* Traditional analysis solves the trivial cases, and can yield invaluable insight to the solution of the difficult ones. But the bottom line is that the difficult cases must be treated numerically.

You are probably familiar with the initial value problem, in which you have a differential equation such as $y''(x) = f(x, y, y')$ and the initial conditions $y(0) = a$, $y'(0) = b$. Equations of this form are quite common, and we'll develop several methods suitable for their solution. There is another type of problem that is also of considerable importance to physics, which we'll also address in this chapter: the boundary value problem. Here, rather than having information about the derivative, you are told about the function at various points on the *boundary* of the integration region.

Unfortunately, there is no "best" method to solve all differential equations. Each equation has a character all its own, and a method that works well on one may work poorly, or even fail, on another. What we will do is develop some general ideas concerning the numerical solution of differential equations, and implement these ideas in a code that will work reasonably well for a wide variety of problems. Keep in mind, however, that if you are faced with solving a difficult problem, say one involving large sets of differential equations to be solved over a wide range of the independent variable, you might be better off investigating a solution specifically tailored to the problem you're confronting.

5.1 Euler Methods

The most prolific mathematician of the eighteenth century, or perhaps of any century, was the Swiss born Leonhard Euler (1707–1783). It has been said that Euler could calculate with no apparent effort, just as men breathe and eagles fly, and would compose his memoirs while playing with his thirteen children. He lost the sight in his right eye when he was 28, and in the left when he was 59, but with no effect on his mathematical production. Aided by a phenomenal memory, and having practiced writing on a chalk board before becoming blind, he continued to publish his mathematical discoveries by dictating to his children. During his life, he published over 500 books and papers; the complete bibliography of Euler's work, including posthumous items, has 886 entries.

Euler made contributions to virtually every field of eighteenth century mathematics, particularly the theory of numbers, and wrote textbooks on algebra and calculus. The prestige of his books established his notation as the standard; the modern usage of the symbols e, π, and i (for $\sqrt{-1}$) are directly attributable to Euler. He also made significant contributions in areas of applied mathematics: Euler wrote books on ship construction and artillery, on optics and music, and ventured into the areas of physics and astronomy. But our current interest, which represents only a minute fraction of Euler's, is in methods due to him in solving differential equations.

Consider the differential equation

$$y'(x) = f(x, y). \tag{5.1}$$

(If f is a function of x alone, we can immediately "solve" for y:

$$y(x) = \int^x f(\chi)\, d\chi. \tag{5.2}$$

Since this is an "uninteresting" situation, we'll assume that f is a function of x and y.) Now, one might try to solve Equation 5.1 by Taylor's series; that is, if we knew all the derivatives, we could construct the solution from the expansion

$$y(x) = y(x_0) + (x - x_0)y'(x_0) + \frac{(x - x_0)^2}{2!}y''(x_0) + \cdots. \tag{5.3}$$

Since $y'(x)$ is known, we can obtain the higher derivatives—but it takes a little work. The second derivative, for example, is

$$y''(x) = \frac{\partial}{\partial x}f(x, y) + \frac{dy}{dx}\frac{\partial}{\partial y}f(x, y)$$

$$= \frac{\partial}{\partial x}f(x, y) + f(x, y)\frac{\partial}{\partial y}f(x, y). \tag{5.4}$$

Clearly, this is leading to some complicated expressions, and the situation degenerates as we move to higher derivatives. As a practical matter, the Taylor's series solution is not very helpful. However, it provides a standard against which other methods can be measured. To that end, we write

$$y(x) = y_0 + (x - x_0)f(x_0, y_0) + \frac{(x - x_0)^2}{2!}$$

$$\times \left[\frac{\partial f(x_0, y_0)}{\partial x} + f(x_0, y_0)\frac{\partial f(x_0, y_0)}{\partial y} \right] + \frac{(x - x_0)^3}{3!}y'''(\xi), \qquad (5.5)$$

where $y_0 = y(x_0)$.

The original differential equation gives us the derivative y' at any point; if we're given the value of y at some point x_0, then we could approximate the function by a Taylor series, truncated to two terms:

$$y(x) \approx y(x_0) + (x - x_0)y'(x_0). \qquad (5.6)$$

As simpleminded as it is, this method actually works! (But not well!) Denoting the size of the step $x - x_0$ by h, we can write Equation 5.6 as an equality

$$y(x_0 + h) = y(x_0) + hf\big(x_0, y(x_0)\big) = y_0 + hf_0, \qquad (5.7)$$

where we've defined $y_0 = y(x_0)$ and $f_0 = f(x_0, y_0)$. This is known as the *simple Euler method*, and it allows us to move the solution along, one step at a time, as indicated in Figure 5.1. A typical implementation is to divide the total integration region into steps of size h, and to move the solution along one step at a time in the obvious way. As a check on accuracy, the calculation can be repeated for a different step size, and the results compared.

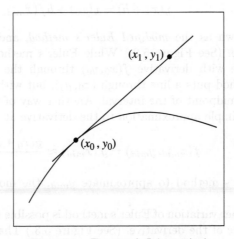

Figure 5.1 The *simple* Euler method.

EXERCISE 5.1

Write a computer code to solve the differential equation

$$y'(x) = y^2 + 1$$

on the region $0 < x < 1$ using Euler's method, with $y(0) = 0$. Plot or graph your results for $h = 0.05$, 0.10, and 0.20, along with the exact result.

The problem with the simple Euler method is that the derivative at the beginning of the interval is assumed constant over the entire step; the derivative at the end of the interval is not used (in this interval). But we've already seen that such asymmetric treatments always lead to low levels of accuracy in the solution. Wouldn't it be better to use some *median* value of the derivative, say the value halfway through the step? Of course—but how is the derivative at the midpoint evaluated, when the derivative is itself a function of y? Good question.

Let's use Euler's method to give us a *guess* at what the solution should be at the midpoint, $x_{mid} = x_0 + \frac{h}{2}$. That is,

$$y(x_{mid}) = y_0 + \frac{h}{2}y_0' = y_0 + \frac{h}{2}f_0, \tag{5.8}$$

where we've again associated the derivative of y with the function f—that is, we've used the differential equation we're trying to solve. With this expression for $y(x_{mid})$, we can evaluate the derivative at the midpoint, $f(x_{mid}, y_{mid})$, and using *that* as our approximation to the derivative over the entire interval we find

$$y(x_0 + h) = y(x_0) + hf(x_{mid}, y_{mid}). \tag{5.9}$$

This is known as the *modified Euler's method*, and has an interesting geometrical picture. (See Figure 5.2.) While Euler's method corresponds to drawing a straight line with derivative $f(x_0, y_0)$ through the point (x_0, y_0), the modified Euler's method puts a line through (x_0, y_0), but with (approximately) the derivative at the midpoint of the interval. Another way of thinking of this method is to consider a simple approximation to the derivative at the midpoint,

$$f(x_{mid}, y_{mid}) = y'(x_{mid}) \approx \frac{y(x_0 + h) - y(x_0)}{h}. \tag{5.10}$$

Using Euler's method to approximate y_{mid}, the modified Euler method quickly follows.

Yet another variation of Euler's method is possible if we attempt a solution using a *mean* value of the derivative. (See Figure 5.3.) That is, we use Euler's equation to guess at $y(x_0 + h)$, which we use to evaluate the derivative at the end of the interval. This derivative is averaged with the "known" derivative at the start of the

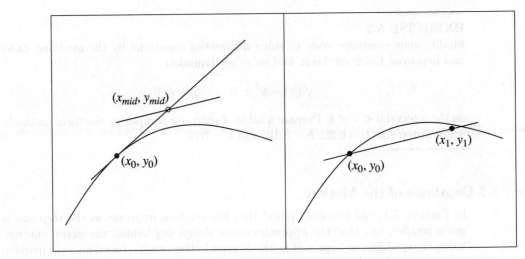

Figure 5.2   The *modified* Euler method.

interval, and this mean derivative is used to advance the solution. The *improved Euler Method* is thus given as

$$y(x_0 + h) = y(x_0) + h\frac{f_0 + f(x_0 + h, y_0 + hf_0)}{2}. \qquad (5.11)$$

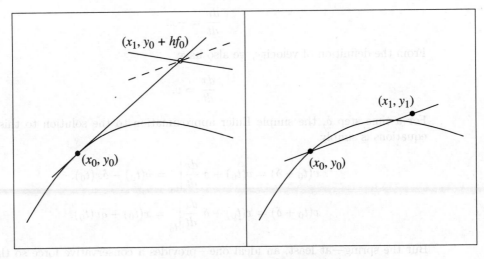

Figure 5.3   The *improved* Euler method.

EXERCISE 5.2

Modify your computer code to solve differential equations by the modified Euler and improved Euler methods, and solve the equation

$$y'(x) = y^2 + 1, \qquad y(0) = 0$$

on the interval $0 < x < 1$. Prepare a table of solutions comparing the three methods, using a step size $h = 0.20$, $h = 0.10$, and $h = 0.05$.

5.2 Constants of the Motion

In Exercise 5.1, you probably found that the solution improves as the step size is made smaller, but that the approximations always lag behind the exact solution. Using the modified or improved methods gives better results, based on a comparison among approximations or against the exact result. But before we explore even better approximations, we should note that there are other ways to judge the quality of a solution: on physical grounds, it might happen that a particular quantity is conserved. In that situation, the degree to which that quantity is calculated to be constant is indicative of the quality of the solution. For example, consider a mass on a spring—the velocity of the mass is determined from the equation

$$\frac{dv}{dt} = a = \frac{F}{m} = \frac{-kx}{m}. \tag{5.12}$$

For simplicity, take the mass and the force constant to equal one, so that we have

$$\frac{dv}{dt} = -x. \tag{5.13}$$

From the definition of velocity, we also have

$$\frac{dx}{dt} = v. \tag{5.14}$$

For a time step δ, the simple Euler approximation to the solution to this set of equations is simply

$$v(t_0 + \delta) = v(t_0) + \delta \left.\frac{dv}{dt}\right|_{t_0} = v(t_0) - \delta x(t_0), \tag{5.15}$$

$$x(t_0 + \delta) = x(t_0) + \delta \left.\frac{dx}{dt}\right|_{t_0} = x(t_0) + \delta v(t_0). \tag{5.16}$$

But the spring—at least, an ideal one—provides a conservative force so that the energy of the system, $E = mv^2/2 + kx^2/2$, is a constant of the motion. Imagine that the system is set in motion at $t = 0$, $x = 0$ with $v = 1$. Using time steps of $\delta = 0.1$, the equations can be solved, and the "solutions" thus determined. At each step, we can derive the energy from the calculated positions and velocities, and exhibit these quantities as in Figure 5.4. Needless to say, something is not working here.

But we already knew that the simple Euler method had its problems; do the modified or improved methods do a better job? Applying the modified Euler method to Equations 5.13 and 5.14, we first use the simple Euler's method to approximate v and x halfway through the time increment,

$$v\left(t_0 + \frac{\delta}{2}\right) = v(t_0) + \frac{\delta}{2}\left.\frac{dv}{dt}\right|_{t_0} = v(t_0) - \frac{\delta}{2}x(t_0), \tag{5.17}$$

$$x\left(t_0 + \frac{\delta}{2}\right) = x(t_0) + \frac{\delta}{2}\left.\frac{dx}{dt}\right|_{t_0} = x(t_0) + \frac{\delta}{2}v(t_0). \tag{5.18}$$

These values are then used over the entire time increment to determine v and x at $t = t_0 + \delta$:

$$v(t_0 + \delta) = v(t_0) + \delta\left.\frac{dv}{dt}\right|_{t_0+\frac{\delta}{2}} = v(t_0) - \delta x\left(t_0 + \frac{\delta}{2}\right), \tag{5.19}$$

$$x(t_0 + \delta) = x(t_0) + \delta\left.\frac{dx}{dt}\right|_{t_0+\frac{\delta}{2}} = x(t_0) + \delta v\left(t_0 + \frac{\delta}{2}\right). \tag{5.20}$$

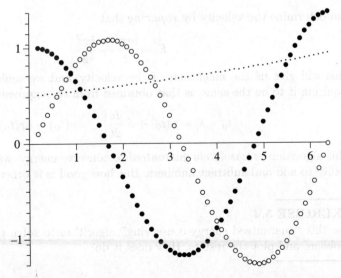

Figure 5.4   Position (o), velocity (•), and energy (·) as a function of time, for the simple harmonic oscillator, as calculated by the simple Euler method.

The code to implement the modified Euler method is only a slight modification of that used for the simple Euler method—simply add the evaluation of xmid and vmid to the code, and use these values to evaluate xnew and vnew from the previous xold and vold values.

EXERCISE 5.3
Use the modified Euler method with a time step of 0.1 to solve the "mass on a spring" problem, and present your results in a plot similar to Figure 5.4. How well is the energy conserved?

It might seem that a numerical method that preserves constants of the motion is inherently "better" than one that does not. Certainly, the improved and modified Euler methods are to be preferred over the simple Euler method. But this preference is derived from improvements made in the algorithm, as *verified* by the computation of constants of the motion, not because the constants were *guaranteed* to be preserved.

It is possible to *construct* an algorithm that preserves constants of the motion. For example, consider the mass-on-a-spring problem. We might use the simple Euler expression to determine position,

$$x(t_0 + \delta) = x(t_0) + \delta \left. \frac{dx}{dt} \right|_{t_0} = x(t_0) + \delta v(t_0), \qquad (5.21)$$

and determine the velocity by *requiring* that

$$E = \frac{mv^2}{2} + \frac{kx^2}{2}. \qquad (5.22)$$

This will give us the *magnitude* of the velocity, and we could obtain its *sign* by requiring it to be the same as that obtained from the expression

$$v(t_0 + \delta) = v(t_0) + \delta \left. \frac{dv}{dt} \right|_{t_0} = v(t_0) - \delta x(t_0). \qquad (5.23)$$

This algorithm *is absolutely guaranteed* to conserve energy, within the computer's ability to add and subtract numbers. But how good is it otherwise?

EXERCISE 5.4
Use this "guaranteed energy-conserving" algorithm to solve the mass-on-a-spring problem, and plot the results. How does it do?

The point to be made here is that all algorithms have errors associated with them, and focusing on a single feature of a particular algorithm while ignoring others is not necessarily the best way to choose the appropriate algorithm for a particular problem.

5.3 Runge-Kutta Methods

The Euler methods are examples of a general class of approximations known as Runge-Kutta methods, characterized by expressing the solution in terms of the derivative $f(x, y)$ evaluated with different arguments. This is in contrast to the Taylor's series solution that requires many different derivatives, all evaluated with the same arguments. Runge-Kutta methods are extremely popular, in part due to the ease with which they can be implemented on computers.

We notice that all the Euler methods can be written in the form

$$y(x_0 + h) = y(x_0) + h[\alpha f(x_0, y_0) + \beta f(x_0 + \gamma h, y_0 + \delta h f_0)]. \tag{5.24}$$

Let's see how well this expression agrees with Taylor's series. A function $f(x, y)$ of two variables can be expanded as

$$f(x, y) = f(x_0, y_0) + (x - x_0)\frac{\partial f(x_0, y_0)}{\partial x} + (y - y_0)\frac{\partial f(x_0, y_0)}{\partial y}$$

$$+ \frac{(x - x_0)^2}{2}\frac{\partial^2 f(\xi, \eta)}{\partial x^2} + (x - x_0)(y - y_0)\frac{\partial^2 f(\xi, \eta)}{\partial x \partial y}$$

$$+ \frac{(y - y_0)^2}{2}\frac{\partial^2 f(\xi, \eta)}{\partial y^2} + \cdots, \tag{5.25}$$

where $x_0 \leq \xi \leq x$ and $y_0 \leq \eta \leq y$. Using this expression to expand $f(x_0 + \gamma h, y_0 + \delta h f_0)$ of Equation 5.24, we find that

$$y(x) = y_0 + h\alpha f(x_0, y_0)$$

$$+ h\beta \left[f(x_0, y_0) + h\gamma\frac{\partial f(x_0, y_0)}{\partial x} + h\delta f(x_0, y_0)\frac{\partial f(x_0, y_0)}{\partial y} + O(h^2) \right]$$

$$= y_0 + h(\alpha + \beta)f(x_0, y_0)$$

$$+ h^2\beta \left[\gamma\frac{\partial f(x_0, y_0)}{\partial x} + \delta f(x_0, y_0)\frac{\partial f(x_0, y_0)}{\partial y} \right] + O(h^3). \tag{5.26}$$

This expression agrees with the Taylor series expression of Equation 5.5 through terms involving h^2, if we require that

$$\alpha + \beta = 1,$$
$$\beta\gamma = 1/2,$$
$$\text{and} \quad \beta\delta = 1/2. \tag{5.27}$$

Thus the improved and modified Euler methods both agree with the Taylor series through terms involving h^2, and are said to be second-order Runge-Kutta methods. Although these equations require that $\gamma = \delta$, otherwise there is considerable flexibility in choosing the parameters; the optimum second-order method, in the sense that the coefficient multiplying the h^3 term is minimized, has $\alpha = 1/3$, $\beta = 2/3$, and $\gamma = \delta = 3/4$.

While the Euler method jumps right in to find a solution, the improved and modified methods are more conservative, testing the water (so to speak) before taking the plunge. These methods can actually be derived in terms of an integral: since $y' = f(x, y)$, then clearly

$$y(x_0 + h) = y(x_0) + \int_{x_0}^{x_0+h} f(\tau, y) \, d\tau. \tag{5.28}$$

The only problem, of course, is that the sought after solution y appears under the integral on the right side of the equation, as well as on the left side of the equation. Approximating the integral by the midpoint rule, we have

$$y(x_0 + h) = y(x_0) + h f\left(x_0 + \frac{h}{2}, y_{mid}\right). \tag{5.29}$$

y_{mid} is then approximated by a Taylor series expansion,

$$y_{mid} \approx y(x_0) + \frac{h}{2} f(x_0, y_0). \tag{5.30}$$

Since the integral is already in error $O(h^2)$, there is no point in using a more accurate series expansion. With these approximations, Equation 5.28 then reads

$$y(x_0 + h) = y(x_0) + h f\left(x_0 + \frac{h}{2}, y_0 + \frac{h}{2} f_0\right), \tag{5.31}$$

which we recognize as the modified Euler method. In a similar fashion, the improved Euler method can be derived by approximating the integral in Equation 5.28 by the trapezoid rule.

The methods outlined can be used to derive higher-order Runge-Kutta methods. Perhaps the most popular integration method ever devised, the fourth-order Runge-Kutta method, is written in terms of intermediate quantities defined as

$$\begin{aligned}
f_0 &= f(x_0, y_0), \\
f_1 &= f\left(x_0 + \frac{h}{2}, y_0 + \frac{h}{2} f_0\right), \\
f_2 &= f\left(x_0 + \frac{h}{2}, y_0 + \frac{h}{2} f_1\right), \\
f_3 &= f(x_0 + h, y_0 + h f_2).
\end{aligned} \tag{5.32}$$

The solution is then expressed as

$$y(x_0 + h) = y(x_0) + \frac{h}{6}(f_0 + 2f_1 + 2f_2 + f_3). \tag{5.33}$$

This is the standard, classic result often referred to as simply *the* Runge-Kutta method, and is a mainstay in the arsenal of numerical analysts. For the special case that $f = f(x)$, this result is obtained by evaluating the integral of Equation 5.28 by Simpson's rule.

EXERCISE 5.5

Write a computer code to solve differential equations using this 4th-order Runge-Kutta algorithm. Solve the differential equation

$$y'(x) = y^2 + 1, \qquad y(0) = 0$$

on the interval $0 \le x \le 1$. The RK4 algorithm is much more powerful than this particular differential equation requires, but it's always good to test new approaches on simple, familiar problems.

5.4 Convergence

Clearly, the methods we've discussed have been increasingly better and better. We can quantify this somewhat by looking at a plot of the results versus the time step h (Figure 5.5).

Clearly, the modified and improved Euler algorithms are superior to the Simple Euler. (On the scale of this figure, the RK4 results would all be at the same value.)

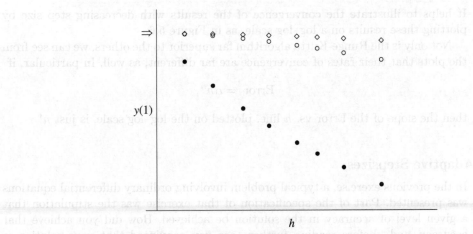

Figure 5.5   Convergence of the various algorithms as a function of h for the example of Exercise 5.5. The results from the Simple Euler (●), Modified Euler (○), and Improved Euler (◇) algorithms all converge to the exact result, indicated by the arrow.

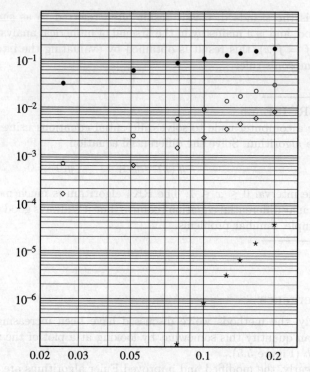

Figure 5.6   Log–log plot of relative error versus h. The RK4 results are indicated by a *star*.

It helps to illustrate the convergence of the results with decreasing step size by plotting these results on a log–log scale, as in Figure 5.6.

Not only is the Runge-Kutta algorithm far superior to the others, we can see from the plots that their rates of convergence are far different, as well. In particular, if

$$\text{Error } = \alpha h^n,$$

then the slope of the Error vs. h line, plotted on the log–log scale, is just n!

5.5 Adaptive Stepsizes

In the previous exercise, a typical problem involving ordinary differential equations was presented. Part of the specification of that exercise was the stipulation that a given level of accuracy in the solution be achieved. How did you achieve that accuracy, and—before reading further—are you convinced that your solution is *really* that accurate?

Probably the most common way to ascertain the accuracy of a solution is to calculate it twice, with two different stepsizes, and compare the results. This comparison could be made after many propagation steps, i.e., after integrating the solution for some distance. But the nature of the solution might change considerably from one region to another—a smaller stepsize might be necessary *here* and not *there*—so that the calculated results should be compared often, allowing for a decrease (or increase!) of the stepsize where appropriate.

By far the easiest way to accomplish this comparison is to use stepsizes h and $h/2$, and compare immediately—if the difference is small, then the error is assumed small. In fact, this estimate of the error is used to adjust the size of the step. If the error is larger than tolerated, then the stepsize is halved. Likewise, if the error is less than some predetermined value, the steps are too small and too much work is being performed; the stepsize is increased. Such an adaptive stepsize modification to the classic Runge-Kutta method greatly enhances its utility, so much so that methods without some form of adaptation simply should not be used.

An additional benefit of having two approximations to the result is that Richardson's extrapolation can be used to obtain a "better" estimate of the solution. Since the Runge-Kutta method is accurate through h^4, the two solutions can be combined to eliminate the first term of the error ($\sim h^5$): if $y_{(h)}$ and $y_{(h/2)}$ are the two solutions, the extrapolated value is

$$y_{extrapolated} = \frac{16y_{(h/2)} - y_{(h)}}{15}. \tag{5.34}$$

EXERCISE 5.6

One of the standard problems of first year physics is one-dimensional projectile motion—but contrary to standard practice, let's include air resistance to see how large an effect it is. The time rate of change of the momentum is

$$\frac{dp}{dt} = mg - kv^2,$$

where m is the mass of the object, $g = 9.8\text{m/s}^2$ is the acceleration due to gravity, and k is a drag coefficient. For a particular sphere of mass 10^{-2} kg the drag coefficient was determined to be $k = 10^{-4}\text{kg/m}$. Modify your Runge-Kutta program to take adaptive stepsizes, and use this modified code to solve the projectile problem. Letting $p = mv$, find the velocity of the sphere released from rest as a function of time for $0 < t < 10$ seconds. Choose a step size to ensure four significant digit accuracy. Compare your calculation to the zero-th order approximation, e.g., the analytic solution obtained by ignoring air resistance.

5.6 Runge-Kutta-Fehlberg

Rather than interval halving and doubling, even with Richardson's extrapolation, there's another, more interesting way that we can utilize our knowledge of the error to our benefit. Let's devise a scheme in which we maintain a given accuracy at each step in the solution of the differential equation. For an n-th order Runge-Kutta solution we have

$$y(x_0 + h) = y_{exact} + kh^{n+1}, \tag{5.35}$$

where y_{exact} is the exact solution, while for an $(n+1)$-th order solution we have

$$\hat{y}(x_0 + h) = y_{exact} + \hat{k}h^{n+2}. \tag{5.36}$$

The difference between these two solutions is simply

$$y(x_0 + h) - \hat{y}(x_0 + h) = kh^{n+1} - \hat{k}h^{n+2} \approx kh^{n+1}, \tag{5.37}$$

where the approximation is valid for small h. We can then solve for k,

$$k \approx \frac{y - \hat{y}}{h^{n+1}}. \tag{5.38}$$

But the difference between the two solutions is also a measure of the error, which is to be maintained at a predetermined acceptable error level of $\bar{\varepsilon}$. The question is then, what stepsize h_{new} would generate an error $\bar{\varepsilon}$ or less? That is, we require that

$$kh_{new}^{n+1} = \frac{y - \hat{y}}{h^{n+1}} h_{new}^{n+1} \leq \bar{\varepsilon}. \tag{5.39}$$

Equation 5.39 is easily solved for h_{new}, with the result

$$h_{new} \leq h \sqrt[n+1]{\frac{\bar{\varepsilon}}{|y(x_0 + h) - \hat{y}(x_0 + h)|}}. \tag{5.40}$$

Now, we need to interpret this result just a bit. Using the stepsize h both y and $\hat{y}$ can be calculated, and so a direct numerical estimate of the error $|y - \hat{y}|$ can be calculated. But we know how this error depends on h, and so can calculate the coefficient k from Equation 5.38. And knowing k allows us to evaluate an h_{new} that would have given an error of $\bar{\varepsilon}$. *Voila!* If the calculated error is greater than the acceptable error, then too large a step will have been taken and h will be greater than h_{new}. Since the error has been determined to be larger than acceptable, we'll repeat the step using a smaller stepsize. On the other hand, it can happen that the calculated error is smaller than we've specified as acceptable, h is less than h_{new}, so that we could have taken a larger step. Of course, it would be wasteful to actually repeat the step—but we can use h_{new} as a guess for the next step to be taken! This leads to a very efficient algorithm in which the step size is continually adjusted so that the actual error is near, but always less than, the prescribed tolerance.

Beginning with an initial value of $y(x_0)$ and an initial h, the algorithm consists of the following steps:

1. Calculate $y(x_0 + h)$ and $\hat{y}(x_0 + h)$ from $y(x_0)$.

2. Calculate h_{new}. If h_{new} is less than h, *reject* the propagation to $x_0 + h$, redefine h, and repeat Step 1. If h_{new} is greater than h, *accept* the propagation step, replace x_0 by $x_0 + h$, redefine h, and go to Step 1 to continue propagating the solution.

Since the cost of repeating a step is relatively high, we'll intentionally be conservative and use a step size somewhat smaller than that predicted, say only 90% of the value, so that corrective action is only rarely required.

This discussion has addressed the case of absolute error, but in general we prefer to use relative errors. That case is easily obtained by dividing the numerator and denominator of the term inside the radical by (a good approximation to) the exact result, $\hat{y}$. Then

$$h_{new} = h \sqrt[n+1]{\left| \frac{\bar{\varepsilon}/\hat{y}}{(y - \hat{y})/\hat{y}} \right|}. \tag{5.41}$$

Clearly, the numerator is the prescribed, allowed relative error while the denominator is the calculated one. Introducing ε to denote the maximum allowed *relative* error, we have

$$h_{new} = h \sqrt[n+1]{\frac{\varepsilon}{|(y - \hat{y})/\hat{y}|}}. \tag{5.42}$$

So far so good, but it's not obvious that much effort, if any, has been saved. Fehlberg provided the real key to this method by developing Runge-Kutta methods of different order that use *exactly the same* intermediate function evaluations. Once the first approximation to the solution has been found, it's trivial to calculate the second. The method we will use is the fourth-order/fifth order method, defined in terms of the following intermediate function evaluations:

$$f_0 = f(x_0, y_0), \tag{5.43}$$

$$f_1 = f\left(x_0 + \frac{h}{4}, y_0 + \frac{h}{4} f_0 \right), \tag{5.44}$$

$$f_2 = f\left(x_0 + \frac{3h}{8}, y_0 + \frac{3h}{32} f_0 + \frac{9h}{32} f_1 \right), \tag{5.45}$$

$$f_3 = f\left(x_0 + \frac{12h}{13}, y_0 + \frac{1932h}{2197} f_0 - \frac{7200h}{2197} f_1 + \frac{7296h}{2197} f_2 \right), \tag{5.46}$$

$$f_4 = f\left(x_0 + h, y_0 + \frac{439h}{216} f_0 - 8hf_1 + \frac{3680h}{513} f_2 - \frac{845h}{4104} f_3 \right), \tag{5.47}$$

$$f_5 = f\left(x_0 + \frac{h}{2}, y_0 - \frac{8h}{27} f_0 + 2hf_1 - \frac{3544h}{2565} f_2 + \frac{1859h}{4104} f_3 - \frac{11h}{40} f_4 \right). \tag{5.48}$$

With these definitions, the fourth-order approximation is given as

$$y = y_0 + h \left(\frac{25}{216} f_0 + \frac{1408}{2565} f_2 + \frac{2197}{4104} f_3 - \frac{1}{5} f_4 \right) \tag{5.49}$$

and the fifth-order is given as

$$\hat{y} = y_0 + h \left(\frac{16}{135} f_0 + \frac{6656}{12825} f_2 + \frac{28561}{56430} f_3 - \frac{9}{50} f_4 + \frac{2}{55} f_5 \right). \tag{5.50}$$

The error can be evaluated directly from these expressions,

$$Err = \hat{y} - y = h \left(\frac{1}{360} f_0 - \frac{128}{4275} f_2 - \frac{2197}{75240} f_3 + \frac{1}{50} f_4 + \frac{2}{55} f_5 \right), \tag{5.51}$$

so that y need never be explicitly calculated. Since we're using a fourth-order method, an appropriate (conservative) expression for the step size is

$$h_{new} = 0.9h \sqrt[5]{\frac{\varepsilon}{|(y - \hat{y})/\hat{y}|}}, \tag{5.52}$$

where ε is the specified maximum relative error.

The computer coding of these expressions is actually quite straightforward, although a little tedious. In particular, the coefficients entering into the expressions must be entered very carefully. In the following computer code, these coefficients are specified separately from their actual use, and most are specified by expressions involving operations as well as numerical values. Twelve divided by thirteen is not easily expressed as a decimal, and should be expressed to the full precision of the computer if it were; it's easier, and more accurate, to let the computer do the division. By using symbolic names in the actual expressions of the algorithm, the clarity of the code is enhanced. Some of the computer code might look like the following:

```
% This program solves differential equations by the
% Runge-Kutta-Fehlberg adaptive step algorithm.
function rkf
% Specify relative error tolerance.
epsilon = 1.e-5;
% Specify coefficients used in the R-K-F algorithm:
%    The coefficients Am are used to determine the 'x' at
%    which the derivative is evaluated.
a1 = 0.25; a2 = 0.375; a3 = 12.0/13.0; a4 = 1.0; a5 = 0.5;

%    The coefficients Bmn are used to determine the 'y' at
%    which the derivative is evaluated.
b10 =    0.25;         b20 =       3.0/ 32.0; b21 =       9.0/ 32.0;
b30 =1932.0/2197.0;    b31 = -7200.0/2197.0; b32 =  7296.0/2197.0;
```

```
b40 = 439.0/ 216.0;   b41 =     -8.0;      b42 =  3680.0/ 513.0;
                       b43 = -845.0/4104.0;
b50 =  -8.0  /27.0;    b51 =      2.0;      b52 = -3544.0/2565.0;
                       b53 =1859.0/4104.0;  b54 =    -11.0/  40.0;


%   The Cn are used to evaluate the solution YHAT.
c0  =    16.0/  135.0; c2 = 6656.0/12825.0; c3 = 28561.0/56430.0;
                       c4 =     -0.18;      c5 = 2.0/55.0;


%   The Dn are used to evaluate the error.
d0  =     1.0/  360.0; d2 = -128.0/4275.0;  d3  = -2197.0/75240.0;
                       d4 =      0.02;      d5  = 2.0/55.0;
    % Initialize the integration:
    % Note: here  x ==> time, y ==> velocity
    a  =               % initial time
    b  =               % final time
    h  =               % step size
    x0 =               % initial conditions
    ...
% The current point is specified as (x0,y0) and the
% step size to be used is H. The function DERIVS evaluates
% the derivative function at (X,Y). The solution is
% moved forward one step by:
while (x0 < b)
    f0 = derivs(x0,y0);
    x  = x0 + a1*h;
    y  = y0 + b10*h*f0;
    f1 = derivs(x,y);
    x  = x0 + a2*h;
    y  = y0 + b20*h*f0 + b21*h*f1;
    f2 = derivs(x,y);
    x  = x0 + a3*h;
    y  = y0 + h*(b30*f0+b31*f1+b32*f2);
    f3 = derivs(x,y);
    x  = x0 + a4*h;
    y  = y0 + h*(b40*f0+b41*f1+b42*f2+b43*f3);
    f4 = derivs(x,y);
    x  = x0 + a5*h;
    y  = y0 + h*(b50*f0+b51*f1+b52*f2+b53*f3+b54*f4);
    f5 = derivs(x,y);

    yhat   = y0 + h*(c0*f0+c2*f2+c3*f3+c4*f4+c5*f5);
    RelErr = abs(h*(d0*f0+d2*f2+d3*f3+d4*f4+d5*f5)/yhat);
    hnew   = h * (epsilon/RelErr)^0.2;

    if( hnew >= h )           % The error is small enough. Accept the
        x0   = x0 + h;        %   solution, and move it along.
```

```
        y0    = yhat;      %
      end                  % Redefine h. If the error was too large,
      h = 0.9 * hnew       %   we'd now repeat the step with a
    end                    %   smaller h.

    function [der] = derivs(x,y)
    % This function evaluates the derivative of the function
      ...
```

Note that the algorithm has been written as a separate function, in keeping with our discussion in Chapter 1 regarding writing modular code. For the moment, you should just loop through this code until x is greater than the maximum desired, at which time the program should terminate. As it stands, there is no printout, which you'll probably want to change.

EXERCISE 5.7

Repeat the problem of projectile motion with air resistance, with all the parameters the same, but using the Fehlberg algorithm. You can start the integration with almost any h—if it's too large, the program will redefine it and try again, and if it's too small, well, there's no harm done and the second step will be larger. Use a maximum error tolerance of 10^{-5}, and print out the accepted x and y values (that is, time and velocity) at each step.

Before we can go much farther in our investigation of the solutions of differential equations, we need to make some practical modifications to our Fehlberg integrator. Let's separate the algorithm from any specific problem by taking the specification of the initial conditions and the integration limits out of the function, and passing this information to the function as parameters. We'll also make epsilon a global variable. In the same spirit, we'll have the function return the solution in arrays, rather than printing the results itself. The function statement will then be something like

```
function [xx, yy] = rkf(Xinitial,XFinal,Yinitial)
```

where xx and yy are arrays containing the solution. Of course, these changes necessitate other changes in the code as well. (This *modularization* of the code is something we'll always want to do, as functions become sufficiently large and complicated.)

As for the algorithm itself, by this time you've probably found that the integrator works very well, and you might suspect that further refinement isn't necessary. And you're probably right! But we want to develop a code that is going to do its job, without a lot of intervention from us, for a large variety of problems. That is, we want it to be smart enough to deal with most situations, and even more important, smart enough to tell us when it can't!

One of the things that can happen, occasionally, is that the *very nature* of the solution can change; in such a case, it's possible for the integrator to "get confused." To avoid this problem, we will impose an additional constraint upon the step size predictions: the step size shouldn't change too much from one step to the next. That is, if the prediction is to take a step one hundred times greater than the current one, then it's a good bet that something "funny" is going on. So, we won't allow the prediction to be larger than a factor of four times the current size. Likewise, we shouldn't let h decrease too rapidly either; we'll only accept a factor of ten decrease in h. (While it might appear that overriding the stepsize prediction would automatically introduce an error, such is not the case since the accuracy of the step is verified after its completion and repeated if the error isn't within the specified limit. It does ensure that the integrator isn't tricked into taking *too small* of a step.) And while we're at this, let's impose maximum and minimum step sizes: if the predicted h exceeds h_{max}, h will simply be redefined; but if h falls less than h_{min}, it's probably an indication that something is seriously amiss, and the integration should be stopped and an appropriate message displayed. These modifications should be made to your code, so that the result looks something like the following.

```
...
global RKF_epsilon RKF_hmin RKF_hmax;
...
h = RKF_hmax;        % Initial step size
index = 1;
xx(1) = x0;          % 1st elements of arrays being returned
yy(1) = y0;
...
hnew = h * (RKF_epsilon/RelErr)^0.2;
%
% Check for increase/decrease in H, as well as H-limits.
%
if( hnew > 4.0*h),    hnew = 4.0*h; end;
if( hnew < 0.1*h),    hnew = 0.1*h; end; % Always "cover your decimal points"
if( hnew > RKF_hmax), hnew = RKF_hmax; end;
if( hnew < RKF_hmin)
    error(strcat('\n Possible Problem: "hnew" is TOO SMALL\n',...
       'x0   = %11.8f\n hnew = %8.4gf < hmin = \%8.4g'),x0,hnew,RKF_hmin)
end
%
if( hnew >= h )           % The error is small enough. Accept the
    x0 = x0 + h;          %   solution, and move it along.
    y0 = yhat;
    index = index + 1;
    xx(index) = x0;       % Store x and solution in return arrays.
    yy(index) = yhat;
end
```

```
h = 0.9 * hnew;          % Redefine h.
...
```

Note that we can conveniently initialize the integrator with $h = h_{max}$. These modifications to **hnew** *do not* change the conditions under which the "current" step is accepted or rejected; they simply restrict the range of acceptable stepsizes. If the step taken is acceptable, the results at the current step are stored in the arrays for subsequent return. After making these modifications, test them on the following project.

EXERCISE 5.8
Attempt to find the solution of

$$y' = \frac{1}{x^2}, \quad y(-1) = 1$$

on the interval $-1 \leq x \leq 1$. Take $h_{max} = 0.1$, $h_{min} = 0.001$, and **Epsilon** = 5×10^{-5}.

At this point, perhaps we should make one more modification to **rkf**. As it stands, the integration begins at a specified **xInitial**, but it stops only after it has passed **xFinal**, not *precisely* at **xFinal**. This can be corrected by adding a couple of lines of code toward the end of the "while-loop,"

```
    if(x0 + h > xFinal)h = xFinal - x0; end
    if(abs((xFinal-x0)/xFinal) < 1.e-10)break;end; % Break out of while loop
  end                                              % End of while loop
```

The first statement redefines **h** so that the last step integrates to **xFinal**, and the second breaks out of the while loop.

As we've come to expect, MATLAB has its own differential equation solvers. Prime among them is **ode45**, which is very similar in spirit to the RKF algorithm. It's also based on an explicit Runge-Kutta formula, using the Dormand-Prince pair for the 4th and 5th order methods. As always, entering **help ode45** or **doc ode45** at the MATLAB prompt will provide you with detailed information on the function, and on other solvers as well. (Since **ode45** was written with MATLAB, the actual code can be inspected by entering **edit ode45**.) Their recommendation is that, in general, **ode45** is the best function to apply as a first try for most problems. Further information is also available at their website,

http://www.mathworks.com/access/helpdesk/help/techdoc/index.html

5.7 Several Dependent Variables

Many problems of physics involve several dependent variables, such as the components of a vector. These differential equations might be written as

$$\frac{dv_x}{dt} = f_x(t, v_x, v_y),$$

$$\frac{dv_y}{dt} = f_y(t, v_x, v_y), \qquad (5.53)$$

where v_x, v_y are the components of a vector and f_x and f_y are functions describing how those components change with time. It's a very small step to extend our comments regarding Euler (and Runge-Kutta) algorithms to this situation.

To avoid some possible confusion between variable names, we'll use t as the independent variable so that we can use v_x and v_y as our dependent variables. We then write the two component equations above as a single vector equation,

$$\frac{d\vec{v}}{dt} = \vec{f}(t, \vec{v}). \qquad (5.54)$$

We can now simply repeat the previous Taylor series arguments: expanding $\vec{v}(t)$ about t_o, we find

$$\vec{v}(t) = \vec{v}(t_o) + (t - t_0)\frac{d\vec{v}}{dt}\bigg|_{t=t_o} + \cdots. \qquad (5.55)$$

Keeping only the first two terms, and using the definition of $\vec{f}$, we find the simple Euler approximation

$$\vec{v}(t) = \vec{v}(t_o) + (t - t_0)\vec{f}(t_o, \vec{v}(t_o)). \qquad (5.56)$$

The *modified* and *improved* approximations follow in an obvious fashion, as do the Runge-Kutta algorithms.

What we've found here is that the methods used for a scalar differential equation can be extended and applied to vector differential equations in a very straightforward manner. The one difficulty that we must always remember, however, is that (in general) *each* component of $\vec{f}$ depends upon *all* the components of $\vec{v}$. This has quite practical ramifications, which must be incorporated into the computer code.

MATLAB treats all variables as arrays. As a result, there are remarkably few changes needed in our existing code to treat this "new" problem. We will make some cosmetic changes to enhance the generality of our computer code. For example, we'll use t as the independent variable, and introduce S as the "solution" array. We'll also rename the RHS of the equation F, which is now an array. We thus see that this problem *is not* fundamentally different from the scalar problem we've been working with—it just has more components! Instead of stepping our one solution along, we'll step our two components along. We thus see that the modifications in our existing code are rather trivial, and consist primarily of replacing scalar quantities by arrays and renaming them. The independent variable t is still a scalar, but the dependent variables S and Shat, and the intermediate quantities F0, F1, ..., all become dimensioned arrays. (Note that F0 and F1 are arrays, not elements of an array.) The computer code might look something like

```
function [tt,SS] = RKF(tInitial, tFinal, SInitial)
%
% This function solves ordinary differential equations
%   having SEVERAL dependent variables, i.e., components,
%   by the Runge-Kutta-Fehlberg adaptive step algorithm.
%   Note that the solution and the intermediate function
%   evaluations are now stored in ARRAYS, and are treated
%   as components of COLUMN VECTORS.
%
%
%  Input:  tInitial    starting t value (the independent variable)
%          tFinal      ending t value
%          SInitial    initial value of S, i.e., S(tInitial)
%
%  Output: tt          an array of t values
%          SS          an array of solutions, corresponding to the t's in tt
%
global RKF_epsilon RKF_hmin RKF_hmax;
clear tt SS;

    ...

% Specify coefficients used in the R-K-F algorithm:
%   The coefficients Am are used to determine the 't' at
%   which the derivative is evaluated.
a1=0.25; a2=0.375; a3=1.2e1/1.3e1; a4=1.0; a5=0.5;
    ...

% Initialize the integration:
h    =                    % step size
t0   =                    % initial conditions
S0   =                    % S0 is a column vector array
index   = 1;
tt(1)   = tInitial;       % return arrays...
SS(:,1) = SInitial;
% -----------------------------------------------------------*
%  Remember: S, S0, SHAT, and all the intermediate           *
%  quantities F0, F1, etc., are dimensioned arrays!          *
% -----------------------------------------------------------*
% The current point is specified as (t0,S0) and the
% step size to be used is H. The function DERIVS evaluates
% the derivative function at (t,S). The solution is
% moved forward one step by:
```

```
while (t0 < tFinal)
    F0 = derivs(t0,S0); % F0, F1, F2, F3, F4, F5 are column vectors
    t  = t0 + a1*h;
    S  = S0 + b10*h*F0;
    F1 = derivs(t,S);
    t  = t0 + a2*h;
    S  = S0 + b20*h*F0 + b21*h*F1;
    F2 = derivs(t,S);

    ...

    Shat = S0 + h*(c0*F0+c2*F2+c3*F3+c4*F4+c5*F5);
    %
    RMS = sqrt(sum((h*(d0*F0+d2*F2+d3*F3+d4*F4+d5*F5)./Shat).^2)/length(Shat));
    hnew =  h * (RKF_epsilon/RMS) ^0.2;
    % Check for increase/decrease in H, as well as H-limits.
    if(hnew > 4.0*h), hnew = 4.0*h; end
        ...
    if( hnew >= h )
        t0          = t0 + h;   % The error is small enough. Accept the
        S0          = Shat;     %    solution, and move it along.
        index       = index + 1;
        tt(index)   = t0;       % Store t and S in return arrays.
        SS(:,index) = Shat;
    end
    h = 0.9 * hnew              % Redefine h.
    if(t0 + h > tFinal)...
    if( abs(tFinal-t0)...
end

function [der] = derivs(t,S)
% This function evaluates all the components of the
% derivative vector, putting the results in the array 'der'.
    ...
```

The biggest change, of course, is that the pertinent quantities are now arrays. In particular, we have chosen to make these column vectors rather than row vectors. We've also changed the error criteria, adopting a root-mean-square definition for the relative error. We've also put almost all the information about the particular differential equation to be solved into the function `derivs`, which calculates all the components of the derivative vector.

Let's apply this to a specific example. Consider the elementary problem of projectile motion, described by the vector equation

$$\frac{d\vec{v}}{dt} = \vec{g}, \tag{5.57}$$

where $\vec{g}$ is the acceleration due to gravity. This problem can be solved analytically. But imagine, for example, introducing air resistance into this problem. In general, the problem of projectile motion with air resistance is governed by the vector equation

$$\frac{d\vec{v}}{dt} = \vec{g} - c|v|\vec{v}, \tag{5.58}$$

where $\vec{g}$ is the acceleration due to gravity and c is a coefficient of air resistance. Note that the air exerts a force proportional to $-|v|\vec{v}$ on the projectile, opposing its motion. In terms of components, we can write

$$\frac{dv_x}{dt} = -c\sqrt{v_x^2 + v_y^2}\ v_x,$$

$$\frac{dv_y}{dt} = -g - c\sqrt{v_x^2 + v_y^2}\ v_y. \tag{5.59}$$

(Note that a standard right-handed coordinate system has been imposed, so that $-g$ indicates that the force of gravity is downward.) As forewarned, both components of velocity appear in each of the component differential equations. That is, we can't "separate" the equations as we could in the much simpler airless projectile problem. The physics of the problem is entirely contained in the derivative function, something like

```
function [der] = derivs(t,S)
% This function evaluates all the components of the
% derivative vector, putting the results in the array 'der'.
%
% For this problem, we'll let S(1) = x-component of velocity
%                             S(2) = y-component of velocity
Vx = S(1);
Vy = S(2);
% With constants defined as
c = 0.1;
g = 9.8;
%
% The column vector containing the derivatives is evaluated as
%
der = [  -c * sqrt( Vx*Vx + Vy*Vy ) * Vx;    % the time derivative of Vx
         -g-c * sqrt( Vx*Vx + Vy*Vy ) * Vy ]; % the time derivative of Vy
%
% Note:  It is not necessary to use the intermediate variables
% Vx and Vy as above; the computer could evaluate
%
%     der = [  -c * sqrt( S(1)*S(1) + S(2)*S(2) ) * S(1);
%              -g-c * sqrt( S(1)*S(1) + S(2)*S(2) ) * S(2) ];
%
% just as easily. However, for US to understand it, this
% coding has advantages.
```

EXERCISE 5.9

Write a computer code implementing the Runge-Kutta-Fehlberg algorithm to solve the vector differential equation describing this projectile motion. With $h_{min} = 0.0001$ and $h_{max} = 0.1$, use the code to solve for the motion of a projectile, with

$$g = 9.8 \, \text{m/s}^2 \quad \text{and} \quad c = 0.1 \, \text{m}^{-1},$$

subject to the initial conditions that

$$v_x = 20 \, \text{m/s} \quad \text{and} \quad v_y = 0.$$

Display both components of the velocity for $0 \leq t \leq 10$ seconds.

5.8 The N-Particle Linear Chain Model

Consider a simple model of wave motion inside a crystal. Each plane is represented by a particle of mass m_i—the particles are fixed in the x-direction, but allowed to move in the y-direction, so that we're only investigating the effects of a transverse wave as in Figure 5.7. The force on each particle is assumed to be proportional to the displacement of its neighboring particles á là Hooke's Law. In this *nearest neighbor* model the force on the i-th particle is thus

$$f_i = k(y_{i+1} - y_i) + k(y_i - y_{i-1}) = k(y_{i+1} - 2y_i + y_{i-1}). \qquad (5.60)$$

The particles at the ends of the chain are taken to be fixed in space, so that $y_1 = y_N = 0$. We are interested in computing the y-displacement of the particles as a function of time. By definition,

$$\frac{dy_i}{dt} = v_i \qquad (5.61)$$

where v_i is the velocity of the particle, and

$$\frac{dv_i}{dt} = \frac{f_i}{m_i} = k(y_{i+1} - 2y_i + y_{i-1}), \qquad i = 2, \ldots, N - 1. \qquad (5.62)$$

Note that for an N-particle chain, there are only $N-2$ interior particles free to move.

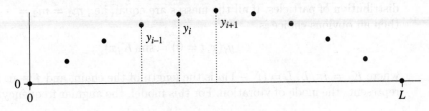

Figure 5.7 N-Particle linear chain.

A familiar differential equation solver can then be employed to obtain the subsequent positions and velocities as a function of time. An outline of the code might look as follows:

```
% oscillatorchain.m
% Fragment for the development of the N-particle oscillator chain model.
% Note that we're only solving for the motion of the P (= N-2) interior points.

function oscillatorchain

L   =            % length of chain
k   =            % spring constant
P   =            % number of interior particles
x0  =            % x positions for P particles, evenly spaced
M   =            % particles' masses
t0  =            % initial and final times
tf  =
y0  =            % y initial positions (row vector)
v0  =            % v initial velocites (row vector)
[t,y] = RKF( t0, tf, [y0';v0'];
...
% Plot the height of the particles at each x position every time
...

function [der] = derivs(t,y)
% This function evaluates all the components of the
% derivative vector, putting the results in the array 'der'.
% y(1:P):      positions of the P particles
% y(P+1:P+P): velocities of the P particles
for i=1:P
    der(i) = y(P+i); % velocities
end
for i=2:P-1
    der(i) = k*(y(i+1)-2*y(i)+y(i-1))/M(i); % accelerations
end
der(P+1)  = k*(y( 2 ) -2*y(1) +  0.0   )/M(1);
der(P+P)  = k*( 0.0   -2*y(P) + y(P-1) )/M(P);
der = transpose(der);
```

To investigate how this array changes in time we need to assume an initial distribution of particles. If all the masses are equal, i.e., $m_1 = m_2 = \cdots = m_i = m$, then an obvious choice is

$$y_j(x, t = 0) = \sin(K_j x), \tag{5.63}$$

where $K_j = j\pi/L$, $L = (N-1)a$ is the length of the chain, and j is an integer that represents the mode of vibration. For this model, the angular frequency for the j-th mode is known to be

$$\omega_j = 2\sqrt{k/m}\sin\left(\frac{K_j a}{2}\right) = 2\sqrt{k/m}\sin\left(\frac{j\pi a}{2(N-1)}\right). \tag{5.64}$$

EXERCISE 5.10

Develop a code to simulate the time-dependent motion of a system of 26 oscillator particles equidistantly spaced over a total length of 10 meters with a spring constant $k = 10\,\text{N/m}$ and mass $= 1\,\text{kg}$. Take the fundamental mode of vibration, $j = 1$, as the initial distribution of particles and confirm its corresponding vibrational period.

EXERCISE 5.11

Repeat the previous exercise for $j = 2, 3$, and 4, the higher harmonic modes.

EXERCISE 5.12

Simulate the motion of the linear chain model with 50 particles and an initial Gaussian-shaped pulse given by

$$y(x_i, t = 0) = \exp(-3(x_i - x_{25})^2), \quad i = 2, \ldots, N - 1. \tag{5.65}$$

Follow the motion for 20 seconds.

EXERCISE 5.13

This time, let the initial displacements of the chain be zero, but the initial velocities be

$$\dot{y}(x_i, t = 0) = \sin\frac{4\pi x_i}{L}, \quad i = 1, \ldots, N/4,$$
$$= 0, \qquad\quad i > N/4.$$

Follow the motion for 20 seconds.

The chain in the previous exercises was rather heavy, but the physics being discussed applies to various situations. Consider, for example, the motion of a transverse wave through a solid. We can simulate this motion as a linear chain of atoms. Consider a chain of Copper atoms, each with mass 1.05×10^{-25} kg, separated by the lattice constant 2.56×10^{-10} meters. The (atomic scale) spring constant k is related to the (macroscopic) bulk modulus B by

$$k = Ba,$$

where the bulk modulus for Copper is $1.42 \times 10^{11}\,\text{N/m}^2$.

EXERCISE 5.14

Let the initial distribution of positions be given by Equation 5.63, and follow the motion long enough to verify that its frequency is given by Equation 5.64.

EXERCISE 5.15

Let the initial conditions be those given in Exercise 5.13, and determine the velocity of the wave through the chain.

5.9 Second Order Differential Equations

So far we've been quite successful in finding numerical solutions to our differential equations. However, we've mostly been concerned with first order equations of the form

$$y' = f(x, y) \tag{5.66}$$

or, with time as the independent variable,

$$\frac{dy}{dt} \equiv \dot{y} = f(t, y). \tag{5.67}$$

And we've even extended our basic approach to include vector differential equations, such as

$$\frac{d\mathbf{S}}{dt} \equiv \dot{\mathbf{S}} = \mathbf{F}(t, \mathbf{S}). \tag{5.68}$$

In physics, *second order* differential equations are much more important to us in that they describe a much larger number of real physical systems. We thus need to work with equations of the form

$$\frac{d^2 y}{dt^2} \equiv \ddot{y} = f(t, y, \dot{y}). \tag{5.69}$$

Now, it might appear that this is a totally new and different problem. There are, in fact, numerical approaches specifically developed to treat second order differential equations. However, it is also possible to *reduce* this problem to a more familiar form.

In fact, we've already done this when we looked at the "mass on the spring" problem. You'll recall that we were able to treat the problem by considering two quantities, the position and the velocity, each of which was governed by a first order differential equation but involving both quantities. Although our notation was clumsy, we were able to solve the problem.

To facilitate the general solution to Equation 5.69, let's introduce some new variables; in particular, let's let $S_1 = y$, and $S_2 = \dot{y}$, two components of the "solution" vector. Aside from the computational advantages that we're seeking, this just makes a lot of sense: $\dot{y}$ is a *different thing* than is y—position and velocity are different—and so why shouldn't it have its own name and be treated on an equal basis with y? We then find that the original second order differential equation can be written as a set of two, first order differential equations,

$$\dot{S}_1 = S_2, \tag{5.70}$$

$$\dot{S}_2 = f(t, S_1, S_2). \tag{5.71}$$

At this point, we *could* go back and rederive all our methods—Euler, Runge-Kutta, and Fehlberg—but we don't have to do that. Instead, we note that these look like equations involving multiple dependent variables, or *vector* components, an observation further enhanced if we define

$$F_1 = S_2, \tag{5.72}$$

and

$$F_2 = f(t, S_1, S_2). \tag{5.73}$$

Our equations can then be written in vector form

$$\begin{bmatrix} \dot{S}_1 \\ \dot{S}_2 \end{bmatrix} = \begin{bmatrix} S_2 \\ f(t, S_1, S_2) \end{bmatrix} = \begin{bmatrix} F_1 \\ F_2 \end{bmatrix}, \tag{5.74}$$

or

$$\frac{d}{dt} \begin{bmatrix} S_1 \\ S_2 \end{bmatrix} = \begin{bmatrix} F_1 \\ F_2 \end{bmatrix}, \tag{5.75}$$

or

$$\dot{\mathbf{S}} = \mathbf{F}(t, \mathbf{S}), g$$

where $\mathbf{S}$ and $\mathbf{F}$ denote vectors, containing the solution and the derivatives. We thus see that this problem *is not* fundamentally different from the first order problem we've been working with at all—it's just that some of the components are essentially "definitions." In general, an n-th order differential equation can always be turned into a set of n first order equations. The function evaluating these derivatives might look something like

```
function [der]=derivs(t,S)
% This function evaluates all the components of the
% derivative vector, putting the results in the array 'der'.
%
der(1) = S(2);                    % Equation 5.72
der(2) = "f (t, S(1), S(2))";     % Equation 5.73
```

EXERCISE 5.16

Make the necessary modifications to your code, and test it on the differential equation

$$\ddot{y}(t) = -4y(t), \qquad y(0) = 1, \qquad y'(0) = 0,$$

on the interval $0 \leq t \leq 2\pi$. Compare to the analytic result. Use the computer to plot these results as well—the visualization of the result is much more useful than a pile of numbers in understanding what's going on.

At this juncture, it is not a major modification to write the Runge-Kutta-Fehlberg algorithm as an independent function, not tied to a specific problem being solved. This has the tremendous advantage that, once written, we never again need to be concerned with the code. Note, however, that this modification requires derivs to be independent as well, and that a few other (relatively minor) changes be made.

Let's begin with the driving program, say TEST.m, that will call RKF to solve a particular problem. This program should, at a minimum, provide input to RKF, such as initial and final integration times, initial conditions for the problem, and the integration parameters. RKF should then return, for example, the times at which the solution was determined, and the solution itself. The driving program will be left with printing the results, or drawing a graph, or whatever—RKF should only be concerned with the solution of the differential equation.

But there is an obstacle: to be useful for various problems, the actual name of the function that calculates the derivatives, and called by RKF, should itself be a "variable." MATLAB overcomes this obstacle with a *function handle*, which we'll demonstrate.

Each of these functions, TEST.m, RKF.m, and MyDerivatives.m must all be stored in their own files. First, the driving program:

```
%  TEST.m
%  This script demonstrates the use of independent, stand-alone
%     functions. It calls RKF to solve the problem of Exercise 5.16.
%
global RKF_epsilon RKF_hmin RKF_hmax;   % Parameters used by RKF
RKF_epsilon = 0.000001;
RKF_hmin    = 0.0001;
RKF_hmax    = 0.1;
tInitial    = 0.0;                          % Initial conditions
tFinal      = 1.0;
solution0   = [ 1.0; 0.0];
%
% Use RKF to solve the problem.  Note the "@" sign !!!
%
```

```
[t, s] = RKF(tInitial, tFinal, solution0, @MyDerivatives)
%
% The results are returned in "t" and in "s".  Print them,
%    graph them, whatever...
```

The most critical element of this code is the function handle, MyDerivatives. Essentially, this tells RKF where the function MyDerivatives can be found. To be explicit, the derivative function itself is

```
% MyDerivatives.m
function [der] = MyDerivatives(t,S)
% This function evaluates the necessary derivatives for the
%    differential equation
%
%          y" = -4y
%
der = [ S(2);
        -4*S(1)];
```

Finally, we need to look at RKF.m itself. Actually, it's very straightforward,

```
% This function solves ordinary differential equations having SEVERAL
%    dependent variables, i.e., components, by the Runge-Kutta-Fehlberg
%    adaptive step algorithm.  It is designed to be quite general, with
%    the name of the derivative function (which actually defines the
%    differential equation) being passed to it as an argument.  WITHIN
%    this function, the derivative function is known as "derivs".
%
%  Usage:  [tt,SS] = RKF( tInitial, tFinal, SInitial, @filename )
%
%  Input:  tInitial    starting t value (the independent variable)
%          tFinal      ending t value
%          SInitial    initial value of S, i.e., S(tInitial)
%          @filename   The handle of the function that contains the
%                      derivative definition, stored in the file
%                      "filename.m".  Within this function (RKF),
%                      it is referred to as "derivs".
%
% Output: tt   an array of t values at which the solution was calculated
%         SS   an array of solutions, corresponding to the t's in tt
%
function [tt,SS] = RKF(tInitial, tFinal, SInitial, derivs )
clear tt SS;
global RKF_epsilon RKF_hmin RKF_hmax;
...
... % The RKF function itself is virtually unchanged...
...
```

EXERCISE 5.17

Verify that this reorganization of the program works, using it to solve the previous exercise. Its value, of course, is in the ease with which a new problem can be addressed, without modifying RKF.m. To that end, re-examine Exercise 5.9. Note that parameters like g and c really only need to be defined within the derivative function.

5.10 The van der Pol Oscillator

In the 1920s, Balthasar van der Pol experimented with some novel electrical circuits involving triodes (vacuum tubes). One of those circuits is now known as the van der Pol oscillator, and is described by the differential equation

$$\ddot{x} = -x - \varepsilon(x^2 - 1)\dot{x}. \tag{5.76}$$

Interestingly, this equation pops up frequently, and is seen in the theory of the laser. If $\varepsilon = 0$, then this is a simple harmonic oscillator. But for $\varepsilon \neq 0$, this oscillator departs from the harmonic oscillator, and in a *nonlinear* way. Thus, many of the analytic methods normally applied to differential equations are not applicable to this problem!

If ε is small, then this problem can be treated by a form of perturbation theory, in which the effect of the nonlinear term is averaged over one cycle of the oscillation. But this is valid only if ε is small. Fortunately, our numerical methods *do not* rely on the linearity of the differential equation, and are perfectly happy to solve this equation for us.

EXERCISE 5.18

Use our friendly integrator to solve Equation 5.76, for $\varepsilon = 1$ (a value much greater than zero). As initial conditions, let $x(0) = 0.5$, and $\dot{x}(0) = 0$. Follow the solution for several oscillations, say on the interval $0 \leq t \leq 8\pi$, and plot the position and velocity as a function of time.

5.11 Phase Space

Although following the solution as a function of time is interesting, an alternate form of viewing the dynamics of a problem has also been developed. In a *phase space* description, the position and velocity (momentum) of a system are the quantities of interest. As time evolves, the point in phase space specifying the current state of the system changes, thereby tracing out a *phase trajectory*. For example, consider

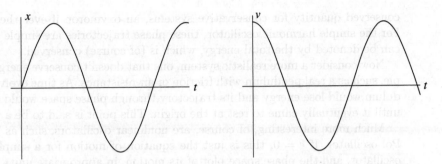

Figure 5.8   Position and velocity as functions of time for the simple harmonic oscillator.

a simple harmonic oscillator, with

$$x(t) = \sin t \qquad (5.77)$$

and

$$v(t) = \cos t. \qquad (5.78)$$

The position and velocity are plotted as functions of time in Figure 5.8. This is certainly a useful picture, but it's not the *only* picture. While the figure illustrates how position and velocity are (individually) related to time, it doesn't do a very good job of relating position and velocity to one another.

But certainly position and velocity are related; we know that the total energy of the system is conserved. We can remove the explicit time dependence, thereby obtaining a direct relationship between them. Such a curve, directly relating position and velocity, is shown in Figure 5.9. Of course, the time at which the system passes through a particular point can be noted, if desired.

By adopting a phase space picture, many results of advanced mechanics are immediately applicable. For example, the area enclosed by a phase trajectory is a

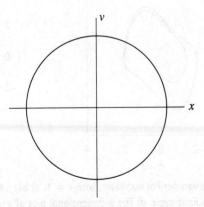

Figure 5.9   The trajectory in phase space of the simple harmonic oscillator.

conserved quantity for conservative systems, an oxymoron if ever there was one. For the simple harmonic oscillator, these phase trajectories are simple ellipses and can be denoted by the total energy, which is (of course) conserved.

Now consider a more realistic system, one that doesn't conserve energy for example, such as a real pendulum with friction or air resistance. As time evolves, the pendulum would lose energy and its trajectory through phase space would spiral down until it eventually came to rest at the origin. This point is said to be a *fixed point*.

Much more interesting, of course, are nonlinear oscillators, such as the van der Pol oscillator. If $\epsilon = 0$, this is just the equation of motion for a simple harmonic oscillator, and the phase space plot of its motion, in appropriate units, is simply a circle. If $\epsilon \neq 0$, the plot is not so simple. But after a long enough time, the plot settles down to a *limit cycle*, simply repeating its motion *ad infinitum*. And this limit cycle is *independent* of the initial conditions. An example is shown in Figure 5.10.

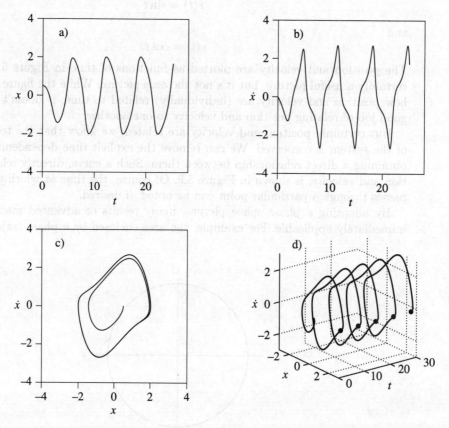

Figure 5.10   The van der Pol oscillator, with $\epsilon = 1$. a) $x(t)$. b) $\dot{x}(t)$. c) The phase space plot showing the approach to a limit cycle. d) The 3-dimensional plot of $x(t)$ and $\dot{x}(t)$ as a function of t. The solid dots are placed on the graph every time one cycle of the motion is completed. The initial conditions are $x(0) = 0.5$ and $\dot{x}(0) = 0$.

Because the initial conditions were such that they fell within the limit cycle, the orbit spiraled outward toward the limit cycle. In contrast, if we had started with initial conditions putting the oscillator outside the limit cycle, the system would have spiraled inward toward the limit cycle.

Both the fixed point and the limit cycle are examples of an *attractor*. For a fixed point, the dimensionality of the attractor is zero, and for a limit cycle, the dimensionality is one. In neither case is the motion chaotic, a topic to be encountered in Chapter 6.

EXERCISE 5.19

Investigate the trajectory of the van der Pol oscillator in phase space, for $0 \leq t \leq 8\pi$ and $\epsilon = 1$. Try different initial conditions, say with $\dot{x}(0) = 0$ but $x(0) = 1, 2, 3$, and plot your results as trajectories in phase space. Satisfy yourself that the asymptotic motion is a limit cycle, independent of the initial conditions.

To study the motion of nonlinear systems, the French Mathematician Henri Poincaré (1854–1912) developed the idea of a Poincaré section. (Poincaré was a polymath and is described as *The Last Universalist*, as he excelled in all the areas of mathematics that existed during his lifetime.) We've seen that initial conditions can lead to different initial paths in phase space, but that eventually a path can evolve to a fixed path, such as a limit cycle. But we're often *not* interested in the initial motion, but only in the long time, *asymptotic* motion of the system. Such motion through time and phase space is depicted in Figure 5.10.

Because phase space diagrams can become quite complicated, Poincaré invented a method to simplify the analysis of phase space diagrams. His method involves a "stroboscopic" view of a phase space diagram. That is, take a snapshot of the path at specific times, and look at the collection of snapshots. In particular, we plot the path in phase space at increments of the limit cycle's frequency. This is depicted in Part d) of the Figure, in which a solid dot indicates the position in phase space at equal time intervals. If you look carefully at the Figure, you will notice the phase space position of the dot is identical for every cycle. (Not at first, but after sufficiently long times, in the asymptotic region.) This plot is a portion of the full phase space, the *Poincaré section*. In this example, in which the asymptotic motion is a limit cycle and the time increment is the period of the oscillator, the dots fall on top of each other and the Poincaré section is a single point, reflecting the periodic motion of the system.

Essentially, this set of points corresponds to intersections made by the coordinate pair with parallel planes perpendicular to the t-axis but placed at equal time intervals. The Poincaré section plot is the sequence of points formed by the intersections of the phase space path with these parallel planes, and projected onto one plane. The Poincaré section actually becomes particularly useful when we deal with a system under an applied external oscillatory force. The force has the effect of adding energy to the system, and motivates us to look at the system in a different way. A system could develop motion with more than one period. So we wish to learn whether the system's phase space settles to a single point, a single loop, etc. as is the case of an attractor, or many unrelated points as is the case of a strange attractor. While we will come back to this later in Chapter 6, it suffices to say that the idea is to learn about the long time phase space behavior of the system as a multiple of the applied external force's frequency.

5.12 The Finite Amplitude Pendulum

Back when we were talking about integrals in Chapter 4, we discussed the "simple" pendulum, whose motion is described by the differential equation

$$\ddot{\theta} = -\frac{g}{l}\sin\theta. \tag{5.79}$$

We found that the period of this pendulum was given in terms of an elliptic integral. We now want to solve for θ as a function of time. In the usual introductory treatments of the pendulum, $\sin\theta$ is approximated by θ and Equation 5.79 becomes the equation for a simple harmonic oscillator. In more advanced presentations, more terms in the expansion of the sine function might be retained and a series solution to Equation 5.79 be developed; but even then, the solution is valid only to the extent that the expansion for the sine is valid. But a numerical solution is not constrained in this way. With our handy-dandy second order integrator up and running, it's nearly trivial to generate accurate numerical solutions. In fact, we can generate several different solutions, corresponding to different initial conditions, to produce a family of trajectories in phase space, a *phase portrait* of the system. Such a portrait contains a lot of information. For example, at small amplitudes $\sin\theta$ *is* approximately θ, so that the path in phase space should look very similar to those for a simple harmonic oscillator. With larger amplitudes, the trajectories should look somewhat different.

Let's recall some facts about the simple pendulum. The total energy, E, is the sum of kinetic and potential energies,

$$E = T + V, \tag{5.80}$$

where

$$T = \frac{1}{2}ml^2\dot{\theta}^2 \tag{5.81}$$

and

$$V = mgl(1 - \cos\theta). \tag{5.82}$$

For $\theta_0 = 0$ we then have

$$E = T = \frac{1}{2}ml^2\dot{\theta}_0^2 \tag{5.83}$$

or

$$\dot{\theta}_0 = \sqrt{\frac{2E}{ml^2}}. \tag{5.84}$$

Using these initial conditions, Equation 5.79 can be solved to find θ and $\dot{\theta}$ as a function of time, for various total energies. Is there a physical significance to energies greater than $2mgl$?

EXERCISE 5.20

Solve the "simple" pendulum for arbitrary amplitudes. In particular, create a phase portrait of the physical system. For simplicity, choose units such that $g = l = 1$ and $m = 0.5$, and plot θ in the range $-3\pi < \theta < 3\pi$. Include $\theta_0 = \pm 2\pi$, and consider both positive and negative initial velocities. Identify trajectories in phase space by their energy; include trajectories for $E = 0.25$, 0.5, 0.75, 1, 1.25, and 1.5. (Why should you take particular care with the $E = 1$ trajectory? This particular trajectory is called the *separatrix*—I wonder why?)

5.13 The Animated Pendulum

As we noted, the phase space approach is achieved by removing the explicit time dependence. This yields valuable information, and presents it in a useful manner—the significance of an *attractor* is immediately obvious, for example. The presentation is *static*, however—quite acceptable for textbook publication, but not really in the "modern" spirit of things. With a microcomputer, you can generate the solution as a function of time—why don't you display the solution as time evolves? In particular, why don't you *animate* your display? Actually, it's not that difficult!

Animation is achieved by displaying different images on the screen in quick succession. On television and at the cinema, the images are displayed at a rate of about 30 images per second. About 15 images per second is the lower limit; less that this, and the mind/eye sees "jitter" rather than "motion." MATLAB's graphics capabilities are sufficient to display animation in "real time" for many problems of our interest, and can also save the individual frames and compile them to create an .avi file for viewing later.

Imagine a "picture" of our pendulum, simply a line drawn from the point of suspension to the location of the pendulum bob. The next image is simply another line, drawn to the new location of the bob. For such simple line plots, we can achieve animation by clearing the screen of the old image and writing the new one.

The logic for the computer code might be something like the following:

```
function animate
clear;
global ...;              % Parameters required by RKF

...

S0 = [3.1 ; 0.0];        % Initial position and velocity of pendulum
dt = 0.05;               % time between successive frames of animation
```

```
for t=dt:dt:20.0
    [t,S] = RKF(t-dt, t, S0, @Pendulum);
    for j=1:2                              % RKF returns all computed solutions.
        S0(j) = S(j,length(t));            % We're only interested in the last
    end                                    % one, which is the initial condition
                                           % for the next time step.
    theta = S0(1);
    x = sin(theta);                        % ANIMATION :
    y = 1-cos(theta);
    clf;                                   % clear the screen
    axis([-1.5 1.5 -0.5 2.5]);             % create a plot window
    axis image                             % window to fit axis tightly
    hold on                                % overlay commands
    line([0,x],[1,y]);                     % draw pendulum string
    plot(x,y,'bo','MarkerSize',5,...       % draw big blue pendulum bob
        'MarkerFaceColor',[0 0 1]);
    pause(0.02);                           % pause a moment
end
```

The `for` loop is clearly where the action takes place. Some calculations are performed, the screen is cleared, the new image is drawn, and the program pauses, so that the animation doesn't proceed too rapidly. For the animation to accurately simulate the motion of the pendulum, we would need to ensure that the images are redrawn/drawn at a constant rate, perhaps by adding a timing loop to the code. But for purposes of illustration, drawing at equal time steps is sufficient.

EXERCISE 5.21
Animate your pendulum.

In general, the RKF parameters should be chosen to ensure the accuracy of the calculation. However, for the fidelity of the animation, only frames separated by a constant time step should be displayed. For a sufficiently time-consuming calculation, this may not be possible to accomplish in "real time." That is, the calculation can take longer than allowed for the appropriate frame rate to be achieved. In this case, using MATLAB's `movie` facility, each frame can be stored as calculated, and the entire movie played back at an appropriate frame rate. The movie can also be transformed to an `.avi` file and saved.

5.14 Another Little Quantum Mechanics Problem

Way back in Chapter 2 we discussed the one-dimensional Schrödinger equation

$$-\frac{\hbar^2}{2m}\frac{d^2\psi}{dx^2} + V(x)\psi(x) = E\psi(x), \qquad (5.85)$$

and found solutions for the problem of an electron in a finite square well. Those solutions were facilitated by knowing the analytic solutions for the different regions of the potential. Well, that was then, and this is now!

Let's imagine a different physical problem, that of an electron bound in the anharmonic potential

$$V(x) = \alpha x^2 + \beta x^4, \tag{5.86}$$

where α and β are constants. In a qualitative sense, the solutions to this problem must be similar to those for the finite square well; that is, an oscillatory solution between the classical turning points, and a decaying solution as you move into the forbidden region. The sought-for solution should look something like Figure 5.11.

The computer code you presently have should work just fine, except for one small problem: what are the initial conditions? In this problem, you don't have them! Rather, you have *boundary conditions*. That is, instead of knowing ψ and $d\psi/dx$ at some specific point, you know how ψ should behave as $x \rightarrow \pm\infty$. That's a little different, and takes some getting used to.

Let's revisit a boundary value problem you do know, the infinite square well, and consider how a numerical solution to it would proceed. First, you would guess an energy. And you know that $\psi(x_0) = 0$, just as in the present case, so you would then guess $\psi'(x_0)$ and numerically solve Equation 5.85. Your results, for two different guesses for $\psi'(x_0)$, might look like those in Figure 5.12

What we see is that the choice of ψ'_o is not really critical. While the numerical solutions are different, one has exactly the same validity as the other, since they differ only in an overall multiplicative constant. After all, if $\psi(x)$ is a valid solution, then so is $5\psi(x)$. Neither of these functions reached the boundary at $x = a$ with the correct value. On the other hand, a different energy would lead to a distinctly different $\psi(x)$, one that might satisfy the boundary condition at $x = a$.

Returning to the current problem, we simply *guess* initial conditions and observe their consequences. Deep in Region I, we know that ψ should be small but increasing

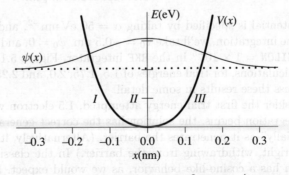

Figure 5.11 The anharmonic potential $V(x) = 50x^2 + 2500x^4$, and its least energetic eigenfunction. (Recall that the convention is to align the zero baseline of the wavefunction with the energy eigenvalue, $\approx 2.05\,\text{eV}$ for this problem. However, in subsequent figures we will not usually include this baseline.)

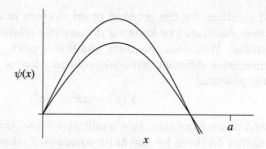

Figure 5.12   Two attempts at a numerical solution to the infinite square well problem, with different initial derivatives $\psi'(0)$. Neither satisfy the boundary condition at $x = a$, the right side of the well.

as x increases; let's guess that

$$\psi(x_0) = 0,$$

and

$$\psi'(x_0) = \psi_0', \qquad (5.87)$$

where ψ_0' is a positive number. As with the infinite square well, this choice is not critical. We can then make an initial guess for the energy E, and "solve" the differential equation using the Runge-Kutta-Fehlberg integrator. Plotting the solution, we can see how good our guess for the energy was, and try again, based on the result. This is called the *shooting method* since, in essence, you're trying to hit the target at the other boundary.

Before we can do the calculation, however, we need specific values for the constants. As noted earlier, the computer deals with pure numbers only, and not units, so that we need to exercise some care. Using an appropriate system of units is extremely advantageous. As before, we choose to use electron masses, nanometers, and eV's. In these units, we have

$$\hbar^2 = 0.076199682 \text{ eV } m_e \text{ nm}^2. \qquad (5.88)$$

The potential is specified by taking $\alpha = 50$ eV nm^{-2}, and $\beta = 2500$ eV nm^{-4}. To start the integration, we'll take $x_0 = -0.5$ nm, $\psi_0 = 0$, and $\psi_0' = 1 \times 10^{-5}$, and we'll set EPSILON $= 1 \times 10^{-5}$ in the RKF integrator. Figure 5.13 contains the results of such calculations, for trial energies of 1.5, 1.75, 2.0, and 2.25 electron volts. We need to discuss these results in some detail.

Consider the first trial energy attempted, 1.5 electron volts. In Region I, where the integration begins, the solution has the correct general shape, decreasing "exponentially" as it penetrates the barrier. (Alternatively, it's increasing as it moves to the right, withdrawing from the barrier.) In the classically allowed region the solution has a cosine-like behavior, as we would expect. But the behavior to the right of the well in Region III is clearly incorrect, with the solution becoming very large instead of very small. Recall that in this region there are two mathematically permitted solutions: one that is increasing, and one that is decreasing; it is on

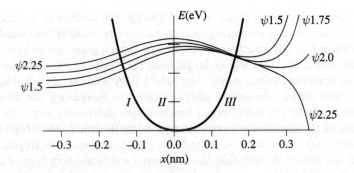

Figure 5.13   Numerical solutions of the anharmonic potential for trial energies of 1.5, 1.75, 2.0, and 2.25 electron volts. The numerical solution must satisfy the boundary conditions to be physically acceptable.

the basis of our *physical* understanding that only the decreasing one is permitted. But of course, our trial energy is not the correct energy, it's only a first guess, and a rather poor one at that, as evidenced by the unphysical behavior of the solution. Recall that we want to find that energy that leads to a strictly decaying solution in this region. That is, we want to "hit" the solution that has a zero coefficient multiplying the increasing component.

Let's try another energy, say 1.75 electron volts. The behavior of the numerical solution is much as before, including a rapid increase to the right of the potential well. However, the onset of this rapid increase has been postponed until farther into the barrier, so that it is (arguably) a better solution than we had previously. (We're getting closer to the "target.") Let's try again: at 2.0 electron volts, the onset is delayed even further. We're coming closer and closer to the correct energy, finding solutions with smaller amounts of the increasing solution in them. So we try again, but as shown in the figure, we get a quite different behavior of the solution for 2.25 electron volts: instead of becoming very large and positive, it becomes very large and negative!

What has happened, of course, is that our trial energy has gotten too large. The correct energy, yielding a wavefunction that tends toward zero at large x, is between 2 and 2.25 electron volts, and we see a drastic change in behavior as we go from below to above the correct energy. This suggests the use of a root finder to determine the precise energy that we seek. But can we ever expect to find that correct energy by this method? That is, can we ever find a solution that strictly decays in Region *III*? And why aren't we seeing any of this "explosion of the solution" *to the left* of the potential well?

Recall that there are two linearly independent solutions to a second order differential equation; in the classically forbidden region, one of the solutions increases, and one decreases. Any solution can be written as a linear combination of these two: what we want is that *specific* solution that has the coefficient of the increasing solution exactly equal to zero. As the trial energy comes closer to the correct energy, that coefficient decreases—but we saw that our numerical solution always "blew up" at some point. Why? Although the coefficient is small, it's multiplying a function that is *increasing* as x increases—no matter how small the coefficient, as long as it is not *exactly* zero, there will come a point where this coefficient times the increasing function will be larger than the desired function, which is *decreasing*, and the numerical solution will "explode"! Why wasn't this behavior seen in Region I? In that region, the sought after solution was *increasing*, not decreasing—the contribution from the nonphysical function was *decreasing* as the integration proceeded out of the classically forbidden region. In Region I, we integrated in the direction such that the unwanted contribution vanished, while in Region III, we integrated in the direction such that the unwanted solution *overwhelmed* our desired one. *We integrated in the wrong direction!*

> Always propagate the numerical solution in the same direction as the physically meaningful solution increases.

The cure for our disease is obvious: we need to always begin the integration in a classically forbidden region, and integrate toward a classically allowed region. In the case of the potential well, we'll have two solutions, integrated from the left and right, and require that they match up properly in the middle. (This would be accomplished with an appropriate root finder.) For symmetric potentials, such as the anharmonic potential we've been discussing, the situation is particularly simple since the solutions must be either even or odd: the even solutions have a zero derivative at $x = 0$, and the odd solutions must have the wavefunction zero at $x = 0$. As a result, we only need to propagate one solution.

(As discussed earlier, the numerical value for the initial derivative is not critical, since different choices simply lead to wavefunctions with different overall multiplicative factors. Ultimately, this ambiguity can be removed by normalizing the wavefunction, e.g., requiring that

$$\int_{-\infty}^{\infty} \psi^*(x)\psi(x)\,dx = 1. \tag{5.89}$$

But even then there remains an uncertainty in the overall phase of the wavefunction. That is, if ψ is a normalized solution, so is $i\psi$. For the bound state problem discussed here, however, the wavefunction can be taken to be real, and the complex conjugate indicated in the integral is unnecessary.)

We begin as before, deep in Region I, with $\psi_o = 0$ and ψ'_o small, such as 1×10^{-5}. We then solve the differential equation to determine $\psi(x = 0, E)$ and $\psi'(x = 0, E)$. For the even states, we require $\psi'(x = 0, E) = 0$, and for the odd states $\psi(x = 0, E) = 0$.

Now, we're almost done; all that remains is to ensure that the calculation is accurate. If a (poor) choice of the tolerance yields 5 significant digits in the Runge-Kutta-Fehlberg integration, for example, then it's meaningless to try to find the root of $\psi'(x = 0, E) = 0$ to 8 significant digits. The overall accuracy can never be greater than the least accurate step in the calculation. We also need to verify that the x_0 is "deep enough" in the forbidden region that the eigenvalue doesn't depend upon its value.

EXERCISE 5.22
Find the lowest three eigenvalues, two even and one odd, of the anharmonic potential $V(x) = 50x^2 + 2500x^4$, and plot the potential and the eigenfunctions. Discuss the measures you've taken to ensure 8 significant digit accuracy in the eigenvalues.

We should not leave you with the impression that all the problems of quantum mechanics involve symmetric potentials—quite the contrary is true. Symmetry is a terrifically useful characteristic, and should be exploited whenever present. But the more usual situation is the one in which the potential is *not* symmetric. For example, let's consider the force between two atoms. When they are far apart, the electrons of one atom interact with the electrons and nucleus of the other atom giving rise to an attractive force, the *van der Waals attraction*. But as the distance between the atoms becomes very small, the force becomes repulsive as the nuclei (or the ionic core in many-electron atoms) interact with one another. Thus the general shape of the potential must be repulsive at small distances and repulsive at large ones, thus necessitating an energy minimum somewhere in the middle. As an example, the potential energy curve for the hydrogen molecule is presented in Figure 5.14. (More precisely, it's the electronic potential as a function of interatomic separation in molecular hydrogen in its ground electronic state. Finding the eigenvalues of this

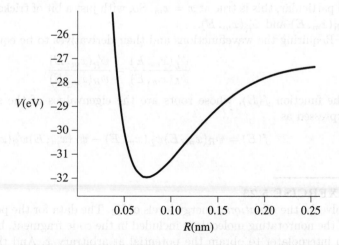

Figure 5.14   An accurate ground state potential for molecular hydrogen. (Data taken from W. Kolos and L. Wolniewicz, "Potential-Energy Curves for the $X^1\Sigma_g^+$, $b^3\Sigma_u^+$, and $C^1\Pi_u$ States of the Hydrogen Molecule," *Journal of Chemical Physics* **43**, 2429, 1965.)

potential give us the vibrational energy levels of the nonrotating molecule. Inclusion of rotation is easily accomplished.)

Clearly, the potential is not symmetric. And since it *is not* symmetric, the eigenfunctions *are not* purely even or odd functions. Still, the method of solution is essentially the same as before: choose a *matching point*, x_m, say near the minimum of the potential well. Then, beginning far to the left, integrate to the matching point as before to find $\psi_L(x_m, E)$ and $\psi'_L(x_m, E)$. Because the potential is not symmetric, we must actually perform the second integration, as discussed earlier. Starting far to the right, with $\psi_R(x_\infty, E) = 0$ and $\psi'_R(x_\infty, E)$ being a small number, integrate *to the left* until $x = x_m$ is reached, so that $\psi_R(x_m, E)$ and $\psi'_R(x_m, E)$ are obtained. Unfortunately the RKF integrator, as we've developed it, is incapable of this second integration. When we wrote the while condition as

```
while (x0 < xFinal)
```

we implicitly assumed that x0 was increasing, so that the required integration can't be performed. However, we can use RKF to solve a *different problem* that leads to the *same solution*.

Let's reflect the potential about the y-axis, extending the potential to negative values. Instead of doing the second integration by starting at a large positive x with $\psi_R(x_\infty, E)$ and $\psi'_R(x_\infty, E)$ and integrating down to x_m, we instead start at a large negative value with $\psi_R(x_{-\infty}, E)$ and $\psi'_R(x_{-\infty}, E)$ and integrate up to $x = -x_m$. This wavefunction will just be the mirror image of $\psi_R(x, E)$, for $x > 0$. That is,

$$\psi_R(x, E) = \psi_R(-x, E)$$

and

$$\psi'_R(x, E) = -\psi'_R(-x, E).$$

In particular, this is true at $x = x_m$. So, with just a bit of trickery, we *have* obtained $\psi_R(x_m, E)$ and $\psi'_R(x_m, E)$.

Requiring the wavefunctions and their derivatives to be equal, we find that

$$\frac{\psi'_L(x_m, E)}{\psi_L(x_m, E)} = \frac{\psi'_R(x_m, E)}{\psi_R(x_m, E)}. \tag{5.90}$$

The function $f(E)$, whose roots are the eigenvalues of the system, can then be expressed as

$$f(E) = \psi_R(x_m, E)\psi'_L(x_m, E) - \psi_L(x_m, E)\psi'_R(x_m, E). \tag{5.91}$$

EXERCISE 5.23

Solve for the *vibrational* energy levels of H_2. The data for the potential energy curve of the nonrotating molecule is included in the code fragment, but you'll need to use an interpolator to obtain the potential at arbitrary x. And then, of course, you'll need to use a root finder to determine the eigenvalues.

5.15 A Second Order Differential Equation in Two Dimensions

At this point, it should be obvious how to approach such a problem. To be specific, let's reconsider our projectile motion problem and simply ask: How can we find the *position* of the projectile? First, of course, we need a differential equation involving the position—the very *definition* of velocity should do the trick. That is,

$$\frac{d\vec{r}}{dt} = \vec{v}, \tag{5.92}$$

or in terms of components,

$$\frac{dx}{dt} = v_x,$$
$$\frac{dy}{dt} = v_y. \tag{5.93}$$

This looks very much like what we've already done, except that instead of having two differential equations, we now have four. The manner of solution should be clear, but let's be explicit: define a "vector" $\vec{s}$ such that

$$\vec{s} = \begin{pmatrix} x \\ v_x \\ y \\ v_y \end{pmatrix}.$$

Then we have

$$\frac{d\vec{s}}{dt} = \frac{d}{dt} \begin{pmatrix} x \\ v_x \\ y \\ v_y \end{pmatrix} = \begin{pmatrix} dx/dt \\ dv_x/dt \\ dy/dt \\ dv_y/dt \end{pmatrix} = \begin{pmatrix} v_x \\ -c\sqrt{v_x^2 + v_y^2}\, v_x \\ v_y \\ -g - c\sqrt{v_x^2 + v_y^2}\, v_y \end{pmatrix} = \vec{f},$$

where we've used our previous expressions from Equation 5.59 for the velocity derivatives. We can now employ *exactly* the same algorithm we used previously, except that our solution vector now has four components. As before, all the physics is contained in the function evaluating the derivative vector.

EXERCISE 5.24

Use your computer code to solve for the position, as well as the velocity, of the projectile with

$$g = 9.8 \text{ m/s}^2 \quad \text{and} \quad c = 0.1 \text{ m}^{-1},$$

subject to the initial conditions that

$$x = y = 0, \quad v_x = 20\text{m/s}, \quad \text{and} \quad v_y = 0.$$

Display both components of the position and the velocity for $0 \le t \le 10$ seconds.

5.16 Shoot the Moon

Newton tells us that the gravitational force of attraction between two bodies is

$$\mathbf{F} = -G\frac{mM}{r^2}\mathbf{e_r}. \tag{5.94}$$

We already know that $\mathbf{F} = m\mathbf{a}$, so I suppose we know all there is to know about the motion of bodies under the influence of gravity.

In principle, maybe; in practice, there's a little more to it. Let's start with a little review of a problem from freshman mechanics. Imagine that we have two bodies, say the Earth and the Moon, that are orbiting one another. Or to put it another way, each body is orbiting about their common center-of-mass (Figure 5.15). This makes it convenient to use a coordinate system to describe the system that is fixed in space and has its origin located at the center-of-mass. In general, the orbital trajectories are ellipses, with one focus at the origin, but for the Earth–Moon system the eccentricity of the orbit is so small, 0.055, that we'll approximate them as circles. If d is the (mean) center-to-center distance between the Earth and the Moon, then

$$r_E = \frac{m_M}{m_M + m_E}d \tag{5.95}$$

and

$$r_M = \frac{m_E}{m_M + m_E}d \tag{5.96}$$

where m_E is the mass of the Earth and m_M the mass of the Moon. Clearly, $d = r_E + r_M$.

The Earth–Moon system revolves about its common center of mass with a sidereal orbital period T, or with an angular frequency $\omega = 2\pi/T$. If the Moon lies on the positive x-axis at $t = 0$, then

$$\phi_M = \omega t \tag{5.97}$$

and

$$\phi_E = \omega t + \pi, \tag{5.98}$$

where ϕ_M is the angular location of the Moon and ϕ_E is the angular location of the Earth. The relationship between T, d, and the masses is not accidental, of course.

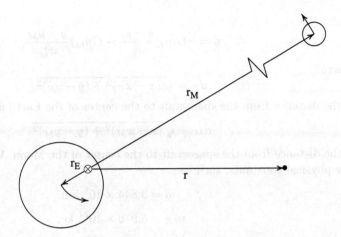

Figure 5.15   Center-of-mass coordinates for the Earth–Moon system. The view is from Polaris, looking down on the plane of rotation, with the counterclockwise motion of the Earth and Moon indicated. The relative sizes of the Earth and Moon, and the location of the center of mass ⊗, are drawn to scale.

To remain in uniform circular motion a body must be constantly accelerated, the acceleration being generated by the gravitational force of attraction. Thus we have Kepler's third law of planetary motion, first published in *Harmonices Mundi* in 1619, that the square of the orbital period is proportional to the cube of the mean separation.

We now have a reasonable description of the Earth–Moon system. Let's add to the equation mankind's innate desire to explore the unknown, and ask: How do we journey from the Earth to the Moon?

Let's imagine that a spacecraft has been placed in a "parking orbit" 400 km above the Earth, so that the radius of the orbit is 6800 km. At time $t = 0$ the spacecraft reaches the angular position α in its circular orbit about the Earth, the rockets fire, and the spacecraft attains the velocity of v_0 in a direction tangent to its parking orbit. Since the rockets fire for only a brief time compared to the duration of the voyage, we'll assume it to be instantaneous. But of course, as the spacecraft moves toward the Moon, the Moon continues its revolution about the Earth–Moon center-of-mass. All the while, the motion of the spacecraft is dictated by Newton's laws,

$$\mathbf{F} = m\mathbf{a} = -G\frac{m\,m_E}{|\mathbf{r} - \mathbf{r_E}|^3}(\mathbf{r} - \mathbf{r_E}) - G\frac{m\,m_M}{|\mathbf{r} - \mathbf{r_M}|^3}(\mathbf{r} - \mathbf{r_M}). \qquad (5.99)$$

As we had expected, the mass of the spacecraft doesn't enter into these equations. They can be written in component form as

$$\ddot{x} = -Gm_E\frac{x - x_e}{d_E^3} - Gm_M\frac{x - x_M}{d_M^3}, \qquad (5.100)$$

and

$$\ddot{y} = -Gm_E \frac{y - y_e}{d_E^3} - Gm_M \frac{y - y_M}{d_M^3}, \tag{5.101}$$

where

$$d_E = \sqrt{(x - x_E)^2 + (y - y_E)^2} \tag{5.102}$$

is the distance from the spacecraft to the center of the Earth and

$$d_M = \sqrt{(x - x_M)^2 + (y - y_M)^2} \tag{5.103}$$

is the distance from the spacecraft to the center of the Moon. With knowledge of a few physical constants, such as

$$d = 3.844 \times 10^5 \text{ km},$$

$$m_E = 5.976 \times 10^{24} \text{ kg},$$

$$m_M = 7.35 \times 10^{22} \text{ kg},$$

$$T = 27.322 \text{ days},$$

and

$$G = 6.67 \times 10^{-11} \text{N m}^2/\text{kg}^2,$$

we're ready to explore!

EXERCISE 5.25

As a preliminary exercise, and to check that all the parameters have been correctly entered, set the mass of the Moon to zero and see if you can verify the freshman calculation for the velocity needed for the spacecraft to have a circular orbit about the Earth at this altitude.

Now, for the "real thing":

EXERCISE 5.26

Find a set of initial conditions, α and v_0, that will send the spacecraft from the parking orbit to the Moon. For starters, just try to hit the Moon. (Score a hit if you come within 3500 km of the center of the Moon.)

EXERCISE 5.27

For more intrepid voyagers, find initial conditions that will cause the spacecraft to loop around the Moon and return to Earth. This orbit is of real significance: see "Apollo 13" under the heading NEAR DISASTERS in your history text.

5.17 Celestial Mechanics

To say that "celestial mechanics has had an impact of the development of physics" would be an incredible understatement. As early as Newton, the question of the stability of the Moon's orbit about the Earth was a serious concern. (Today, we might argue that the age of the solar system itself is evidence that the system is stable, but in Newton's day, the age of the Earth wasn't known. Newton himself argued that it was only a few thousand years old.)

In 1888 King Oscar II of Sweden established a prize for whomever could solve, or make the most progress toward solving, the n-body problem. Newton had solved the 2-body problem, but the general n-body problem has too many unknowns for the number of equations available, and hence can't be solved by any of the obvious techniques. (Even today, the general problem remains, necessarily, unsolved.) This is not to say that tremendous insight into the problem, and to certain aspects in mathematics, can't be gleaned from the investigation.

Two periodic solutions to the 3-body problem, though incomplete, were known due to Euler (1767) and Lagrange (1772). (It's interesting to note that both of these solutions have each of the three bodies moving on an ellipse, the same orbit that Newton found for the two-body problem.) However, these solutions are unstable. The prize was ultimately awarded to Henri Poincaré. While he didn't actually solve the problem, he introduced the methods of surfaces of section, phase space, and deterministic chaos that have influenced much of the work that has followed.

Since the equations of motion can't be solved analytically, a computational approach is an obvious alternative to the solution of this problem. To trace all the work on this problem is clearly inappropriate for this text, but a couple of examples are well worth the investigation.

In the late 1800s, Meissel and Burreau proposed the Pythagorean problem: Consider three bodies of mass proportional to three, four, and five located at the vertices of a three-four-five right triangle. (See Figure 5.16.) If the bodies are initially at rest, and their motion dictated solely by Newton's laws of motion under Newtonian gravitation, what is their subsequent evolution?

The force on any one body is simply the sum of gravitational forces exerted by the other bodies,

$$\vec{F}_i = m_i \vec{a}_i = -G \sum_{j \neq i} m_i m_j \frac{\vec{r}_i - \vec{r}_j}{|\vec{r}_i - \vec{r}_j|^3}, \tag{5.104}$$

where $\vec{r}_i$ locates the i-th body in the center-of-mass frame of reference. We can use scaled units, in which the masses are simply 3, 4, and 5 mass units, the distances are in terms of the unit distance, and time is in unit time. In these units, $G = 4\pi^2$. Although obviously specialized, close encounters of a few bodies, such as the one being examined here, are exceedingly common between stars in stellar clusters.

Body	mass	x	y
A	3	1	3
B	4	-2	-1
C	5	1	-1

A problem like this really deserves, if not requires, a graphical representation.

EXERCISE 5.28

Investigate the Pythagorean problem. In particular, investigate the motion of the system from $t = 0$ until $t = 1$.

In the previous exercise, you should have observed two close encounters between the stars. Numerically, these encounters require the differential equation solver to take more steps, to ensure the accuracy of the calculation. As a result, the "real time" between the display of successive frames can increase, so that the frames are not being displayed at a constant rate. This can cause the animation to appear jumpy. (The possiblity of this occurring was briefly mentioned in conjunction with the animated pendulum, Exercise 5.21.)

There are several remedies to this situation, including the use of MATLAB's `movie` facility to save each frame as it's calculated, and then subsequently to display the full animation. This is particularly appropriate if the image on each of the frames are complicated, requiring substantial time just to draw them. In the present situation, however, the drawing time is minimal and so a different approach can be

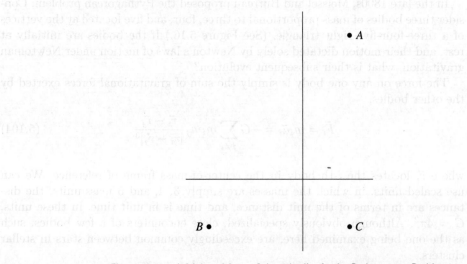

Figure 5.16   Initial positions of the 3 bodies in the Pythagorean Problem.

adopted: Simply store the results as the calculation proceeds, and then draw them all at one time. With this modification, your code should display the frames at a more constant rate, adding substantially to the visual display.

EXERCISE 5.29
Try the Pythagorean problem with this improved animation.

The problem itself is, of course, quite difficult. It's necessary to follow the first encounter very carefully, so that the "initial conditions" for the second encounter are correct, and so on. The investigation of the long-term behavior of the system requires careful attention to all aspects of the calculation.

EXERCISE 5.30
Investigate the Pythagorean problem up to $t = 10$.

Suffice it to say that the N-body problem involving many closely interacting particles is a significant problem. In particular, special methods must be introduced to treat the case seen here, namely, the temporary formation of binaries.

You might expect that for a problem as old and well-studied as this 3-body problem, all the interesting and novel solutions would have already been discovered. Thus it was somewhat surprising that a stable, periodic orbit was discovered in 2000. [A. Chenciner and R. Montgomery, Ann. Math. **152**: 881–901.] While the derivation of this orbit is well beyond us, we can numerically verify that it works. Using the same coordinates and units as in the previous exercise, with all masses equal to unity, the initial conditions for the three bodies are

Body	x	y	v_x	v_y
A	3.3030197	−0.82771837	1.587433767	1.47221479
B	−3.3030197	0.82771837	1.587433767	1.47221479
C	0.0000000	0.00000000	−3.174867535	−2.94442961

This problem is considerably less difficult than the last, so you should have no difficulty using the existing computer program to investigate it.

EXERCISE 5.31
Use your program to determine the motion of the three bodies. Do you see why this is called the "figure eight" orbit?

Of perhaps greater interest than the orbit itself is that the orbit is stable. That is, if one of the bodies is displaced from the initial conditions specified, the orbit remains essentially the same. (That is, they don't all suddenly fly off in different directions.)

EXERCISE 5.32
Investigate the stability of the orbit with respect to varying the initial conditions. What effect does changing the initial conditions have? Clearly, this exercise is just the beginning of what could be a substantial investigation into these problems.

5.18 Finite Differences

There is another approach to boundary value problems that's considerably different from the method we've been discussing. In it, we replace the given *differential* equation by the equivalent *difference* equation. Since we have approximations for derivatives in terms of finite differences, this shouldn't be too difficult. For example, consider the differential equation

$$y''(x) - 5y'(x) + 10y(x) = 10x \tag{5.105}$$

subject to the boundary conditions

$$y(0) = 0, \quad y(1) = 100. \tag{5.106}$$

The first step is to impose a *grid* on this problem and to derive the appropriate finite difference equation. We will then seek the solution of the difference equation at the grid points. Since we are replacing the *continuous* differential equation by the *discrete* finite difference equation, we can only ask for the solution on the finite grid. We would hope, of course, that the solution to this problem is (at least approximately) a solution to the original one. For our example, we'll choose the grid to be $x = 0.0, 0.1, 0.2, \ldots, 1.0$, and solve for the function on the interior points—the solutions at $x = 0$ and $x = 1$ are fixed by the boundary condition, and are not subject to change! To derive the finite difference equation, consider some arbitrary grid point, x_i; at this point, we have (approximately)

$$y_i' \approx \frac{y_{i+1} - y_{i-1}}{2h}, \tag{5.107}$$

and

$$y_i'' \approx \frac{y_{i+1} - 2y_i + y_{i-1}}{h^2}, \tag{5.108}$$

where $h = x_{i+1} - x_i$ and we've introduced the notation $y_i = y(x_i)$. (Note that the expressions for the derivatives we're using are of the same order of accuracy, having error $O(h^2)$—there would be no advantage to using an expression for one term in the differential equation that is more accurate than the expressions for any other term.) These approximations are substituted into the original differential equation to obtain the finite difference equation

$$\frac{y_{i+1} - 2y_i + y_{i-1}}{h^2} - 5\frac{y_{i+1} - y_{i-1}}{2h} + 10y_i = 10x_i. \tag{5.109}$$

This equation has the same structure as some of the equations we investigated in Chapter 2, and can be solved in the same manner. That is, we can write the equation in matrix form, and use Gauss elimination to obtain a solution. However, there are other ways of solving such equations, which we should investigate. Rather than solving the problem in a *direct* manner, we'll develop an *indirect* one. Solving for y_i, we find

$$y_i = \frac{1}{2 - 10h^2}\left[\left(1 - \frac{5h}{2}\right)y_{i+1} + \left(1 + \frac{5h}{2}\right)y_{i-1} - 10h^2 x_i\right]. \tag{5.110}$$

We will find an approximate solution to our differential equation by finding y's that satisfy the derived difference equation, and we'll do that by *iteration*.

Iterative methods are usually not superior to direct methods when applied to ordinary differential equations. However, many physical situations are actually posed in several dimensions, and require the solution to partial differential equations rather than ordinary ones. In these instances, the relative merits are frequently reversed, with iterative methods being immensely superior to direct ones. We should also note that with direct methods the error tends to accumulate as the solution is generated. In Gaussian elimination, for example, the back substitution propagates any error that may be present in one component to all subsequent components. Iterative methods, on the other hand, tend to treat all the components equally and distribute the error uniformly. An iterative solution can almost always be "improved" by iterating again—with a direct solution, what you get is all you got. In Chapter 7 we will explicitly discuss partial differential equations and appropriate methods to investigate them. But those methods are most easily introduced in the context of a single coordinate, e.g., ordinary differential equations, and hence include their discussion at this point.

Let's begin our development of an iterative method by simply guessing values for all the y's—for example, we can guess that y is a linear function and evaluate the y_i's accordingly. These become our *old* y's as we use Equation 5.110 to obtain *new* y's according to the iterative expression

$$y_i^{(j)} = \frac{1}{2 - 10h^2}\left[\left(1 - \frac{5h}{2}\right)y_{i+1}^{(j-1)} + \left(1 + \frac{5h}{2}\right)y_{i-1}^{(j-1)} - 10h^2 x_i\right]. \tag{5.111}$$

The initial guesses are denoted $y_i^{(0)}$, and might be stored in an array Yold. The first iteration at x_i is obtained from $y_{i+1}^{(0)}$ and $y_{i-1}^{(0)}$ by application of Equation 5.111, and stored in the array Ynew. One iteration consists of moving entirely through the array Yold, evaluating the elements of Ynew at all the interior points—remember, the first and last entries are fixed! After all the Ynew entries have been evaluated, Ynew can be copied into Yold, and one cycle of the iteration is complete; the process is then repeated. This is known as the *Jacobi* iteration scheme, and will converge to the correct result. However, we can speed it up a bit with no additional effort.

In the Jacobi scheme, the old values of y are used to evaluate the new ones. But think about that: you've just determined $y_i^{(j)}$, and are ready to evaluate $y_{i+1}^{(j)}$. Jacobi would have you use $y_i^{(j-1)}$ in this evaluation, although you've just calculated a better value! Let's use the better value: in moving through the y-array from left to right, replace Equation 5.111 by the *Gauss-Seidel* iteration scheme

$$y_i^{(j)} = \frac{1}{2 - 10h^2}\left[\left(1 - \frac{5h}{2}\right)y_{i+1}^{(j-1)} + \left(1 + \frac{5h}{2}\right)y_{i-1}^{(j)} - 10h^2 x_i\right].\qquad (5.112)$$

Of course, if moving through the array from right to left, you would use

$$y_i^{(j)} = \frac{1}{2 - 10h^2}\left[\left(1 - \frac{5h}{2}\right)y_{i+1}^{(j)} + \left(1 + \frac{5h}{2}\right)y_{i-1}^{(j-1)} - 10h^2 x_i\right].\qquad (5.113)$$

Not only is this a more rapidly convergent scheme, it eliminates the need for two different arrays of data. The iteration is continued until a specified level of accuracy is obtained, for *all* points.

Previously we've discussed how the accuracy of a single quantity is determined; in the present case, we would require that the successive iterates $y_i^{(j)}$ and $y_i^{(j-1)}$ be the same to some specified number of significant digits. But here we need to require that this accuracy be met at *all* the grid points. We find it very convenient to use *logical variables* to do this, as suggested in the example computer code:

```
% gauss_seidel.m
% The GAUSS-SEIDEL iteration method of finite differences
clear;
tolerance = 2.e-4;
h =
c1 = 1.0 - 2.5*h;
c2 = 1.0 + 2.5*h;
c3 = -10.0*h*h;
```

```
c4 = 2.0+c3;
% Initial guess:
y=...
iteration = 0;
% Iterate until done...or have iterated too many times.
x=...
done=false;
while done==false
    done=true;
    iteration=iteration+1;
    if (iteration >= 100), error ('Too many iterations!'), end
    % Evaluate the function at all the interior points:
    for i = 2:10
        yy=(c1*y(i+1)+c2*y(i-1)+c3*x(i))/c4;
        if (abs( (yy-y(i))/yy ) > tolerance ) % one failure flags "false"
            done=false;
            y(i) = yy;
        end
    end
end
```

The variable DONE is declared to be a logical variable, and is set to TRUE at the start of every iteration. As the iteration proceeds, the accuracy of each point is tested. Any time the error exceeds the specified accuracy, DONE is set to FALSE—of course, it only takes one such instance for DONE to become FALSE. The final accuracy check is then very simple, "if not done, iterate again." By choosing the appropriate type of variable, and a suitable name for it, the convergence checking has been made very clear.

The accuracy we've specified is not great, for several reasons. First, it's always wise to be conservative when starting a problem—try to develop some feel for the problem and the method of solution before you turn the computer loose on it. And secondly, we shouldn't lose sight of the fact that this is a derived problem, not the original differential equation. Is an exact solution to an approximate problem any better than an approximate solution to the exact problem? To solve the difference equation to higher accuracy is unwarranted, since the difference equation is only a finite representation of the differential equation given. As a final comment on the computer code, note that, as should be done with any iterative method, the number of iterations is counted and a graceful exit is provided if convergence is not obtained. The maximum iteration count is set rather large; the method is guaranteed to converge, but it can be slow. The code fragment was used as a base to develop a computer program to solve the finite difference equation, with the results as shown in Table 5.1.

Table 5.1   Relaxation

iter	$y(0.0)$	$y(0.1)$	$y(0.2)$	$y(0.3)$	$y(0.4)$	$y(0.5)$	$y(0.6)$	$y(0.7)$	$y(0.8)$	$y(0.9)$	$y(1.0)$
0	0.00	10.00	20.00	30.00	40.00	50.00	60.00	70.00	80.00	90.00	100.00
1	0.00	7.89	17.02	26.97	37.46	48.30	59.38	70.61	81.94	93.33	100.00
2	0.00	6.71	15.05	24.68	35.28	46.62	58.51	70.80	83.38	94.28	100.00
3	0.00	5.94	13.64	22.88	33.44	45.07	57.57	70.75	83.72	94.50	100.00
4	0.00	5.38	12.56	21.45	31.88	43.67	56.63	70.26	83.49	94.35	100.00
5	0.00	4.95	11.71	20.27	30.55	42.43	55.62	69.51	82.93	93.99	100.00
·											
·											
·											
87	0.00	1.99	5.04	9.48	15.68	23.94	34.57	47.75	63.42	81.17	100.00

Although the calculation has converged, note that *87* iterations were necessary to obtain the specified accuracy.

EXERCISE 5.33

Write a computer program to solve Equation 5.105 by the method described, subject to the boundary conditions of Equation 5.106 and compare your results to those above.

5.19 Successive Over Relaxation (SOR)

This whole method is referred to as *relaxation*—the finite difference equations are derived and programmed, and with successive iterations the solution *relaxes* to its correct value. As with any iterative procedure, the better the initial guess, the faster the method will converge. Once a "sufficiently accurate" approximation is available, either through good initialization or after cycling through a sufficient number of iterations, the relaxation is monotonic—that is, each iteration takes the approximate solution a step closer to its converged limit, each step being a little less than the previous one. (In Table 5.1, we see that the relaxation becomes monotonic after the third iteration.) This suggests an improved method, in which the *change* in the function from one iteration to the next is used to generate a better approximation: Let's *guess* that the converged result is equal to the most recent iterate plus some multiplicative factor times the difference between the two most recent iterations. That is, we *exaggerate* the difference in order to get closer to the correct result, and guess the solution $\bar{y}^{(j)}$

to be

$$\bar{y}_i^{(j)} = y_i^{(j)} + \alpha \left[y_i^{(j)} - y_i^{(j-1)} \right],$$ (5.114)

where α lies between 0 and 1. (The optimal value for α depends on the exact structure of the difference equation.) This is called *over relaxation*; since it's repeated at each iteration, the method is referred to as *Successive Over Relaxation (SOR)*.

EXERCISE 5.34

Modify your program to use the SOR method to solve the problem of the previous exercise. Experiment with different values of α to find the one requiring the fewest iterations. For that alpha, you should see a dramatic improvement in the rate of convergence over the Gauss-Seidel method.

5.20 Discretization Error

We noted earlier that demanding excessive accuracy in the solution of the finite difference equations is not appropriate. The reason, of course, is that the finite difference equation is only an *approximation* to the differential equation that we want to solve. Recall that the finite difference equation was obtained by approximating the derivative on a grid—no amount of effort spent on solving the finite difference equation itself will overcome the error incurred in making that approximation. Of course, we could try a different grid. . . .

To make our point, we've solved the finite difference equation for three different grids, with $h = 0.2$, 0.1, and 0.05. We pushed the calculation to eight significant digits, far more than is actually appropriate, to demonstrate that the error is associated with the finite difference equation itself, and not the method of solution. That is, our results are essentially *exact*, for each particular grid used. Any differences in our results for different grids are due to the intrinsic error associated with the discretization of the grid! These results are presented in Table 5.2.

As expected, the results become more accurate as h is decreased. But the *magnitude* of the discretization error *is* surprising: at $x = 0.2$, for example, the calculated value changes by 16% as the grid decreases from $h = 0.2$ to 0.1, and another 3% when h is further reduced to 0.05. Again, these changes are due to the discretization of the grid itself, not the accuracy of the solution of the finite difference equations. Clearly, it is a serious mistake to ask for many significant digit accuracy with a coarse grid—the results are not *relevant* to the actual problem you're trying to solve!

Since the error is due to the approximation of the derivatives, which we know to be $O(h^2)$, we can use Richardson's extrapolation to better our results. Using just the $h = 0.2$ and 0.1 data yields extrapolated results superior to the $h = 0.05$ ones. The extrapolations can themselves be extrapolated, with remarkable success.

Table 5.2   Discretization Error

	$y(0.2)$	$y(0.4)$	$y(0.6)$	$y(0.8)$
Finite Difference				
$h = 0.20$	4.3019	13.9258	31.9767	61.0280
$h = 0.10$	5.0037	15.5634	34.3741	63.2003
$h = 0.05$	5.1586	15.9131	34.8676	63.6292
Richardson Extrapolation				
0.20/0.10	5.2376	16.0193	35.1732	63.9244
0.10/0.05	5.2103	16.0296	35.0321	63.7721
0.20/0.10/.05	5.2085	16.0243	35.0227	63.7619
Analytic Result	5.2088	16.0253	35.0247	63.7644

EXERCISE 5.35

Verify the results of Table 5.2. Without Richardson Extrapolation, how small must h be to obtain results accurate to 4 significant digits?

Another approach to generating more accurate results would be to use a more accurate approximation for the derivatives in the first place. By using a higher-order approximation, the truncation error incurred by discarding the higher terms in the derivative expressions would be reduced. For the interior points, we can use the approximations developed in Chapter 3,

$$f'(x) = \frac{f(x - 2h) - 8f(x - h) + 8f(x + h) - f(x + 2h)}{12h} + O(h^4) \qquad (5.115)$$

and

$$f''(x) = \frac{-f(x - 2h) + 16f(x - h) - 30f(x) + 16f(x + h) - f(x + 2h)}{12h^2} + O(h^4). \qquad (5.116)$$

These expressions have error $O(h^4)$, but are not applicable for the points immediately adjoining the endpoints, since either $f(x - 2h)$ or $f(x + 2h)$ will lie outside the range being considered. For these points, we must devise alternate expressions for the derivatives.

In Chapter 3, we used Taylor series expansions for $f(x + h)$, $f(x + 2h)$, etc., to develop approximations for the derivatives. Let's try that again—the relevant expansions are

$$f(x - h) = f_{-1} = f_0 - hf_0' + \frac{h^2}{2!} f_0'' - \frac{h^3}{3!} f_0''' + \frac{h^4}{4!} f_0^{iv} - \frac{h^5}{5!} f_0^v + O(h^6),$$

$$f(x) = f_0,$$

$$f(x + h) = f_1 = f_0 + hf_0' + \frac{h^2}{2!} f_0'' + \frac{h^3}{3!} f_0''' + \frac{h^4}{4!} f_0^{iv} + \frac{h^5}{5!} f_0^v + O(h^6),$$

$$f(x + 2h) = f_2 = f_0 + 2hf_0' + \frac{4h^2}{2!} f_0'' + \frac{8h^3}{3!} f_0''' + \frac{16h^4}{4!} f_0^{iv} + \frac{32h^5}{5!} f_0^v + O(h^6),$$

$$f(x + 3h) = f_3 = f_0 + 3hf_0' + \frac{9h^2}{2!} f_0'' + \frac{27h^3}{3!} f_0''' + \frac{81h^4}{4!} f_0^{iv} + \frac{243h^5}{5!} f_0^v + O(h^6),$$

$$f(x + 4h) = f_4 = f_0 + 4hf_0' + \frac{16h^2}{2!} f_0'' + \frac{64h^3}{3!} f_0''' + \frac{256h^4}{4!} f_0^{iv} + \frac{1024h^5}{5!} f_0^v$$
$$+ O(h^6). \tag{5.117}$$

Since we are seeking a more accurate approximation, it's necessary that we retain more terms in the expansion than before. And since the derivative is desired at a non-symmetric location, we'll need to evaluate the function at more points as well. Taking a linear combination of these expressions, we find

$$a_{-1}f_{-1} + a_0f_0 + a_1f_1 + a_2f_2 + a_3f_3 + a_4f_4$$
$$= f_0 [a_{-1} + a_0 + a_1 + a_2 + a_3 + a_4]$$
$$+ hf_0' [-a_{-1} + a_1 + 2a_2 + 3a_3 + 4a_4]$$
$$+ \frac{h^2}{2!} f_0'' [a_{-1} + a_1 + 4a_2 + 9a_3 + 16a_4]$$
$$+ \frac{h^3}{3!} f_0''' [-a_{-1} + a_1 + 8a_2 + 27a_3 + 64a_4]$$
$$+ \frac{h^4}{4!} f_0^{iv} [a_{-1} + a_1 + 16a_2 + 81a_3 + 256a_4]$$
$$+ \frac{h^5}{5!} f_0^v [-a_{-1} + a_1 + 32a_2 + 243a_3 + 1024a_4]$$
$$+ O(h^6). \tag{5.118}$$

To obtain an expression for f_0', we require that the coefficients of the higher-order derivatives vanish. To have an error of $O(h^4)$, it's sufficient to set $a_4 = 0$ and to choose the remaining coefficients such that

$$a_{-1} + a_1 + 4a_2 + 9a_3 = 0,$$
$$-a_{-1} + a_1 + 8a_2 + 27a_3 = 0,$$
$$a_{-1} + a_1 + 16a_2 + 81a_3 = 0. \tag{5.119}$$

With $a_{-1} = -3a_3$, $a_1 = 18a_3$, and $a_2 = -6a_3$, we find

$$f_0' = \frac{-3f_{-1} - 10f_0 + 18f_1 - 6f_2 + f_3}{12h} + O(h^4). \tag{5.120}$$

Similarly, we can—with some effort—find that

$$f_0'' = \frac{10f_{-1} - 15f_0 - 4f_1 + 14f_2 - 6f_3 + f_4}{12h^2} + O(h^4). \tag{5.121}$$

As you can see, this approach leads to a rather more complicated scheme. And we have yet to derive the finite difference equations themselves. Using these expressions for the derivatives, however, the difference equations are within sight. Note that there will be three distinct cases to be treated: 1) an endpoint, which is held constant; 2) a point adjacent to an endpoint, for which Equations 5.120 and 5.121 are used to derive the difference equation; and 3) points that are at least one point removed from an endpoint, for which the central difference approximations can be used to derive the appropriate difference equation.

EXERCISE 5.36
Modify your existing SOR program to use this higher-order approximation to solve Equation 5.105, subject to the boundary conditions of Equation 5.106. Note that the optimal acceleration parameter determined previously will not be optimal for this new situation, although it should be a reasonable value to use. What value of h was necessary to obtain results accurate to 4 significant digits?

Every physical situation is unique, but the general consensus is that the additional effort required for the higher-order approximations is usually not justified. On a coarse grid, they perform no better than the 3-pt rule, and for fine grids the extra level of accuracy can be more easily obtained by using Richardson extrapolation to "polish" the coarse results.

5.21 A Vibrating String

You probably recall that the vibration of a string, fixed at both ends and under uniform tension, is described by the differential equation

$$\frac{\partial^2 u(x,t)}{\partial t^2} = \frac{T}{\mu(x)} \frac{\partial^2 u(x,t)}{\partial x^2}, \tag{5.122}$$

where T is the tension in the string and $\mu(x)$ is the mass of the string per unit length. A standard way to solve this problem is *to guess a solution* of the form

$$u(x,t) = y(x)\tau(t) \tag{5.123}$$

and see if it works! After making the substitution and rearranging, we find that

$$\frac{1}{y(x)}\frac{T}{\mu(x)}\frac{d^2y}{dx^2} = \frac{1}{\tau(t)}\frac{d^2\tau}{dt^2}. \tag{5.124}$$

Now, the left side of this equation is a function of x alone, and the right side a function of t alone. The only way this relation can be valid for all x and t is for both sides of the equation to equal a constant, which we take to be $-\omega^2$. We then have the *two* equations

$$\frac{1}{\tau(t)}\frac{d^2\tau}{dt^2} = -\omega^2 \tag{5.125}$$

and

$$\frac{1}{y(x)}\frac{T}{\mu(x)}\frac{d^2y}{dx^2} = -\omega^2. \tag{5.126}$$

Multiplying Equation 5.125 by $\tau(t)$ we find the differential equation

$$\frac{d^2\tau}{dt^2} + \omega^2\tau = 0, \tag{5.127}$$

with solution

$$\tau(t) = a\sin\omega t + b\cos\omega t. \tag{5.128}$$

The constant ω, which we introduced in order to separate our two equations, is an angular frequency with units of radians/second, and is related to the simple frequency ν, having units cycles/second, by

$$\omega = 2\pi\nu. \tag{5.129}$$

In like manner, Equation 5.126 leads us to the equation

$$\frac{T}{\mu(x)}\frac{d^2y(x)}{dx^2} + \omega^2y(x) = 0. \tag{5.130}$$

This looks similar to the problems we've solved earlier, but with a crucial difference: *we don't know ω!*

For the moment, let's assume that μ is a constant, μ_o. Then the differential equation 5.130 can be written as

$$\frac{d^2y(x)}{dx^2} + \frac{\omega^2\mu_o}{T}y(x) = 0. \tag{5.131}$$

We recognize this equation, and know that its general solution is simply

$$y(x) = \alpha\sin\omega\sqrt{\frac{\mu_o}{T}}x + \beta\cos\omega\sqrt{\frac{\mu_o}{T}}x. \tag{5.132}$$

Now we impose the boundary conditions: the string is fixed at each end, i.e., $y(x) = 0$ at $x = 0$ and $x = L$. For $y(x)$ to be zero at $x = 0$, we must have that $\beta = 0$. And to ensure that $y(L) = 0$, we must have that

$$\sin \omega \sqrt{\frac{\mu_o}{T}} L = 0 \tag{5.133}$$

or that

$$\omega \sqrt{\frac{\mu_o}{T}} L = n\pi, \qquad n = 1, 2, \dots . \tag{5.134}$$

Thus only certain values of ω are possible, those for which

$$\omega = \frac{n\pi}{L} \sqrt{\frac{T}{\mu}}, \qquad n = 1, 2, \dots . \tag{5.135}$$

This is the expected result—a string vibrates at only certain frequencies, determined by the string's mass density μ, length L, and tension T.

   Imagine, for a moment, that we had not recognized the analytic solution to Equation 5.131. Could we have tried to solve it numerically? Of course we could, using the shooting method developed for finding the eigenvalues of the anharmonic quantum oscillator. $y(0)$ is fixed, and we'd make a reasonable guess for the derivative $y'(0)$. Then by making repeated guesses for k, in combination with a root finder, we'd find that k for which $y(L) = 0$.

EXERCISE 5.37

Consider a piano wire 1 meter long, of mass 0.954 grams, stretched with a tension of 1000 Newtons. Use the *shooting method* we've described to find the lowest eigenvalue of the vibrating string problem, e.g., the frequency of its fundamental note.

   This particular example is useful for purposes of illustration, but you already knew the answer. Consider a slightly different problem, one for which $\mu(x)$ *is not constant*. For example, the string might increase in thickness as you move along its length, so that its mass can be described by the expression

$$\mu(x) = \mu_0 + \left(x - \frac{L}{2} \right) \Delta. \tag{5.136}$$

μ_0 is the average mass density, and Δ is its variation per unit length.

EXERCISE 5.38

Reconsider the piano wire problem, with $\mu_0 = 0.954$ g/m and $\Delta = 0.5$ g/m^2. By how much does the fundamental frequency change, compared to the uniform string? Plot the shape of the string, $y(x)$, and compare to the sinusoidal shape of the string in the previous exercise.

5.22 Eigenvalues via Finite Differences

For problems involving one dimension, the shooting method is nearly always adequate in finding the solution to boundary value problems. However, the method is severely limited in two or more dimensions. The reason is simply that in one dimension the boundary condition is at a *point*, while in two dimensions, for example, the boundary is along a *curve*, i.e., an *infinite number of points*. If we are to solve multidimensional problems, then we must have an alternate method of solution. Such an alternate is obtained from the finite difference approach. In Chapter 7 this approach will be applied to two-dimensional problems; the presentation here will be in one dimension, to demonstrate how it proceeds.

Let's consider the nonuniform vibrating string problem we've investigated earlier. We'll solve for the displacement of the string f on a grid of $N + 1$ equally spaced x coordinates, indexed $i = 0, 1, \ldots, N$. Replacing the derivatives in Equation 5.130 by their finite difference approximations, we obtain the difference equations

$$\frac{T}{\mu_i} \frac{f_{i-1} - 2f_i + f_{i+1}}{h^2} + \omega^2 f_i = 0, \qquad i = 1, 2, \ldots, N - 1, \qquad (5.137)$$

for the $N-1$ (unknown) interior points; the endpoints are fixed, so that $f_0 = f_N = 0$. We can rewrite these equations as a single matrix equation, of the form

$$\begin{bmatrix} -2\dfrac{T}{\mu_1 h^2} & \dfrac{T}{\mu_1 h^2} & 0 & & & \\ \dfrac{T}{\mu_2 h^2} & -2\dfrac{T}{\mu_2 h^2} & \dfrac{T}{\mu_2 h^2} & & & \\ & \ddots & & \ddots & & \\ & & \dfrac{T}{\mu_{N-2} h^2} & -2\dfrac{T}{\mu_{N-2} h^2} & \dfrac{T}{\mu_{N-2} h^2} \\ & & & \dfrac{T}{\mu_{N-1} h^2} & -2\dfrac{T}{\mu_{N-1} h^2} \end{bmatrix} \begin{bmatrix} f_1 \\ f_2 \\ \vdots \\ f_{N-2} \\ f_{N-1} \end{bmatrix}$$

$$= \omega^2 \begin{bmatrix} f_1 \\ f_2 \\ \vdots \\ f_{N-2} \\ f_{N-1} \end{bmatrix}. \qquad (5.138)$$

Using matrix notation, we can write this as

$$\mathbf{A}\mathbf{x} = \lambda\mathbf{x}, \tag{5.139}$$

which we recognize as the matrix eigenvalue equation with eigenvalue $\lambda = \omega^2$. Eigenvalue equations are quite common in physics, appearing frequently and in many different contexts. Moving the right side of the equation to the left, we have

$$(\mathbf{A} - \lambda\mathbf{I})\mathbf{x} = 0, \tag{5.140}$$

where $\mathbf{I}$ is the identity matrix. Written in this form, we can now bring all the power of linear algebra to bear upon the problem. In particular, we know that the only way for this equation to have a solution, other than the trivial one $\mathbf{x} = 0$, is for the determinant of the coefficient matrix to be zero,

$$\det(\mathbf{A} - \lambda\mathbf{I}) = 0. \tag{5.141}$$

This is the *secular equation*. Those values of λ for which the determinant vanishes are the *eigenvalues* of the matrix $\mathbf{A}$.

For an arbitrary matrix $\mathbf{A}$, finding the eigenvalues can be a formidable task. When expanded, the determinant of an $N \times N$ matrix will be an N-th order polynomial in λ. For the example we've been investigating, however, the matrix $\mathbf{A}$ is tridiagonal and hence much simpler than the general problem. Let's write the matrix as

$$\mathbf{A} - \lambda\mathbf{I} = \begin{bmatrix} b_1 - \lambda & c_1 & & & & \\ a_2 & b_2 - \lambda & c_2 & & & \\ & a_3 & b_3 - \lambda & c_3 & & \\ & & \ddots & \ddots & \ddots & \\ & & & a_{N-1} & b_{N-1} - \lambda & c_{N-1} \\ & & & & a_N & b_N - \lambda \end{bmatrix}. \tag{5.142}$$

Because of the unique structure of the tridiagonal system, we can easily evaluate its determinant. Imagine that $\mathbf{A} - \lambda\mathbf{I}$ were a 1×1 matrix. Then its determinant, D_1, would simply be $b_1 - \lambda$. If it were 2×2, then

$$D_2 = (b_2 - \lambda)D_1 - a_2 c_1, \tag{5.143}$$

and if 3×3,

$$D_3 = (b_3 - \lambda)D_2 - a_3 c_2 D_1. \tag{5.144}$$

In general, we have the recurrence relation

$$D_j = (b_j - \lambda)D_{j-1} - a_j c_{j-1} D_{j-2}, \quad j = 3, \ldots, N. \tag{5.145}$$

After evaluating D_1 and D_2, Equation 5.145 can be used to generate all the determinants up to N, which is the determinant we want. If we combine a root search with the evaluation of the determinant, we obtain an eigenvalue solver for the tridiagonal system. An outline of the program investigating the frequencies of the nonuniform piano wire might look like the following:

```
% trieigen.m
% Code fragment to evaluate the fundamental frequency of
%   vibration of the nonuniform piano wire.

function trieigen
...
% Initialize a, b, and c.
x  = ...
% Note that there are (N+1) points, but the solution is already known
%   at the endpoints f(0) and f(N). (fixed boundary conditions)
nx = length(x);        % the number of INTERIOR points!
mu = mu0+(x-L/2.0)*delta;
a  = -T./(h*h*mu);
b  = -2*a;
c  = a;
lambda = TriEigen(a,b,c,nx);
% We actually want the frequency, which is the
%   square root of the eigenvalue lambda.
omega = sqrt(lambda);
...

function [Lambda] = TriEigen(a,b,c,n)
% This function searches DETER, as a function of LAMBDA,
%   for its first zero. One of the root-finding routines
%   from Chapter 2 should be used here.
...

function [determ] = deter(lambda,a,b,c,n)
determ = b(1) - lambda;
if(n ~= 1)
    d1 = determ;
    determ = (b(2)-lambda) * d1 - a(2)*c(1);
    if(n ~= 2)
        d2 = determ;
        for j = 3:n
            determ = (b(j)-lambda)*d2-a(j)*c(j-1)*d1;
            d1      = d2;
            d2      = determ;
        end
    end
end
```

EXERCISE 5.39

Fill in the missing pieces in this program, and use it to determine the fundamental frequency of vibration of the nonuniform piano wire. (Actually, it's always good practice to first test your program on a known problem. Thus, you might want to solve the problem with a uniform piano wire, to verify that your program is working correctly.)

5.23 The Power Method

Since an N-th order polynomial has N roots, there are N eigenvalues to an $N \times N$ matrix. And with each of these eigenvalues λ_j is associated an eigenvector $\mathbf{u}_j$, e.g.,

$$\mathbf{A}\mathbf{u}_j = \lambda_j \mathbf{u}_j, \qquad j = 1, 2, \ldots, N. \tag{5.146}$$

One of the simplest ways of finding eigenvalues and eigenvectors of a general matrix, at least conceptually, is the so-called *power method*. Let's begin with some arbitrary vector $\mathbf{x}$—such a vector can be written as a linear combination of eigenvectors,

$$\mathbf{x} = \sum_{j=1}^{N} a_j \mathbf{u}_j. \tag{5.147}$$

For convenience, we'll assume that the eigenvalues are ordered such that

$$|\lambda_1| > |\lambda_2| > \cdots > |\lambda_N|. \tag{5.148}$$

Now, let the matrix $\mathbf{A}$ multiply $\mathbf{x}$, with the result that

$$\mathbf{A}\mathbf{x} = \mathbf{A} \sum_{j=1}^{N} a_j \mathbf{u}_j$$

$$= \sum_{j=1}^{N} a_j \mathbf{A}\mathbf{u}_j$$

$$= \sum_{j=1}^{N} a_j \lambda_j \mathbf{u}_j. \tag{5.149}$$

Multiply both sides by $\mathbf{A}$ again, and then again, so that after m multiplications we have

$$\mathbf{A}^m \mathbf{x} = \sum_{j=1}^{N} a_j \lambda_j^m \mathbf{u}_j$$

$$= \lambda_1^m \left[a_1 \mathbf{u}_1 + \sum_{j=2}^{N} a_j \left(\frac{\lambda_j}{\lambda_1} \right)^m \mathbf{u}_j \right]. \tag{5.150}$$

Since λ_1 is the dominant (largest magnitude) eigenvalue, the magnitude of the ratio λ_j/λ_1 is less than one. As $m \to \infty$ this ratio tends to zero leaving only the first term,

$$\lim_{m \to \infty} \mathbf{A}^m \mathbf{x} = \lambda_1^m a_1 \mathbf{u}_1. \tag{5.151}$$

If we have some vector $\mathbf{y}$—and any vector that has some component of $\mathbf{u}_1$, the dominant eigenvector, will do—we can compute the scalar product $\mathbf{y}^T \mathbf{A}^m \mathbf{x}$. Taking the ratio of consecutive scalar products, we have

$$\lim_{m \to \infty} \frac{\mathbf{y}^T \mathbf{A}^{m+1} \mathbf{x}}{\mathbf{y}^T \mathbf{A}^m \mathbf{x}} = \lambda_1. \tag{5.152}$$

EXERCISE 5.40

Write a program implementing the power method to find the dominant eigenvalue of the matrix

$$\mathbf{A} = \begin{bmatrix} 2 & 1 \\ 1 & 0 \end{bmatrix}. \tag{5.153}$$

(As always, MATLAB makes problems like these very easy to program.) Almost any initial vector will work, some better than others. You might try

$$\mathbf{x} = \frac{1}{\sqrt{2}} \begin{bmatrix} 1 \\ 1 \end{bmatrix}. \tag{5.154}$$

You can use $\mathbf{y} = \mathbf{x}$ to approximate λ_1.

5.24 Eigenvectors

In many situations the eigenvalues—such as the frequencies of a vibration—are the primary quantities of interest. In these cases, we don't bother finding the eigenvector $\mathbf{x}$. (Note that in the shooting method, this is not an option; the eigenvector— the approximate $y(x)$—is always generated.) But in other cases, we might want to find the eigenvector. In the nonuniform piano wire problem, for example, it's important to discover that the solution is *not* simply a sine curve. This information is contained in the eigenvector.

Let's return to the discussion of the power method, and let $\mathbf{x}$ be a *normalized* vector so that

$$\mathbf{x}^T \mathbf{x} = 1. \tag{5.155}$$

Being normalized is not a requirement to being an eigenvector, but it's a desirable characteristic in that it can substantially simplify the analysis. Let's define a sequence of such normalized vectors, beginning with

$$\mathbf{x}^{(0)} = \mathbf{x}. \tag{5.156}$$

We then consider the product $\mathbf{A}\mathbf{x}^{(0)}$. The result of this multiplication will be a vector, but it will not be normalized. Let's normalize this vector, and call it $\mathbf{x}^{(1)}$,

$$\mathbf{x}^{(1)} = \frac{\mathbf{A}\mathbf{x}^{(0)}}{\sqrt{|\mathbf{A}\mathbf{x}^{(0)}|^2}}. \tag{5.157}$$

With this definition of $\mathbf{x}^{(1)}$, we thus have

$$\mathbf{A}\mathbf{x}^{(0)} = q^{(1)}\mathbf{x}^{(1)} \tag{5.158}$$

where

$$q^{(1)} = \sqrt{|\mathbf{A}\mathbf{x}^{(0)}|^2}. \tag{5.159}$$

We then consider $\mathbf{x}^{(2)}$ as the normalized vector resulting from the product $\mathbf{A}\mathbf{x}^{(1)}$, so that

$$\mathbf{A}\mathbf{x}^{(1)} = q^{(2)}\mathbf{x}^{(2)}, \tag{5.160}$$

and so on. The sequence of $q^{(m)}$ and $\mathbf{x}^{(m)}$ thus constructed tends toward the dominant eigenvalue and its eigenvector,

$$\lim_{m \to \infty} q^{(m)} = \lambda_1, \quad \text{and} \quad \lim_{m \to \infty} \mathbf{x}^{(m)} = \mathbf{u}_1. \tag{5.161}$$

EXERCISE 5.41
Write a program to calculate the normalized eigenvector associated with the dominant eigenvalue of the matrix

$$\mathbf{A} = \begin{bmatrix} 2 & 1 \\ 1 & 0 \end{bmatrix}. \tag{5.162}$$

To find the eigenvalue of smallest magnitude, we consider the *inverse power method*. If

$$\mathbf{A}\mathbf{u}_j = \lambda_j \mathbf{u}_j, \tag{5.163}$$

then we can multiply by $\lambda_j^{-1}\mathbf{A}^{-1}$ to find that

$$\mathbf{A}^{-1}\mathbf{u}_j = \lambda_j^{-1}\mathbf{u}_j. \tag{5.164}$$

That is, if $\mathbf{A}$ has eigenvalues λ_j and eigenvectors $\mathbf{u}_j$, the inverse of $\mathbf{A}$ has the same eigenvectors $\mathbf{u}_j$ but eigenvalues λ_j^{-1}. Then the eigenvalue of $\mathbf{A}$ having the smallest magnitude will be the dominant eigenvalue of $\mathbf{A}^{-1}$! To find that eigenvalue we use the same iteration scheme as before, but with $\mathbf{A}^{-1}$ in place of $\mathbf{A}$,

$$[\mathbf{A}^{-1}]\mathbf{z}^{(m)} = p^{(m+1)}\mathbf{z}^{(m+1)}, \tag{5.165}$$

where

$$\lim_{m\to\infty} p^{(m)} = \lambda_N^{-1}, \quad \text{and} \quad \lim_{m\to\infty} \mathbf{z}^{(m)} = \mathbf{u}_N. \qquad (5.166)$$

EXERCISE 5.42

Write a program to verify that

$$\mathbf{A}^{-1} = \begin{bmatrix} 0 & 1 \\ 1 & -2 \end{bmatrix} \qquad (5.167)$$

is the inverse of

$$\mathbf{A} = \begin{bmatrix} 2 & 1 \\ 1 & 0 \end{bmatrix}. \qquad (5.168)$$

Then calculate the eigenvalue of $\mathbf{A}$ having the *smallest* magnitude by using the power method to determine the eigenvalue of $\mathbf{A}^{-1}$ with the *largest* magnitude.

Rather than using the matrix inverse explicitly, the inverse power method can be implemented by recognizing that Equation 5.165 is equivalent to

$$\mathbf{A} \left[p^{(m+1)} \mathbf{z}^{(m+1)} \right] = \mathbf{z}^{(m)}. \qquad (5.169)$$

This is of the form

$$\mathbf{Ax} = \mathbf{b}, \qquad (5.170)$$

which we investigated earlier with regard to sets of linear equations. Knowing $\mathbf{A}$ and $\mathbf{z}^{(m)}$, Equation 5.169 can be solved for the unknown $p^{(m+1)}\mathbf{z}^{(m+1)}$, by Gaussian elimination for example. $p^{(m+1)}$ and $\mathbf{z}^{(m+1)}$ can then be found by requiring the vector to be normalized. This solution can then be used in the next iteration and the process repeated.

EXERCISE 5.43

Write a program implementing the inverse power method with Gaussian elimination to solve for the smallest magnitude eigenvalue of the matrix

$$\mathbf{A} = \begin{bmatrix} 2 & 1 \\ 1 & 0 \end{bmatrix}. \qquad (5.171)$$

Note that the inverse is never explicitly needed nor calculated.

The power method, or the inverse power method, can be very slow to converge and by itself is usually not particularly useful in finding eigenvalues. However, the method provides an extremely useful technique for finding *eigenvectors* if we already have a good approximation for the eigenvalue. Consider the eigenvalue equation

$$\mathbf{A}\mathbf{u}_j = \lambda_j \mathbf{u}_j. \tag{5.172}$$

If q is an approximation to λ_j, then we can subtract $q\mathbf{u}_j$ from both sides of the equation to yield

$$(\mathbf{A} - q\mathbf{I})\mathbf{u}_j = (\lambda_j - q)\mathbf{u}_j, \tag{5.173}$$

where $\mathbf{I}$ is the identity matrix. That is, any eigenvector of $\mathbf{A}$ is *also* an eigenvector of $(\mathbf{A} - q\mathbf{I})$. However, the *eigenvalue* of $(\mathbf{A} - q\mathbf{I})$ is $(\lambda_j - q)$, so that if q is a good approximation to λ_j, then $(\lambda_j - q)$ is nearly zero! If we now use the inverse power method to find the eigenvector of $(\mathbf{A} - q\mathbf{I})$, the algorithm should converge *very rapidly* since the dominant eigenvalue of $(\mathbf{A} - q\mathbf{I})^{-1}$ is very large—only a few iterations are needed to obtain a good eigenvector!

With the appropriate q, any eigenvalue λ_j can be shifted into the dominant position of $(\mathbf{A} - q\mathbf{I})$, so that this method can be used to find any eigenvector. If it should happen that $\mathbf{A}$ is tridiagonal, then the solution is further simplified and the subroutine TRISOLVE can be used to find the eigenvector.

EXERCISE 5.44

Consider the nonuniform piano wire again. Impose a grid on the problem, say every 0.1 m along its 1 meter length. Since the endpoints are fixed, that leaves 9 points along the wire. Solve for the lowest three frequencies, by searching for roots in the determinant. Then determine the eigenvectors associated with them.

EXERCISE 5.45

Whenever a grid is imposed upon a problem, the error associated with its imposition should be investigated—if you don't know how accurate your approximations are, what confidence can you have in your results? Investigate the discretization error by considering grids with spacing 0.5 m and 0.025 m, and compare to the result of the previous exercise. (Both the eigenvalue and eigenvector will differ.)

A coherent approach to obtaining eigenvectors and eigenvalues emerges when we combine the power method with the above scheme. For example, if we are interested in obtaining the real eigenvalues and eigenvectors of a real matrix, we can search for the roots of its determinant and count the number of sign changes in a certain range. We let the positions of the sign changes be eigenvalue guesses to a root solver function such as those discussed in Chapter 2. The Gaussian elimination function lusolve.m of Chapter 3 can be employed to obtain the determinant. It can also be used to perform all the matrix operations involved in obtaining the eigenvectors as well. One question remains: What range do we use to search for the determinant sign changes? The answer to this question is provided by the power method's ability to produce the smallest and largest eigenvalues. The search range is between and including those two extreme values.

EXERCISE 5.46

Write a computer program implementing this approach, and use it to solve for all the eigenvalues and eigenvectors of the matrix

$$A = \begin{bmatrix} 6 & 3 & 2 & 1 \\ 5 & 4 & 3 & 2 \\ 2 & 1 & 8 & 3 \\ 3 & 2 & 4 & 2 \end{bmatrix}. \tag{5.174}$$

● **5.25 Finite Elements**

In the finite difference approach, a few points were chosen at which the derivatives appearing in the differential equation were approximated by finite differences, and the resulting linear equations solved. The *finite element* method takes a different approach, approximating the exact solution by a (flexible) trial solution, and solving the resulting equations to find the "best" trial function. Both methods have their advantages; certainly, the finite difference approach is easy to understand and is straightforward to program. The finite element method, on the other hand, is a bit more difficult to grasp and to program, but frequently yields superior results for the same computational effort. In many areas of engineering, such as structural analysis, it has essentially replaced the finite difference method. Its use in physics is not presently widespread, but that circumstance is rapidly changing.

Let's begin by considering a simple differential equation, say

$$y'' - 6x = 0, \tag{5.175}$$

subject to the boundary conditions

$$y(0) = 0, \quad y(1) = 1. \tag{5.176}$$

(Clearly, the solution to this equation is $y = x^3$.) Let's guess a solution of the form

$$p(x) = \alpha x^2 + \beta x + \gamma. \tag{5.177}$$

Requiring $p(0) = 0$ and $p(1) = 1$, we find that

$$p(x) = \alpha x^2 + (1 - \alpha)x. \tag{5.178}$$

We now have a trial function, parameterized by α, that satisfies the boundary conditions of the problem. Of course, the true solution also satisfies the differential equation $y'' - 6x = 0$. If we were to substitute our trial solution $p(x)$ for $y(x)$, the left side of the differential equation would not be zero—unless we had happened to have guessed the exact solution! Rather, it would be some function

$$R = p'' - 6x = 2\alpha - 6x, \tag{5.179}$$

which we call the *residual error*. In the finite element method the parameters of the residual error—α in this case—are chosen so that this residual error is minimized (in some sense).

For example, we can consider the integral of the square of the error,

$$I = \int_0^1 R^2 \, dx \tag{5.180}$$

and minimize it with respect to α:

$$\frac{\partial I}{\partial \alpha} = 2 \int_0^1 R \frac{\partial R}{\partial \alpha} \, dx = 2 \int_0^1 (2\alpha - 6x)(2) \, dx = 0. \tag{5.181}$$

Evaluating the integral, we find

$$\alpha = \frac{3}{2}, \tag{5.182}$$

so that

$$p(x) = \frac{3x^2 - x}{2} \tag{5.183}$$

is the best quadratic approximation to the solution of the differential equation, in a least squares sense. This approximation is compared to the exact solution in Figure 5.17.

The basic advantage that the finite element method enjoys over the finite difference method is thus similar to the advantage that the least squares method has over Lagrange interpolation—rather than being overly concerned with point-by-point agreement with the exact solution, the finite element method achieves good overall agreement by forcing the integral of the error small.

To find a better solution to the differential equation we could use a higher-order polynomial for the trial function. Alternatively, we could use relatively low-order trial functions, and break the region of interest into smaller intervals. Both of these approaches are used, but as a practical matter we would rarely want to use higher than a 3rd-order trial function due to the spurious oscillations that occur with higher-order polynomials. Thus a primary avenue to greater accuracy is through using a larger number of intervals.

Let's consider an approximation that involves many intervals and is linear in each one, a *piecewise linear* trial function. A particularly elegant way to express

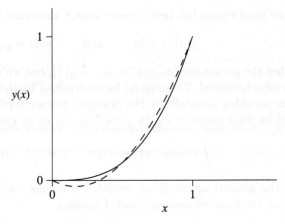

Figure 5.17 Comparison of the exact solution of $y'' - 6x = 0$ to a least squares finite element approximation.

this approximation is in terms of the *basis functions* ϕ_i, where

$$\phi_i(x) = \begin{cases} 0, & x \leq x_{i-1} \\ \dfrac{x - x_{i-1}}{x_i - x_{i-1}}, & x_{i-1} \leq x \leq x_i \\ \dfrac{x_{i+1} - x}{x_{i+1} - x_i}, & x_i \leq x \leq x_{i+1} \\ 0, & x_{i+1} \leq x. \end{cases} \tag{5.184}$$

Such a basis function is illustrated in Figure 5.18. (Does this remind you of linear interpolation?) An arbitrary piecewise linear trial function can then be written as

$$p(x) = \sum_{j=0}^{N} \alpha_i \phi_i(x), \tag{5.185}$$

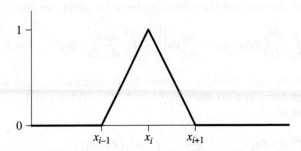

Figure 5.18 Plot of the basis function $\phi_i(x)$.

where the total region has been broken into N intervals. The requirement that

$$p(0) = y(0) \qquad \text{and} \qquad p(1) = y(1) \tag{5.186}$$

establishes the parameters $\alpha_0 = y(0)$, $\alpha_N = y(1)$, but we're left with $N - 1$ parameters to be determined. These could be determined by the method of least squares, but there are other possibilities. For example, we can require that the average error, weighted by some function w_i, be zero. That is, we can require that

$$\int R(x)w_i(x)\,dx = 0, \qquad i = 1, \ldots, N - 1. \tag{5.187}$$

This is the general approach of *weighted residuals*, and is the basis for several versions of the finite element method. Choosing

$$w_i(x) = \frac{\partial R}{\partial \alpha_i} \tag{5.188}$$

we recover the least squares method.

A particularly useful choice of weighting functions are the basis functions $\phi_i(x)$, which then leads to the so-called *Galerkin method,*

$$\int R(x)\phi_i(x) = 0, \qquad i = 1, \ldots, N - 1. \tag{5.189}$$

For our example problem, we have

$$\int_0^1 \left(\frac{d^2 p(x)}{dx^2} - 6x \right) \phi_i(x) = 0, \qquad i = 1, \ldots, N - 1. \tag{5.190}$$

Recall that $p(x)$ is piecewise linear, composed of a series of straight line segments. On each interval the slope is constant—and hence the second derivative is zero—but the slope changes from one interval to the next so that the second derivative is infinite at the endpoints of an interval. This would appear to be a problem, but it's only an illusion—the derivative *is* infinite, but we're only concerned with its *integral.* Integrating the offending term by parts, we have

$$\int_0^1 \frac{d^2 p}{dx^2} \phi_i(x)\,dx = \frac{dp}{dx}\phi_i \Big|_0^1 - \int_0^1 \frac{dp}{dx}\frac{d\phi_i}{dx}\,dx, \qquad i = 1, \ldots, N - 1, \tag{5.191}$$

so that we only need to evaluate finite quantities. And with our choice of basis, the first term is zero since $\phi_i(0) = \phi_i(1) = 0$ for $i = 1, \ldots, N - 1$. The remaining integral is

$$-\int_0^1 \frac{dp}{dx}\frac{d\phi_i}{dx}\,dx = -\sum_{j=0}^N \alpha_j \int_0^1 \frac{d\phi_j(x)}{dx}\frac{d\phi_i(x)}{dx}\,dx, \qquad i = 1, \ldots, N - 1. \tag{5.192}$$

One of the real advantages of using a standard basis set such as $\phi_j(x)$ is that we don't need to evaluate these integrals for every new problem. Rather, we can evaluate them *once*, and use those evaluations in subsequent problems. If the x_i are uniformly spaced between the limits a and b, with $h = x_i - x_{i-1}$, then

$$\int_a^b \frac{d\phi_i(x)}{dx} \frac{d\phi_j(x)}{dx} dx = \begin{cases} \dfrac{2}{h}, & |i-j| = 0, \\[2mm] -\dfrac{1}{h}, & |i-j| = 1, \\[2mm] 0, & |i-j| > 1. \end{cases} \tag{5.193}$$

Thus

$$\int_0^1 \frac{dp(x)}{dx} \frac{d\phi_i}{dx} dx = \sum_{j=0}^{N} \alpha_j \int_0^1 \frac{d\phi_j(x)}{dx} \frac{d\phi_i(x)}{dx} dx = \frac{-\alpha_{i-1} + 2\alpha_i - \alpha_{i+1}}{h}, \tag{5.194}$$

and Equation 5.190 becomes

$$\frac{\alpha_{i-1} - 2\alpha_i + \alpha_{i+1}}{h} - \int_0^1 6x\phi_i(x)\, dx = 0, \qquad i = 1, \dots, N-1. \tag{5.195}$$

In this example, the remaining integral can be performed analytically,

$$\int_0^1 x\phi_i(x)\, dx = hx_i, \qquad i = 1, \dots, N-1. \tag{5.196}$$

For other differential equations, or for a different choice of basis functions, it may be necessary to integrate such a term numerically. For the smoothly varying functions that commonly appear in these applications, Gauss-Legendre quadrature is often the method of choice.

With our evaluation of the integrals, Equation 5.195 thus becomes

$$\frac{\alpha_{i-1} - 2\alpha_i + \alpha_{i+1}}{h} = 6hx_i, \qquad i = 1, \dots, N-1. \tag{5.197}$$

This we recognize as one component of the matrix equation

$$\begin{bmatrix} -2 & 1 & & & \\ 1 & -2 & 1 & & \\ & \ddots & \ddots & \ddots & \\ & & 1 & -2 & 1 \\ & & & 1 & -2 \end{bmatrix} \begin{bmatrix} \alpha_1 \\ \alpha_2 \\ \vdots \\ \alpha_{N-2} \\ \alpha_{N-1} \end{bmatrix} = \begin{bmatrix} 6h^2 x_1 - \alpha_0 \\ 6h^2 x_2 \\ \vdots \\ 6h^2 x_{N-2} \\ 6h^2 x_{N-1} - \alpha_N \end{bmatrix}. \tag{5.198}$$

This tridiagonal system can now be solved with the familiar subroutine TRISOLVE for the unknown α_i.

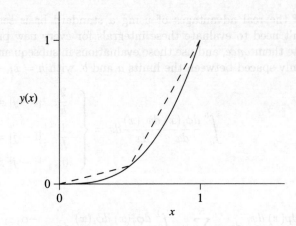

Figure 5.19   Comparison of the exact solution of $y'' - 6x = 0$ to a two-interval piecewise linear approximation obtained with the Galerkin finite element method.

Choosing $N = 2$ leads to the single equation $\alpha_1 = 0.125$, yielding the piecewise linear approximation appearing in Figure 5.19. As we would expect, this result is not as accurate as the quadratic least squares approximation. However, it's relatively easy to improve the result by using more intervals in the piecewise approximation.

EXERCISE 5.47

Use a piecewise linear approximation (that is, use the basis functions of Equation 5.184) over 10 intervals to better approximate the solution to the differential equation. Plot the result, comparing the approximation to the exact solution.

5.26 An Eigenvalue Problem

The finite element method can also be applied to eigenvalue problems. While the derivation of the equations to be solved differs substantially from the derivation with finite differences, the resulting equations are quite similar in appearance. This is unfortunate, in that the principles underlying the two approaches are really quite different.

Let's investigate the vibrating string problem, governed by the differential equation

$$\frac{d^2y}{dx^2} + \frac{\omega^2 \mu(x)}{T} y = 0, \tag{5.199}$$

and approximate $y(x)$ by the piecewise linear approximation

$$p(x) = \sum_{j=0}^{N} \alpha_j \phi_j(x). \tag{5.200}$$

α_0 and α_N are again set by the boundary conditions, $y(0) = y(L) = 0$, so that $\alpha_0 = \alpha_N = 0$. The remaining $N-1$ coefficients α_i are determined from the Galerkin condition,

$$\int_0^L R(x)\phi_i(x)\, dx = 0, \qquad i = 1, \ldots, N-1, \tag{5.201}$$

where the residual error is

$$R(x) = \frac{d^2 p}{dx^2} + \frac{\omega^2 \mu(x)}{T} p. \tag{5.202}$$

Thus the α_i satisfy

$$\int_0^L \left[\frac{d^2 p}{dx^2} + \frac{\omega^2 \mu}{T} p \right] \phi_i\, dx = 0, \qquad i = 1, \ldots, N-1. \tag{5.203}$$

We'll again use integration by parts to evaluate the integral of the second derivative,

$$\int_0^L \frac{d^2 p}{dx^2} \phi_i(x)\, dx = \left. \frac{dp}{dx} \phi_i \right|_0^L - \int_0^L \frac{dp}{dx} \frac{d\phi_i}{dx}\, dx, \qquad i = 1, \ldots, N-1. \tag{5.204}$$

Due to the choice of basis functions, the first term is zero. We now express $p(x)$ in terms of $\phi_j(x)$ and find that the Galerkin condition becomes

$$-\sum_{j=0}^N \alpha_j \int_0^L \frac{d\phi_j}{dx} \frac{d\phi_i}{dx} + \sum_{j=0}^N \alpha_j \frac{\omega^2}{T} \int_0^L \mu(x) \phi_j(x) \phi_i(x)\, dx = 0, \qquad i = 1, \ldots, N-1. \tag{5.205}$$

The first integral we've already done, with the result that

$$-\sum_{j=0}^N \alpha_j \int_0^L \frac{d\phi_j}{dx} \frac{d\phi_i}{dx} = \frac{-\alpha_{i-1} + 2\alpha_i - \alpha_{i+1}}{h}. \tag{5.206}$$

Let's approximate $\mu(x)$ by it's value at x_i, μ_i. Then

$$\int_0^L \mu(x) \phi_j(x) \phi_i(x)\, dx \approx \mu_i \int_0^L \phi_j(x) \phi_i(x)\, dx, \qquad i = 1, \ldots, N-1. \tag{5.207}$$

We again note that the necessary integrals involving the basis functions $\phi_i(x)$ can be performed once, and subsequently used whenever needed. Using the explicit expression for the basis functions, we find

$$\int_0^L \phi_j(x) \phi_i(x)\, dx = \begin{cases} 0, & |i-j| > 1, \\[2mm] \dfrac{h}{6}, & |i-j| = 1, \\[2mm] \dfrac{2h}{3}, & |i-j| = 0. \end{cases} \tag{5.208}$$

We could do a better job of approximating this integral, if we chose. To illustrate, we'll leave $\mu(x)$ arbitrary and evaluate the integral by Gaussian quadrature. Recall that an n-point quadrature is exact for polynomials up to order $(2n-1)$. Since the basis functions are linear, a two-point Gaussian quadrature will yield exact results for a linear μ. There are three cases, $j = i-1, i, i+1$. For the first case, the product $\phi_{i-1}\phi_i$ is zero everywhere except on the interval between x_{i-1} and x_i, so that

$$\int_0^L \mu(x)\phi_{i-1}(x)\phi_i(x)\,dx = \int_{x_{i-1}}^{x_i} \mu(x)\phi_{i-1}(x)\phi_i(x)\,dx$$

$$= \int_{x_{i-1}}^{x_i} \mu(x)\left(\frac{x_i - x}{h}\right)\left(\frac{x - x_{i-1}}{h}\right)\,dx \qquad (5.209)$$

$$= \frac{h}{2}\int_{-1}^{1} \mu\left(x_{i-1} + \frac{h}{2}(y+1)\right)\frac{1}{2}(1-y)\frac{1}{2}(1+y)\,dy,$$

where we've made the substitution

$$y = \frac{2}{h}(x - x_{i-1}) - 1. \qquad (5.210)$$

The integral is now in the form required for Gauss-Legendre integration. Using only a two-point quadrature, we have

$$\int_0^L \mu(x)\phi_{i-1}(x)\phi_i(x)\,dx \approx \frac{h}{12}\left[\mu\left(x_{i-1} + \frac{h}{2}\left(1 - \frac{1}{\sqrt{3}}\right)\right)\right.$$

$$\left. + \mu\left(x_{i-1} + \frac{h}{2}\left(1 + \frac{1}{\sqrt{3}}\right)\right)\right]. \qquad (5.211)$$

Clearly, the case $j = i+1$ will proceed in a nearly identical manner. For the case $j = i$, both the intervals $x_{i-1} \leq x \leq x_i$ and $x_i \leq x \leq x_{i+1}$ need to be considered. Since the basis functions change radically from one interval to the next, while Gauss-Legendre integration presumes a smoothly varying integrand, the two intervals should be considered separately. But we see that performing these integrals, either analytically or numerically, is easily accomplished.

Let's return to our simplified evaluation of the integrals, as given in Equation 5.208. The Galerkin conditions of Equation 5.205 then read

$$\frac{-\alpha_{i-1} + 2\alpha_i - \alpha_{i+1}}{h} + \frac{\omega^2\mu_i}{T}\left[\alpha_{i-1}\frac{h}{6} + \alpha_i\frac{2h}{3} + \alpha_{i+1}\frac{h}{6}\right] = 0, \ i = 1, 2, \ldots, N-1.$$

$$(5.212)$$

The comparison of this equation with its finite difference counterpart, Equation 5.137, is rather interesting. The equations appear rather similar—certainly, the derivatives appear in the same fashion. But note that the term in the brackets represents a weighted average of the α's, with exactly the same coefficients as obtained in Simpson's rule integration! Where the finite difference method simply has a function evaluation, the finite element method has the *average* of the function, as evaluated by integrating over the neighboring intervals!

We can write these equations in matrix form as

$$
\begin{bmatrix}
-2\dfrac{T}{\mu_1 h^2} & \dfrac{T}{\mu_1 h^2} & 0 \\[2mm]
\dfrac{T}{\mu_2 h^2} & -2\dfrac{T}{\mu_2 h^2} & \dfrac{T}{\mu_2 h^2} \\[2mm]
 & \ddots & \ddots & \ddots \\[2mm]
 & & \dfrac{T}{\mu_{N-2} h^2} & -2\dfrac{T}{\mu_{N-2} h^2} & \dfrac{T}{\mu_{N-2} h^2} \\[2mm]
 & & & \dfrac{T}{\mu_{N-1} h^2} & -2\dfrac{T}{\mu_{N-1} h^2}
\end{bmatrix}
\begin{bmatrix}
\alpha_1 \\ \alpha_2 \\ \vdots \\ \alpha_{N-2} \\ \alpha_{N-1}
\end{bmatrix}
$$

$$
= \frac{\omega^2}{6}
\begin{bmatrix}
4 & 1 \\
1 & 4 & 1 \\
 & \ddots & \ddots & \ddots \\
 & & 1 & 4 & 1 \\
 & & & 1 & 4
\end{bmatrix}
\begin{bmatrix}
\alpha_1 \\ \alpha_2 \\ \vdots \\ \alpha_{N-2} \\ \alpha_{N-1}
\end{bmatrix}. \tag{5.213}
$$

In matrix notation, we write this as

$$
\mathbf{Ax} = \lambda \mathbf{Bx}, \tag{5.214}
$$

the *generalized* eigenvalue problem. If we're seeking the smallest eigenvalue, then a modified version of the inverse iteration method can be used. And since the problem is tridiagonal, we can again use TRISOLVE in its solution.

We begin with an initial $\mathbf{x}^{(0)}$, and evaluate the product $\mathbf{Bx}^{(0)}$. Then TRISOLVE is used to solve the equation

$$
\mathbf{Ax}^{(1)} = (\mathbf{Bx}^{(0)}) \tag{5.215}
$$

for the unknown (and unnormalized) $\mathbf{x}^{(1)}$. In general, the iteration proceeds according to

$$
\mathbf{Ax}^{(k)} = \mathbf{Bx}^{(k-1)}. \tag{5.216}
$$

Note that the normalization of $\mathbf{x}^{(k)}$ and $\mathbf{x}^{(k-1)}$ is not the same.

The generalized eigenvalue equation itself provides an exact expression for the eigenvalue in terms of the eigenvector. Multiplying Equation 5.214 by $\mathbf{x}^T$, we have

$$
\mathbf{x}^T \mathbf{Ax} = \lambda \mathbf{x}^T \mathbf{Bx}, \tag{5.217}
$$

or

$$\lambda = \frac{\mathbf{x}^T \mathbf{A} \mathbf{x}}{\mathbf{x}^T \mathbf{B} \mathbf{x}}. \tag{5.218}$$

With this hint, we define the *Rayleigh Quotient* as

$$R = \frac{\mathbf{x}^{(k)^T} \mathbf{A} \mathbf{x}^{(k)}}{\mathbf{x}^{(k)^T} \mathbf{B} \mathbf{x}^{(k)}}. \tag{5.219}$$

As $k \to \infty$, $R \to \lambda$. In practice, the iteration is terminated when two successive iterations agree to within some predetermined tolerance. Of course, the vector needs to be renormalized after every iteration. However, rather than requiring $\mathbf{x}^T \mathbf{x} = 1$, in this problem we require a different type of normalization,

$$\mathbf{x}^T \mathbf{B} \mathbf{x} = 1. \tag{5.220}$$

An appropriate program then looks like

```
% finitelement.m
% Fragment to solve the vibrating piano wire problem for constant
%    linear density using the finite element method.

function finitelement
tolerance = 1.e-5;
L   = 1.0;
mu0 = 0.954e-3;
T   = 1000.0;
n   = 11;
nx  = n+2;
h   = L/(nx-1);
% Initialize a, b, and c.
mu = mu0 + zeros(n); % The case when mu = constant
a  = -T./(h*h*mu);
b  = -2.0*a;
c  = a;
% X0 is x(k-1) --- initially, elements are just 1/sqrt(N)
X0 = ones(1,n)/sqrt(n);
count = 0;
% Initializing for the first pass --- let X1 be A x(0).
%    (This is ONLY for the first pass!!!)
X1(1) = b(1) * X0(1) + c(1) * X0(2);
for i = 2: n-1
    X1(i) = a(i)*X0(i-1) + b(i)*X0(i) + c(i)*X0(i+1);
end
X1(n) = a(n) * X0(n-1) + b(n) * X0(n);

% This is the top of the iteration loop.
```

```
% Evaluate x(k-1) * [ A x(k-1) ] --- result in UP
done = false;
while done==false
    up = X0*X1';
    % Evaluate the product [ B x(k-1) ], store in X1
    X1(1) = (4.0*X0(1)+ X0(2) )/6.0;
    for i = 2: n-1
        X1(i) = (X0(i-1)+4.0*X0(i)+X0(i+1))/6.0;
    end
    X1(n) = (X0(n-1)+4.0*X0(n))/6.0;
    % Evaluate x(k-1) B x(k-1), the denominator
    down = X0*X1';
    % Renormalize the vector in X1
    X1 = X1/sqrt(down);
    % Compute the Rayleigh quotient, UP/DOWN, and iterate until
    %    accurate result is obtained.
    if (count ~= 0)
        error = (up/down - quotient) / (up/down);
        if ( abs(error) <= tolerance), done = true; end
    end
    quotient = up/down;
    count = count + 1;
    fprintf('approximate eigenvalue =%10.4g\n',quotient)
    % Solve the tridiagonal system for X0, the next
    %    approximate eigenvector.
    [X0] = trisolve(a,b,c,X1,n); % numeric solution
end
omega = sqrt(quotient); %  calculate the frequency
freq  = omega/pi/2;
fprintf('Omega=%7.2f, Simple frequency =%7.2f\n',omega,freq)
```

EXERCISE 5.48

Verify that the finite element program we've presented does in fact solve the vibrating string problem. Then modify the program to consider 20 intervals in the piecewise linear approximation, rather than 10, and compare your results.

EXERCISE 5.49

Consider the second string problem, with $\mu(x) = \mu_o + (x - L/2)\Delta$. You will need to evaluate the integrals involving $\mu(x)$—you should be able to do these analytically. What's the fundamental frequency of the vibration? How does this result compare—at the same N—to the finite difference result?

EXERCISE 5.50

Integrals should be performed analytically whenever possible. However, situations arise in which numerical evaluations are justified. Replace the analytic evaluation of integrals in your program by two-point Gauss-Legendre integration. Verify that your replacement is correct by comparing results with the previous exercise. Then, consider a different density function,

$$\mu(x) = \mu_0 + \Delta(x - L/2)^2. \tag{5.221}$$

What is the fundamental frequency of vibration? What is the shape of the string, compared to the two other strings we've been investigating?

5.27 References

Many of the topics discussed in this chapter are routinely covered in Numerical Analysis texts. There are many excellent ones to choose from, the following is just a brief list of the ones we particularly like.

Forman S. Acton, *Numerical Methods That Work,* Harper & Row, New York, 1970. This book is particularly commendable with regard to Acton's philosophy toward computation.

Anthony Ralston, *A First Course in Numerical Analysis,* McGraw–Hill, New York, 1965.

Richard L. Burden and J. Douglas Faires, *Numerical Analysis,* 8th Edition, Thomson Brooks/Cole, Belmont, CA, 2005.

Curtis F. Gerald and Patrick O. Wheatley, *Applied Numerical Analysis,* Addison–Wesley, Reading, MA, 1989.

J. Stoer and R. Bulirsch, *Introduction to Numerical Analysis,* Springer–Verlag, New York, 1980. This text is not as introductory as the title suggests, but it is an excellent reference.

A particularly engaging account of the origins of chaos and stability, including the contributions of Poincaré and a discussion of the Pythagorean 3-body problem, is contained in

Florin Diacu and Philip Holmes, *Celestial Encounters,* Princeton University Press, Princeton, NJ, 1996.

We also recommend

Ivars Peterson, *Newton's Clock: Chaos in the Solar System,* W. H. Freeman and Company, New York, 1993.

For those interested in the music of stringed instruments, *The Journal of the Catgut Acoustical Society* is highly recommended. There are, of course, several texts on "the physics of music," including

Thomas D. Rossing, *The Science of Sound,* Addison–Wesley, Reading, MA, 1990.

Arthur H. Benade, *Fundamentals of Musical Acoustics,* Oxford University Press, New York, 1976.

6

Fourier Analysis

By now, we have all come to appreciate the power and usefulness of the Taylor series, which allows us to expand (most) continuous functions in an infinite series of terms. While Taylor series expressions are very useful in general, there are two situations for which they are not well suited. The first is for periodic functions—the Taylor series utilizes a unique point, about which the series is expanded. But in a periodic function, equivalent points lie just one period away. This inherent property of a periodic function is simply not taken into account in the Taylor series. The second situation that causes problems is in describing a function with discontinuities—Taylor's series requires the function, and *all* of its derivatives, to exist. These requirements result from the derivation of Taylor's series from the Laurent series, which in turn involves the analyticity of the function in the complex plane. Since analyticity is a global property, it's not surprising that the derived Taylor series requires all those derivatives. So the Taylor series can never be used to describe a function with jumps, or even with jumps in some derivative.

In modern terms, the difficulty actually lies in the concept of a *function* itself. Euler had an elementary view, that a function should be representable by a smoothly drawn curve. This is in significant contrast to the modern concept, which simply associates each member of a set $\{x\}$ with an element of the set $\{f(x)\}$. And bridging the gap lies the work of Fourier, Cauchy, and Riemann. While Cauchy and Riemann were primarily mathematicians, Fourier belonged to that element of the French school that believed mathematics should be applied to real-world problems— indeed, modern methods of analysis are deeply dependent upon the work of Fourier, including a sizable chunk of physics.

6.1 The Fourier Series

Both Euler and d'Alembert had solved the "vibrating string" problem using two arbitrary functions, while Daniel Bernoulli had found a solution in terms of an infinite series of trigonometric functions. Since the trigonometric functions seemed to imply a periodic solution, Bernoulli's solution appeared less general. Fourier's contribution was the idea that any function can be expressed in the form

$$f(t) = \frac{a_0}{2} + \sum_{n=1}^{\infty} a_n \cos nt + \sum_{n=1}^{\infty} b_n \sin nt. \tag{6.1}$$

Clearly, this expansion can describe periodic functions. And in contrast to the Taylor series, a Fourier series can be used to describe a discontinuous function, or a function with discontinuous derivatives. Jean Baptiste Joseph Fourier (1768–1830), a teacher of mathematics at the École Normale and the École Polytechnique in Paris and an administrator under Napoleon Bonaparte, submitted an essay on the mathematical theory of heat to the French Academy of Science in 1812. Although he won the Academy prize, the essay was criticized for a certain looseness of reasoning by the panel of referees, Lagrange, Laplace, and Legendre. Lagrange, in particular, did not believe that the series converged! It was not until 1828 that Dirichlet found the mathematically *sufficient* conditions that can be imposed upon the function to ensure convergence, but it is not known if they are *necessary*. And even then, the series may not converge to the value of the function from which it is derived!

Dirichlet's Theorem: *If $f(t)$ is periodic of period 2π, if for $-\pi < t < \pi$ the function $f(t)$ has a finite number of maximum and minimum values and a finite number of discontinuities, and if $\int_{-\pi}^{\pi} f(t)\,dt$ is finite, then the Fourier series converges to $f(t)$ at all points where $f(t)$ is continuous, and at jump-points it converges to the arithmetic mean of the right-hand and left-hand limits of the function.*

In passing, we note that Bernhard Riemann tried to make Dirichlet's conditions less constraining, only to be led down the path leading toward a new definition of the integral: the Riemann integral of conventional calculus. Along the way, he showed that a function $f(x)$ may be integrable and not have a Fourier series representation. The famous Russian mathematician and physicist Andrey Kolmogorov constructed an integrable function with a Fourier series divergent almost everywhere—at the advanced age of 19.

For our purposes, we'll assume that the Fourier series converges for any problem of interest to us; any that are not convergent should promptly be marked *pathological* and sent to the nearest Department of Applied Mathematics.

At a fundamental level, the Fourier series works because the sines and cosines form a complete set, so that they may be used to describe *any* function, and because they are orthogonal on any 2π interval. Equation 6.1 is actually a statement of completeness; the orthogonality is expressed by

$$\int_{-\pi}^{\pi} \sin mt \sin nt \, dt = \begin{cases} \pi\delta_{m,n}, & m \neq 0, \\ 0, & m = 0, \end{cases} \tag{6.2}$$

$$\int_{-\pi}^{\pi} \cos mt \cos nt \, dt = \begin{cases} \pi \delta_{m,n}, & m \neq 0, \\ 2\pi, & m = n = 0, \end{cases} \tag{6.3}$$

$$\int_{-\pi}^{\pi} \sin mt \cos nt \, dt = 0, \quad \text{all integral } m \text{ and } n. \tag{6.4}$$

Using these orthogonality relations, we can easily find that the coefficients are derived from the function by

$$a_n = \frac{1}{\pi} \int_{-\pi}^{\pi} f(t) \cos nt \, dt, \tag{6.5}$$

and

$$b_n = \frac{1}{\pi} \int_{-\pi}^{\pi} f(t) \sin nt \, dt. \tag{6.6}$$

As an example, consider the unit step function

$$f(t) = \begin{cases} -1, & t < 0 \\ 1, & t > 0. \end{cases} \tag{6.7}$$

Since the function is odd, all the a_n must be zero. The b_n are easily found to be

$$\begin{aligned} b_n &= \frac{1}{\pi} \int_{-\pi}^{0} (-1) \sin nt \, dt + \frac{1}{\pi} \int_{0}^{\pi} (+1) \sin nt \, dt \\ &= \frac{2}{\pi} \int_{0}^{\pi} \sin nt \, dt \\ &= \frac{2}{n\pi} [1 - \cos n\pi] \\ &= \begin{cases} 0, & n = 2, 4, 6, \ldots \\ 4/n\pi, & n = 1, 3, 5, \ldots \end{cases} \end{aligned} \tag{6.8}$$

In practice, only a finite number of terms are included in the Fourier series expansion of a function. Since the sines and cosines form an orthogonal set, our remarks made in Chapter 3 concerning approximation by orthogonal functions apply. In particular, we know that these coefficients provide the best possible fit to the original function, in a least squares sense. As more terms are retained in the series, the fit becomes even better. A sequence of such approximations is shown in Figure 6.1.

As the number of terms increases, the approximation does a better and better job of describing the function. Where the function is continuous, the approximations oscillate about the true values of the function, and as more terms are retained the oscillations decrease in magnitude. At the discontinuity, the approximation gives the mean value of the left and right limits of the function, just as Dirichlet

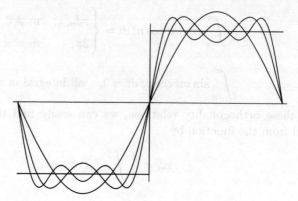

Figure 6.1   Convergence of the Fourier series representation of a unit step function, retaining 1, 2, and 3 terms in the series.

said it would. But near the discontinuity, the oscillations are not decreasing as rapidly as elsewhere. This is called the *overshoot*, and in some sense is the price we pay for being able to describe the discontinuity at all. (Remember, Taylor's series is virtually useless in such situations.) One might think that as more terms are retained in the series, the overshoot would disappear, but that's not the case.

EXERCISE 6.1

Examine the overshoot as the number of terms in the series increases. Evaluate the approximation, and hence the overshoot, in the vicinity of the discontinuity, $0 \leq t \leq 0.1$, retaining 10, 20, 30, 40, and 50 terms in the series. The persistence of the overshoot is known as the Gibbs phenomena.

As another example, consider the function

$$f(t) = |t|, \quad -\pi \leq t \leq \pi. \tag{6.9}$$

Because this function is even, its Fourier series representation will contain only cosine terms, e.g., all the b_n are zero.

EXERCISE 6.2

Evaluate the coefficients of the Fourier series of $f(t) = |t|$. Investigate the convergence of the series by plotting the approximation on the interval $-\pi \leq t \leq \pi$ using N terms, with $N = 2, 4, 6, 8$, and 10. For comparison, plot the original function as well. How rapidly does this series converge, compared to the series describing the unit step function?

While much of our work will be with real functions, the concept of Fourier series is applicable to complex functions as well. And sometimes, it's simply more convenient to use a complex representation. Expressing the sines and cosines as exponentials, Equation 6.1 can be rewritten as

$$f(t) = \sum_{n=-\infty}^{\infty} c_n e^{int} \tag{6.10}$$

in which

$$c_n = \begin{cases} (a_n - ib_n)/2, & n > 0, \\ a_0/2, & n = 0, \\ (a_{|n|} + ib_{|n|})/2, & n < 0. \end{cases} \tag{6.11}$$

The c_n's can, of course, be obtained by integration,

$$c_n = \frac{1}{2\pi} \int_{-\pi}^{\pi} f(t)e^{-int}\, dt. \tag{6.12}$$

6.2 The Fourier Transform

Closely related to the idea of the Fourier series representation of a function is the Fourier Transform of a function. The series representation is useful in describing functions over a limited region, or on the infinite interval $(-\infty, \infty)$ if the function is periodic. Fourier transforms, on the other hand, are useful in describing nonperiodic functions on the infinite interval.

To develop the transform, let's first consider the series representation of a function that is periodic on the interval $[-T, T]$. Making the substitution $t \to \pi t/T$, we have

$$f(t) = \sum_{n=-\infty}^{\infty} c_n e^{in\pi t/T} \tag{6.13}$$

where

$$c_n = \frac{1}{2T} \int_{-T}^{T} f(t)e^{-in\pi t/T}\, dt. \tag{6.14}$$

We can now identify the discrete frequencies appearing in the summations as being

$$\omega = \frac{n\pi}{T}, \tag{6.15}$$

and the differences between successive frequencies as being

$$\Delta\omega = \frac{\pi}{T}. \tag{6.16}$$

Then the series can be written as

$$f(t) = \sum_{n=-\infty}^{\infty} c_n e^{in\Delta\omega t} \tag{6.17}$$

where

$$c_n = \frac{\Delta\omega}{2\pi} \int_{-T}^{T} f(t)e^{-in\Delta\omega t}\, dt. \tag{6.18}$$

We now define

$$c_n = \frac{\Delta\omega}{\sqrt{2\pi}} g(n\Delta\omega), \tag{6.19}$$

so that

$$g(n\Delta\omega) = \frac{1}{\sqrt{2\pi}} \int_{-T}^{T} f(t)e^{-in\Delta\omega t}\, dt \tag{6.20}$$

and

$$f(t) = \frac{1}{\sqrt{2\pi}} \sum_{n=-\infty}^{\infty} \Delta\omega\, g(n\Delta\omega)\, e^{in\Delta\omega t}. \tag{6.21}$$

We now take the limit as $T \to \infty$. In so doing, $n\Delta\omega$ becomes the continuous variable ω and the summation in Equation 6.21 becomes an integral. Thus

$$f(t) = \frac{1}{\sqrt{2\pi}} \int_{-\infty}^{\infty} g(\omega)e^{i\omega t}\, d\omega \tag{6.22}$$

and

$$g(\omega) = \frac{1}{\sqrt{2\pi}} \int_{-\infty}^{\infty} f(t)e^{-i\omega t}\, dt. \tag{6.23}$$

We now *define* $g(\omega)$ to be the Fourier transform of $f(t)$,

$$\mathcal{F}[f(t)] = g(\omega) = \frac{1}{\sqrt{2\pi}} \int_{-\infty}^{\infty} f(t)e^{-i\omega t}\, dt, \tag{6.24}$$

and $f(t)$ to be the *inverse* transform of $g(\omega)$,

$$\mathcal{F}^{-1}[g(\omega)] = f(t) = \frac{1}{\sqrt{2\pi}} \int_{-\infty}^{\infty} g(\omega)e^{i\omega t}\, d\omega. \tag{6.25}$$

According to our definitions, the factor of 2π is distributed symmetrically between the transform and its inverse. This is only a convention, and one that (unfortunately) is not followed universally. Furthermore, there's nothing *special* or *distinguishing* about our choice of time as being the "original" variable—ω could just as easily have been chosen, in which case the definitions of transform and inverse transform would be reversed. Whatever convention is chosen, you must of course remain consistent. Considerable caution should be exercised concerning these points in order to avoid confusion and (potentially) a great loss of time and effort.

EXERCISE 6.3
Write a program to numerically evaluate the Fourier transform of the function

$$f(t) = \begin{cases} a(1 - a|t|), & |t| < \dfrac{1}{a} \\ 0, & |t| > \dfrac{1}{a}, \end{cases}$$

with $a = 10$, for both positive and negative values of ω, using Romberg integration. Perform the analytic integrals to check your numerical work.

EXERCISE 6.4
Consider the function of the previous exercise. To help visualize the transform, to see which frequencies are most important, and to see how the transform depends upon the original function, evaluate the transform of the function with $a = 2, 4, 6, 8$, and 10. In general, the Fourier transform is a complex quantity, but for this function you should find that it is strictly real. Plot $g(\omega)$.

6.3 Properties of the Fourier Transform

There's considerable symmetry in the Fourier transform pair, and they possess several fundamental properties that are significant. From a formal point of view, perhaps the most fundamental property is that the Fourier transform is linear. That is, if $f_1(t)$ and $f_2(t)$ are two functions having Fourier transforms $g_1(\omega)$ and $g_2(\omega)$, then the Fourier transform of $f_1(t) + f_2(t)$ is

$$\begin{aligned} g(\omega) &= \frac{1}{\sqrt{2\pi}} \int_{-\infty}^{\infty} [f_1(t) + f_2(t)]\, e^{-i\omega t}\, dt \\ &= \frac{1}{\sqrt{2\pi}} \int_{-\infty}^{\infty} f_1(t) e^{-i\omega t}\, dt + \frac{1}{\sqrt{2\pi}} \int_{-\infty}^{\infty} f_2(t) e^{-i\omega t}\, dt \\ &= g_1(\omega) + g_2(\omega). \end{aligned} \tag{6.26}$$

Another property is the scaling relation. Let's imagine that $f(t)$ and $g(\omega)$ are Fourier transforms of one another. For α positive,

$$\mathcal{F}[f(\alpha t)] = \frac{1}{\sqrt{2\pi}} \int_{-\infty}^{\infty} f(\alpha t)e^{-i\omega t}\, dt$$

$$= \frac{1}{\sqrt{2\pi}} \frac{1}{\alpha} \int_{-\infty}^{\infty} f(t')e^{-i\omega t'/\alpha}\, dt'$$

$$= \frac{1}{\alpha} g\left(\frac{\omega}{\alpha}\right), \quad \alpha > 0, \tag{6.27}$$

where the substitution $t' = \alpha t$ was made. But if α is negative, the limits of integration are reversed. Consider α to be negative, so that $\alpha = -a < 0$. Then

$$\mathcal{F}[f(\alpha t)] = \mathcal{F}[f(-at)] = \frac{1}{\sqrt{2\pi}} \int_{-\infty}^{\infty} f(-at)e^{-i\omega t}\, dt. \tag{6.28}$$

With the substitution $t' = -at$, we find

$$\mathcal{F}[f(\alpha t)] = \frac{1}{\sqrt{2\pi}} \frac{-1}{a} \int_{\infty}^{-\infty} f(t')e^{i\omega t'/a}\, dt'$$

$$= \frac{1}{\sqrt{2\pi}} \frac{1}{a} \int_{-\infty}^{\infty} f(t')e^{-i(-\omega/a)t'}\, dt'$$

$$= \frac{1}{a} g\left(\frac{-\omega}{a}\right)$$

$$= \frac{1}{-\alpha} g\left(\frac{\omega}{\alpha}\right), \quad \alpha < 0. \tag{6.29}$$

These results can be combined to yield the general expression

$$\mathcal{F}[f(\alpha t)] = \frac{1}{|\alpha|} g\left(\frac{\omega}{\alpha}\right). \tag{6.30}$$

EXERCISE 6.5
Show that there's a similar relation for inverse transforms,

$$\mathcal{F}^{-1}[g(\beta\omega)] = \frac{1}{|\beta|} f\left(\frac{t}{\beta}\right). \tag{6.31}$$

Equations 6.27 and 6.31 are known as *scaling* relations, and provide a key insight into the Fourier transform pair. In Exercise 6.4, you found that as $f(t)$ became broader, $g(\omega)$ became narrower. The essence of this behavior is contained in these scaling relations. Consider $f(\alpha t)$, such as in Figure 6.2. As α is increased, the function becomes narrower in time. Simultaneously, its Fourier transform becomes broader in frequency!

Let's investigate this further and consider a simple example function: the sine function. With only one frequency component, it extends over all of space. If another sine function of the appropriate frequency is added to the first, the sum can be made to cancel in some regions of space while in other regions they will add. With only a few sine and cosine functions, we're limited in what shapes can be reproduced— as with the unit step function, a few terms will give the correct general shape, but the approximation will have oscillations about the true value of the function. Many terms are needed in order to cancel all the oscillations and give an accurate representation of the function, so that an arbitrary function can be described. That's the essence of Fourier convergence—in large part, the role of the additional functions is to cancel the oscillations. Thus, the more localized a function is in time, the more delocalized it is in frequency.

This is more than a casual observation—it's a fundamental property of Fourier transforms, and has direct physical consequences. Usually stated in terms of position and momentum rather than time and frequency, the statement is that the product of the width of the function, Δx, and the width of the transform of the function, Δp, is always greater than or equal to a specific *nonzero* value, $\hbar$—Heisenberg's Uncertainty Principle.

There are also *shifting* relations. For example, the Fourier transform of $f(t - t_0)$ is simply

$$\mathcal{F}[f(t - t_0)] = \frac{1}{\sqrt{2\pi}} \int_{-\infty}^{\infty} f(t - t_0)e^{-i\omega t}\, dt$$

$$= \frac{1}{\sqrt{2\pi}} \int_{-\infty}^{\infty} f(\tau)e^{-i\omega(\tau + t_0)}\, d\tau$$

$$= e^{-i\omega t_0} \frac{1}{\sqrt{2\pi}} \int_{-\infty}^{\infty} f(\tau)e^{-i\omega \tau}\, d\tau$$

$$= e^{-i\omega t_0} g(\omega), \qquad\qquad (6.32)$$

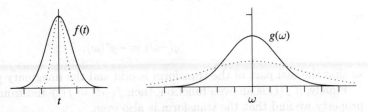

Figure 6.2   The function $f(t)$ and its Fourier transform $g(\omega)$ are plotted by the solid lines. As f is scaled to become narrower, as indicated by the dotted curve, g becomes broader.

where we introduced the variable $\tau = t - t_0$. Likewise, we have the inverse relation

$$\mathcal{F}^{-1}[g(\omega - \omega_0)] = e^{i\omega_0 t} f(t).$$ (6.33)

Time reversal can also be of interest; using the substitution $t = -\tau$, we have

$$\mathcal{F}[f(-t)] = \frac{1}{\sqrt{2\pi}} \int_{-\infty}^{\infty} f(-t) e^{-i\omega t}\, dt$$

$$= \frac{1}{\sqrt{2\pi}} \int_{\infty}^{-\infty} f(\tau) e^{-i\omega(-\tau)}\, (-d\tau)$$

$$= \frac{1}{\sqrt{2\pi}} \int_{-\infty}^{\infty} f(\tau) e^{-i(-\omega)\tau}\, d\tau$$

$$= g(-\omega).$$ (6.34)

Additional properties of the transform pair are associated with particular symmetries of $f(t)$. Consider the relation

$$g(\omega) = \frac{1}{\sqrt{2\pi}} \int_{-\infty}^{\infty} f(t) e^{-i\omega t}\, dt$$ (6.35)

and its complex conjugate

$$g^*(\omega) = \frac{1}{\sqrt{2\pi}} \int_{-\infty}^{\infty} f^*(t) e^{i\omega t}\, dt.$$ (6.36)

If $f(t)$ is *purely real*, then

$$g^*(\omega) = \frac{1}{\sqrt{2\pi}} \int_{-\infty}^{\infty} f(t) e^{-i(-\omega)t}\, dt = g(-\omega).$$ (6.37)

That is, the *real part* of the transform is an even function while the *imaginary part* is odd. Conversely, if $f(t)$ is *purely imaginary*, then

$$g^*(\omega) = -\frac{1}{\sqrt{2\pi}} \int_{-\infty}^{\infty} f(t) e^{-i(-\omega)t}\, dt = -g(-\omega),$$ (6.38)

or

$$g(-\omega) = -g^*(\omega),$$ (6.39)

so that the real part of the transform is odd and the imaginary part is even!

Finally, if $f(t)$ is an even function, then $f(-t) = f(t)$ and from the time reversal property we find that the transform is also even,

$$g(-\omega) = g(\omega).$$ (6.40)

Table 6.1 Symmetry Properties of the Fourier Transform

If $f(t)$ is real,	then $\Re g(\omega)$ is even and $\Im g(\omega)$ is odd;
if $f(t)$ is imaginary,	then $\Re g(\omega)$ is odd and $\Im g(\omega)$ is even;
if $f(t)$ is even,	then $g(\omega)$ is even;
if $f(t)$ is odd,	then $g(\omega)$ is odd;
if $f(t)$ is real and even,	then $g(\omega)$ is real and even;
if $f(t)$ is real and odd,	then $g(\omega)$ is imaginary and odd;
if $f(t)$ is imaginary and even,	then $g(\omega)$ is imaginary and even;
if $f(t)$ is imaginary and odd,	then $g(\omega)$ is real and odd.

Likewise, if $f(t)$ is odd then

$$g(-\omega) = -g(\omega). \tag{6.41}$$

These results are summarized in Table 6.1.

Since derivatives and differential equations play such a central role in physics, we can anticipate a need to calculate the Fourier transform of a derivative such as

$$\mathcal{F}[f'(t)] = \frac{1}{\sqrt{2\pi}} \int_{-\infty}^{\infty} f'(t) e^{-i\omega t} \, dt. \tag{6.42}$$

Integrating by parts, we find

$$\mathcal{F}[f'(t)] = \frac{e^{-i\omega t}}{\sqrt{2\pi}} f(t) \Big|_{-\infty}^{\infty} + \frac{i\omega}{\sqrt{2\pi}} \int_{-\infty}^{\infty} f(t) e^{-i\omega t} \, dt. \tag{6.43}$$

$f(t)$ must vanish as $t \to \pm\infty$, else the Fourier transform $g(\omega)$ will not exist; as a consequence, the first term is evaluated as zero, and we find that

$$\mathcal{F}[f'(t)] = i\omega g(\omega), \tag{6.44}$$

so the Fourier transform of a derivative is easy to evaluate. We'll use this very important property later, in the solution of partial differential equations.

There are some interesting integral relations associated with Fourier transforms as well. For example, consider the Fourier transform

$$g(\omega) = \frac{1}{\sqrt{2\pi}} \int_{-\infty}^{\infty} f(t) e^{-i\omega t} \, dt \tag{6.45}$$

and its inverse

$$f(t) = \frac{1}{\sqrt{2\pi}} \int_{-\infty}^{\infty} g(\omega') e^{i\omega' t} \, d\omega'. \tag{6.46}$$

Note that the variable of integration has been changed to ω'—since it doesn't appear in the evaluated integral, any symbol can be used. Substituting the second expression into the first, we find

$$g(\omega) = \frac{1}{\sqrt{2\pi}} \int_{-\infty}^{\infty} \left[\frac{1}{\sqrt{2\pi}} \int_{-\infty}^{\infty} g(\omega')e^{i\omega' t}\, d\omega' \right] e^{-i\omega t}\, dt$$

$$= \int_{-\infty}^{\infty} \left[\frac{1}{2\pi} \int_{-\infty}^{\infty} e^{i(\omega' - \omega)t}\, dt \right] g(\omega')\, d\omega', \qquad (6.47)$$

or

$$g(\omega) = \int_{-\infty}^{\infty} \delta(\omega' - \omega)g(\omega')\, d\omega', \qquad (6.48)$$

where we've introduced the *Dirac delta function*

$$\delta(\omega' - \omega) = \frac{1}{2\pi} \int_{-\infty}^{\infty} e^{i(\omega' - \omega)t}\, dt. \qquad (6.49)$$

Equation 6.48 is not your typical equation, and you might expect that $\delta(\omega - \omega')$ is not an ordinary function—and you'd be right. To get some idea of what it is, consider the related expression

$$\delta_\tau(\omega - \omega') = \frac{1}{2\pi} \int_{-\tau}^{\tau} e^{i(\omega - \omega')t}\, dt = \frac{\sin\,(\omega - \omega')\tau}{\pi(\omega - \omega')}. \qquad (6.50)$$

This *is* an ordinary function and is plotted in Figure 6.3. In the limit that $\tau \to \infty$, it would seem that $\delta_\tau(\omega - \omega') \to \delta(\omega - \omega')$. For $\omega - \omega' \approx 0$, we have

$$\delta_\tau(\omega - \omega') = \frac{\sin\,(\omega - \omega')\tau}{\pi(\omega - \omega')} \approx \frac{1}{\pi(\omega - \omega')} \left[\tau(\omega - \omega') - \frac{\tau^3(\omega - \omega')^3}{3!} + \cdots \right]$$

$$\approx \frac{\tau}{\pi} - \frac{\tau^3}{3!\pi}(\omega - \omega')^2 + \cdots, \qquad (6.51)$$

so that $\delta_\tau(0) = \tau/\pi$. Thus, as $\tau \to \infty$, we find the function to be larger and larger in magnitude. Meanwhile, the function drops to zero on either side of the origin at $\omega - \omega' \approx \pm\pi/\tau$—judging the width of the function to be the distance between these points, we find it to be $2\pi/\tau$. Thus the magnitude of the function increases linearly with τ while the width is inversely related to τ. The product of height and width, a crude estimate of the area, is a constant!

We can also obtain the integral of the delta function itself. Equation 6.48 is an identity, and so must be true for any function—in particular, it's true for $g(\omega) = 1$ so that

$$\int_{-\infty}^{\infty} \delta(\omega - \omega')\, d\omega' = 1. \qquad (6.52)$$

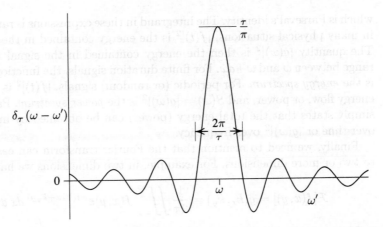

Figure 6.3   A plot of $\delta_\tau(\omega - \omega')$. The height of the function is proportional to τ while the width is inversely proportional to τ. As τ increases, the area under the curve remains (approximately) constant while the curve itself becomes more sharply peaked about $\omega' \approx \omega$.

Thus the integral of the delta function over all ω' is one. And yet, according to Equation 6.49

$$\delta(0) = \infty. \tag{6.53}$$

This is rather strange behavior for a function. In fact, the delta function is not a function at all in the usual sense. Technically, it's a *distribution*, and only has meaning when in appears in an integrand, as in Equation 6.48. Because of its unique characteristics, the Dirac delta has particular significance in several areas of physics, most notably in quantum mechanics.

Another integral of interest is

$$I = \int_{-\infty}^{\infty} f_1^*(t) f_2(t) \, dt. \tag{6.54}$$

Writing $f_1(t)$ and $f_2(t)$ in terms of their Fourier transforms, we find

$$
\begin{aligned}
I &= \int_{-\infty}^{\infty} \left[\frac{1}{\sqrt{2\pi}} \int_{-\infty}^{\infty} g_1(\omega) e^{i\omega t} \, d\omega \right]^* \left[\frac{1}{\sqrt{2\pi}} \int_{-\infty}^{\infty} g_2(\omega') e^{i\omega' t} \, d\omega' \right] dt \\
&= \iint_{-\infty}^{\infty} g_1^*(\omega) g_2(\omega') \left[\frac{1}{2\pi} \int_{-\infty}^{\infty} e^{i(\omega' - \omega)t} \, dt \right] d\omega \, d\omega' \\
&= \iint_{-\infty}^{\infty} g_1^*(\omega) g_2(\omega') \delta(\omega' - \omega) \, d\omega \, d\omega' \\
&= \int_{-\infty}^{\infty} g_1^*(\omega) g_2(\omega) \, d\omega,
\end{aligned}
\tag{6.55}
$$

which is Parseval's identity. The integrand in these expressions is rather important—in many physical situations, $|f(t)|^2$ is the energy contained in the signal at time t. The quantity $|g(\omega)|^2$ is then the energy contained in the signal in the frequency range between ω and $\omega + d\omega$. For finite duration signals, the function $S(\omega) = |g(\omega)|^2$ is the *energy spectrum*. For periodic (or random) signals, $|f(t)|^2$ is usually a rate of energy flow, or power, and $S(\omega) = |g(\omega)|^2$ is the *power spectrum*. Parseval's identity simply states that the total energy (power) can be obtained by integrating $|f(t)|^2$ over time or $|g(\omega)|^2$ over frequency.

Finally, we need to mention that the Fourier transform can easily be extended to two or more dimensions. For example, in two dimensions we have

$$\mathcal{F}[f(x,y)] = g(k_x, k_y) = \frac{1}{2\pi} \iint_{-\infty}^{\infty} f(x,y)e^{-i(k_x x + k_y y)}\, dx\, dy, \qquad (6.56)$$

and in three dimensions

$$\mathcal{F}[f(x,y,z)] = g(k_x, k_y, k_z)$$

$$= \left(\frac{1}{2\pi}\right)^{\frac{3}{2}} \iiint_{-\infty}^{\infty} f(x,y,z)e^{-i(k_x x + k_y y + k_z z)}\, dx\, dy\, dz. \qquad (6.57)$$

Using vector notation, this expression is also recognized as being

$$\mathcal{F}[f(\vec{r})] = g(\vec{k}) = \left(\frac{1}{2\pi}\right)^{\frac{3}{2}} \int f(\vec{r})e^{-i\vec{k}\cdot\vec{r}}\, d\vec{r}, \qquad (6.58)$$

where the integration extends over all of space. And of course, a function can depend upon time as well as space, so that we might have

$$\mathcal{F}[f(\vec{r},t)] = g(\vec{k},\omega) = \left(\frac{1}{2\pi}\right)^{2} \int f(\vec{r},t)e^{-i(\vec{k}\cdot\vec{r}+\omega t)}\, d\vec{r}\, dt, \qquad (6.59)$$

where the integration extends over all time as well as over all of space.

6.4 The Discrete Fourier Transform

Now, let's imagine that we have a physical quantity that's a function of time, and that we measure that quantity in increments Δt. As a result, we have $f(m\Delta t)$, $m = 0, 1, \ldots, N-1$. The Fourier transform $g(\omega)$ is given by the integral

$$g(\omega) = \frac{1}{\sqrt{2\pi}} \int_{-\infty}^{\infty} f(t)e^{-i\omega t}\, dt. \qquad (6.60)$$

Since we have the measurements $f(m\Delta t)$, the integral can be performed numerically, by the trapezoid rule for example. But there are some problems. First, we didn't take any data points before we started taking data. That is, *we don't have data before t=0!* And we don't have *continuous* data, but only data at the times $m\Delta t$! Oops. Maybe this isn't going to be so easy, after all.

Under these conditions, *we cannot calculate the (true) Fourier Transform*—we simply don't have enough to work with! All is not lost, however—we can calculate something that *resembles* the Fourier transform and is extremely useful in many cases. We'll assume that we took data for a sufficiently long time T that all the interesting behavior is contained in the data available. Recalling how we developed the Fourier transform from the Fourier series, we'll retrace the steps of our reasoning to develop a discrete representation of the data. That is, we'll *approximate* the Fourier transform of the true data over an infinite range by something like a Fourier series representation of the actual data, on the interval $0 < t < T$.

The complex representation of the Fourier series on the interval $0 < t < T$ can be written as

$$f(t) = \sum_{n=-\infty}^{\infty} c_n e^{i2\pi nt/T}, \qquad (6.61)$$

with the coefficients given by the integral

$$c_n = \frac{1}{T} \int_0^T f(t) e^{-i2\pi nt/T} \, dt. \qquad (6.62)$$

Note that this representation of the function is periodic with period T. With the goal of making this look more like a Fourier transform, let's define

$$\Delta\omega = \frac{2\pi}{T}. \qquad (6.63)$$

We then approximate the integral by the trapezoid rule, and define the *Discrete Fourier Transform* as

$$g(n\Delta\omega) = \sum_{m=0}^{N-1} f(m\Delta t) e^{-in\Delta\omega m\Delta t} = \sum_{m=0}^{N-1} f(m\Delta t) e^{-i2\pi mn/N}. \qquad (6.64)$$

Since we only have N known quantities, the data taken at N times, we can only determine the transform at N frequencies. Since the $\Delta\omega$ is fixed, the largest frequency we can consider is $(N-1)\Delta\omega$. (Actually, we can only consider frequencies half this large—more on this later.) So the DFT will fail, i.e., give a poor representation, for any function that actually possesses these higher frequencies.

Evaluating the inverse transform is not trivial. Since we have only N frequencies to work with, the summation in the inverse transform can contain only N terms. But it's not obvious that simply truncating the summation of Equation 6.61 is appropriate, or that to do so would not introduce significant error—after all, the trapezoid integration is only accurate to $O(h)$! But in fact, we can find an exact inversion procedure based on the idea of orthogonality. We are acquainted with the idea that functions can be orthogonal to one another, in the sense of performing an integration. They can also be orthogonal in the sense of a summation!

Consider the sum

$$S_N = \sum_{k=0}^{N-1} e^{ik\alpha}. \tag{6.65}$$

If $\alpha = 0$, then every term in the sum is 1 and $S_N = N$. But what if $\alpha \neq 0$? To evaluate the sum, consider the geometric sequence $1, r, r^2, \ldots$. The sum of the first N terms is

$$\sum_{k=0}^{N-1} r^k = r^0 + r^1 + \cdots + r^{N-1} = \frac{1 - r^N}{1 - r}, \tag{6.66}$$

since

$$(1 - r) \sum_{k=0}^{N-1} r^k = r^0 + r^1 + \cdots + r^{N-1} - (r^1 + r^2 + \cdots + r^N) = 1 - r^N. \tag{6.67}$$

But if we let $r = e^{i\alpha}$, Equation 6.66 is just

$$\sum_{k=0}^{N-1} e^{ik\alpha} = \frac{1 - e^{i\alpha N}}{1 - e^{i\alpha}} = S_N. \tag{6.68}$$

In order to generate an orthogonality relation, we need to find a way to force S_N to be zero if $\alpha \neq 0$. We can do this by simply requiring that

$$e^{i\alpha N} = 1,$$

or that

$$\alpha = 2\pi l/N \tag{6.69}$$

with l an integer. This makes $1 - e^{i\alpha N}$, and hence S_N, zero. We can then write

$$\sum_{k=0}^{N-1} e^{i2\pi kl/N} = \begin{cases} N, & l = 0, \\ 0, & l \neq 0. \end{cases} \tag{6.70}$$

We now express l as the difference between the two integers m and n, and find our orthogonality relation

$$\sum_{k=0}^{N-1} e^{i2\pi km/N} e^{-i2\pi kn/N} = N\delta_{m,n}. \tag{6.71}$$

Returning to the DFT given by Equation 6.64, we multiply both sides by $e^{i2\pi kn/N}$ and sum over n to find

$$\sum_{n=0}^{N-1} g(n\Delta\omega)e^{i2\pi kn/N} = \sum_{n=0}^{N-1}\sum_{m=0}^{N-1} f(m\Delta t)e^{-i2\pi mn/N}e^{i2\pi kn/N}$$

$$= \sum_{m=0}^{N-1} f(m\Delta t) \sum_{n=0}^{N-1} e^{-i2\pi mn/N}e^{i2\pi kn/N}$$

$$= \sum_{m=0}^{N-1} f(m\Delta t)N\delta_{k,m}$$

$$= Nf(k\Delta t). \tag{6.72}$$

The *Inverse Discrete Fourier Transform* is then given as

$$f(m\Delta t) = \frac{1}{N}\sum_{n=0}^{N-1} g(n\Delta\omega)e^{i2\pi mn/N}. \tag{6.73}$$

The similarity between the discrete Fourier transforms and the Fourier series or Fourier transforms is unmistakable. However, they are not identical; for example, the DFT uses only finite summations in its evaluations, albeit with particular times and frequencies. These three relations should be thought of as being distinct, although they clearly share a common ancestry.

When making a direct comparison between the Fourier Transform and the DFT, we also need to recognize that they have been normalized differently. That is, the factor Δt—coming from the trapezoid rule integration—is absent in the actual definition of the DFT of Equation 6.64, as is the $\sqrt{2\pi}$, which is included in the definition of the Fourier Transform, Equation 6.60. As a result, letting $\mathcal{F}[f(t)]$ denote the Fourier Transform and $DFT[f(t)]$ the Discrete Fourier Transform, we have

$$\mathcal{F}[f(t)] = \frac{\Delta t}{\sqrt{2\pi}} DFT[f(t)]. \tag{6.74}$$

For the inverse transforms, we have

$$\mathcal{F}^{-1}[g(\omega)] = \frac{\sqrt{2\pi}}{\Delta t} iDFT[g(\omega)], \tag{6.75}$$

where $iDFT$ denotes the inverse Discrete Fourier Transform. Note that these relationships apply only to our definitions—other definitions are possible. However, the numerical factors will always be inverses of one another.

EXERCISE 6.6

Write a program to evaluate the DFT of the function

$$f(t) = \begin{cases} a(1 - a|t|), & |t| < \dfrac{1}{a} \\ 0, & |t| > \dfrac{1}{a}, \end{cases}$$

with $a = 10$ and $N = 100$. At what values of ω can the transform be evaluated? Compare your results to the numerical and analytical Fourier transforms.

6.5 The Fast Fourier Transform

Although the discrete Fourier transform has considerable computational advantages over the Fourier transform, it is still a computationally intensive operation. With N data points, there will be on the order of N operations performed in each summation. And, of course, this only yields one data point in ω-space. To evaluate all the $g(m\Delta\omega)$, we'll need to perform N summations, for a total of N^2 operations. So, if we double the number of points, we quadruple the effort necessary to perform the calculation. And should we move to two dimensions, the effort goes to order N^4. Don't ask about three dimensions.

Fourier analysis is a powerful tool in mathematical physics, but as we've indicated, it's very intensive computationally. Its present status as a premier tool of the computational physicist is due to the existence of a streamlined calculational procedure, the *fast Fourier transform*. This algorithm has apparently been independently discovered, or rediscovered, by many investigators, but Cooley and Tukey are generally credited for the discovery, being the first to discuss the algorithm in detail and to bring it to the attention of the general scientific community. Perhaps the clearest explanation of the algorithm, however, is due to Danielson and Lanczos. If N is an even number, then we can write the DFT as a sum over even-numbered points and a sum over odd-numbered points:

$$g(n\Delta\omega) = \sum_{m=0}^{N-1} f(m\Delta t)e^{-i2\pi mn/N}$$

$$= \sum_{m=0,2,\dots}^{N-1} f(m\Delta t)e^{-i2\pi mn/N} + \sum_{m=1,3\dots}^{N-1} f(m\Delta t)e^{-i2\pi mn/N}$$

$$= \sum_{j=0}^{N/2-1} f(2j\Delta t)e^{-i2\pi 2jn/N} + \sum_{j=0}^{N/2-1} f((2j+1)\Delta t)e^{-i2\pi(2j+1)n/N}, \quad (6.76)$$

where we've let $m = 2j$ in the first term (even points), and $m = 2j + 1$ in the second term (odd points). But this is simply

$$g(n\Delta\omega) = \sum_{j=0}^{N/2-1} f(2j\Delta t)e^{-i2\pi jn/(N/2)}$$

$$+ e^{-i2\pi n/N} \sum_{j=0}^{N/2-1} f((2j+1)\Delta t)e^{-i2\pi jn/(N/2)}$$

$$= g_{even}(n\Delta\omega) + e^{-i2\pi n/N}g_{odd}(n\Delta\omega), \tag{6.77}$$

where we've recognized that the sums are themselves DFT's, with half as many points, over the original even- and odd-numbered points. The original calculation of the DFT was to take on the order of N^2 operations, but this decomposition shows that it actually only requires $2 \times (N/2)^2$ operations! But there's no reason to stop here—each of these DFT's can be decomposed into even and odd points, and so on, as long as they each contain an even number of points. Let's say that $N = 2^k$—then after k steps, there will be N transforms to be evaluated, each containing only one point! The total operation count is thus *not* on the order of N^2, but rather on the order of $N\log_2 N$! If N is a large number, the difference is quite significant. The fast Fourier transform is *fast!* (A collateral advantage, often overlooked, is that it is also more accurate. Since the FFT performs significantly fewer mathematical operations than does the DFT, roundoff error is also significantly less.)

The coding of the FFT is a little complicated, due to the even/odd interweaving that must be done. However, rather than discuss the Cooley-Tukey algorithm itself, let's think about Equation 6.77. Whenever a calculation is stated in this manner, the problem is crying out for a recursive solution. An FFT function might be structured something like

```
function [A]=fft_R(A,m)
% This function performs the Fast Fourier Transform by Recursion.
%
% The array A contains the complex data to be transformed and 'm' is
% log2(N). The variables A(1), u, w, t are complex.
%
% This function computes the Fast Fourier Transform of the input data
% and returns it in the same array. Note that the t's and omega's are
% related in the following way:
%
%    IF      Omega = range of omega's   and    T = range of t's
%    THEN    delta-omega = 2 pi / T     and     delta-t = 2 pi / Omega
%
% When the transform is evaluated, it is assumed that the input data is
% periodic. The output is therefore periodic (you have no choice in this).
% Thus, the transform is periodic in omega-space, with the first N/2 points
```

```
% being 'most significant'. The second N/2 points are the same as the
% Fourier transform at negative omega!!! That is,
%
% FFT(N+1-i) = FFT(-i) ,i = 1,2,....,N/2
%
N = 2^m;
Nd2 = N/2;
if(N==1)
    %  A[1] = A[1];    % don't need to do anything
else
    even = zeros(1,Nd2);  % Data
    odd  = zeros(1,Nd2);  % Data

    for k = 1:Nd2
        even(k) = A(k+k-1);
        odd(k) = A(k+k );
    end
    q = zeros(1,Nd2);  % Data
    r = zeros(1,Nd2);  % Data
    q = fft_R(even, m-1);
    r = fft_R( odd, m-1);

    for k = 1:Nd2
        ang = -2*(k-1)*pi/N;
        ck = complex(cos(ang), sin(ang));
        A( k  ) = q(k)+ck*r(k);
        A(k+Nd2) = q(k)-ck*r(k);
    end
end
```

However, the FFT is such a stalwart of computational science, you can be sure that there's an excellent implementation available for any modern computer language, and MATLAB is certainly no exception. In its simplest form, the FFT is invoked by

```
%  TestFFT.m
%  This is just a little program to test the FFT.
%
function TestFFT
N=8;
for i = 1:N
    a(i)=0;
end
a(3) = 1.;
b = fft(a)
```

The inverse transform is available through the function ifft. Be aware that normalization is always an issue. That is, there's a factor of N that can be associated with either the forward or inverse transform, and there's no established convention on where it should be. As a result, comparing results across different computer languages can sometimes be misleading.

The FFT has some interesting properties that are not particularly obvious. For example, if T is the range of t-values, then the spacing of the ω-values is

$$\Delta\omega = \frac{2\pi}{T}. \tag{6.78}$$

Likewise, if Ω is the range of ω-values, then

$$\Delta t = \frac{2\pi}{\Omega}. \tag{6.79}$$

And, of course, $T = N\Delta t$ and $\Omega = N\Delta\omega$. When the transform is evaluated, it is assumed that the input data is periodic. The output is therefore periodic (you have no choice in this). Thus, the transform is periodic in ω-space, with the first $N/2$ points being "most significant." The second $N/2$ points are the same as the Fourier transform at negative ω!!! That is,

```
FFT(N+1-i) = FFT(-i), i = 1, 2,...., N/2
```

EXERCISE 6.7

Verify that the TestFFT code performs correctly and that the recursive version returns the same results as the MATLAB version. What should the results be? Note that, as often happens when doing numerical work, the computer might give you a number like 10^{-17} where you had expected to find a zero.

Since the FFT is, essentially, just a speedy version of the DFT, the remarks made earlier concerning the direct comparison between the Fourier Transform and the Discrete Fourier Transform apply to the FFT as well.

EXERCISE 6.8

Write a program to evaluate the FFT of the function

$$f(t) = \begin{cases} a(1 - a|t|), & |t| < \dfrac{1}{a} \\ 0, & |t| > \dfrac{1}{a}, \end{cases}$$

with $a = 10$. For the FFT (as presented here) N must be a power of 2, $N = 64$, for example. As with the DFT, the values of ω are then fixed. Compare your results to analytic results for the Fourier Transform obtained earlier. (Accounting for the differences in normalization, of course.)

EXERCISE 6.9

Verify that the symmetry relations between the Fourier pair $f(t)$ and $g(\omega)$, Table 6.1, apply for the Fast Fourier Transform as well.

6.6 Life in the Fast Lane

The development of the Fast Fourier Transform is one of the most significant achievements ever made in the field of numerical analysis. This is due to i) the fact that the Fourier transform is found in a large number of diverse areas, such as electronics, optics, and quantum mechanics, and hence is extremely important, and ii) the FFT is *fast*. For our present purposes, we will consider the sampling of some function at various time steps—the Fourier transform will then be in the frequency domain. Such an analysis is sometimes referred to as being an harmonic analysis, or a function is said to be synthesized (as in electronic music generation).

Earlier, we noted that while it appeared that the highest frequency used in the DFT (or the FFT) was $(N-1)\Delta\omega$, the highest frequency actually used is only half that. The reason is quite simple: while $f(t)$ is periodic in time, $g(\omega)$ is periodic in frequency! (This is obvious, after the fact, since the exponential functions used in the DFT are themselves periodic.) Then the frequencies from $N\Delta\omega/2$ up to $(N-1)\Delta\omega$ are actually the negative frequencies from $-N\Delta\omega/2$ up to $-\Delta\omega$! This frequency, $\omega_{Nyquist} = N\Delta\omega/2$ is called the *Nyquist frequency*, and has a very clear physical basis. Let's imagine that you have a pure cosine function that oscillates twice a second, and that you sample that function every second. What do you see? Remember, you don't know what value the function has except at the times you measure it! So what you see is a *constant* function! How often must you sample the function to get a true picture of how rapidly it's oscillating?

To help investigate the properties of the FFT, you should write a subroutine to plot the magnitude of the transform for you. This can be thought of as a spectral decomposition, or spectrum, of the original data. Since frequencies above the Nyquist frequency are actually negative frequencies, we suggest that you plot these as negative frequencies, so that the spectrum is plotted on the interval $-\omega_{Nyquist} < \omega < \omega_{Nyquist}$. You might find it useful to plot the original data and its spectrum on the same screen.

As suggested by this discussion, the rate at which data is taken is extremely important to the proper utilization of the FFT. In particular, the data must be taken fast enough that nothing dramatic happens *between* the sampled times.

EXERCISE 6.10

Consider the function $f(t) = \cos 6\pi t$. Sample the function every second, for 32 seconds, and evaluate the spectrum of the sampled data. (Use $N = 32$ throughout this exercise.) Repeat the exercise, taking data every half second, for 16 seconds, and then every quarter second, etc. What must the sampling rate be for you to determine the true frequency? (Note that $\Delta\omega$ is different for each of the spectra obtained.)

This exercise addresses the question of sampling rate, and in particular, the perils of *undersampling* the data. It also illustrates the artifact of *aliasing*—if a function is under sampled, the high frequency components don't just go away, but rather they will be *disguised* as low frequency components! This is the case depicted in Figure 6.4, for example. For the FFT to provide a meaningful representation of the data, the data must be sampled at twice the frequency of the highest component contained in it, or higher. And even if the data is sampled at a sufficiently high rate, there can be problems. The FFT assumes that the data is periodic *on the sampled interval*—and if it's not?

EXERCISE 6.11

Consider the function $f(t) = \cos 3t$. Sample the data every second for 8 seconds. This is a sufficiently high rate that undersampling should not be a problem. Evaluate and display the spectrum. What went wrong?

This problem is termed *leakage*. The actual frequency of the data *is not* one of the $m\Delta\omega$ at which the transform is evaluated. So, the FFT *tries* to describe the data by using nearby frequencies, distributing the magnitude of the transform across several frequencies—that is, the magnitude *leaks* into nearby frequency bins. This

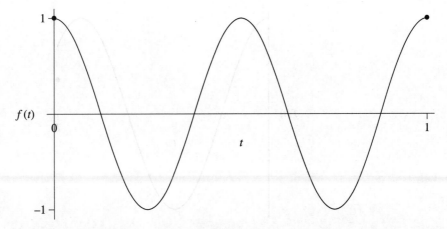

Figure 6.4 The function $f(t) = \cos 4\pi t$. Sampled once a second—or even once every half a second—you would think the function were a constant.

problem can be alleviated by increasing the resolution of the frequencies. Since

$$\Delta\omega = \frac{2\pi}{T},$$

(6.80)

this can be accomplished by sampling the data for a longer time. *Note that the sampling rate is not involved here—only the total observation time!* If we are to sample the function at the same rate, which we must do to avoid undersampling, then we must increase the number of times the function is sampled!

EXERCISE 6.12

Repeat the previous exercise, sampling the function $f(t) = \cos 3t$ every second, but sample for 16, 32, and 64 seconds. Compare the spectra obtained. Note that $\omega_{Nyquist}$ is the same for all the spectra.

An alternate way of viewing the problem of leakage is to note that the sampling interval may not be commensurate with the period of the function, as in Figure 6.5. Sampling the function $f(t) = \cos 3t$ once a second always leads to a discontinuity at the end of the sampling period. Now, if you were to sample at

$$\Delta t = \frac{\pi}{3},$$

you *might* get a different result.

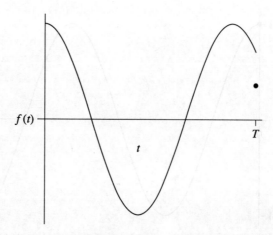

Figure 6.5   A function sampled for a period T incommensurate with the actual period of the function. (Since there is a jump discontinuity in the data, the last data point used should be the mean.)

Line spectra, such as we have been investigating, are quite common in physics. And associated with them are the difficulties sometimes encountered when more than one line is present.

EXERCISE 6.13

Consider the function $f(t) = \sin(2 + \alpha)t + \sin(4 - \alpha)t$, as the parameter α varies from 1 down to 0, with $N = 32, 64$, and 128. Notice anything "unusual" as α gets in the 0.7–0.8 range? Be prepared to explain your results.

6.7 Convolution and Correlation

Although not immediately obvious, the operations of convolution and correlation are closely associated with Fourier transforms. Their formal definitions are quite similar, although their physical interpretation is quite different. First, let's consider *convolution*.

Consider two functions, $p(t)$ and $q(t)$. Mathematically, the convolution of the two functions is defined as

$$p \otimes q = \frac{1}{\sqrt{2\pi}} \int_{-\infty}^{\infty} p(\tau)q(t - \tau)\, d\tau. \tag{6.81}$$

Note that the order is insignificant. That is,

$$p \otimes q = q \otimes p. \tag{6.82}$$

Convolutions arise when we try to predict the response of a physical system to a given input. More on this later.

Now consider the Fourier transform of the convolution,

$$\mathcal{F}[p \otimes q] = \frac{1}{\sqrt{2\pi}} \int_{-\infty}^{\infty} [p \otimes q]e^{-i\omega t}\, dt$$

$$= \frac{1}{\sqrt{2\pi}} \int_{-\infty}^{\infty} \left[\frac{1}{\sqrt{2\pi}} \int_{-\infty}^{\infty} p(\tau)q(t - \tau)\, d\tau \right] e^{-i\omega t}\, dt$$

$$= \frac{1}{\sqrt{2\pi}} \int_{-\infty}^{\infty} p(\tau) \left[\frac{1}{\sqrt{2\pi}} \int_{-\infty}^{\infty} q(t - \tau)e^{-i\omega t}\, dt \right] d\tau. \tag{6.83}$$

With reference to the shifting property, Equation 6.32, we recognize that the term in the square brackets is

$$\frac{1}{\sqrt{2\pi}} \int_{-\infty}^{\infty} q(t - \tau)e^{-i\omega t}\, dt = e^{-i\omega \tau} Q(\omega), \tag{6.84}$$

where $Q(\omega)$ is the Fourier transform of $q(t)$. We then have

$$\mathcal{F}[p \otimes q] = \frac{1}{\sqrt{2\pi}} \int_{-\infty}^{\infty} p(\tau) e^{-i\omega\tau} Q(\omega)\, d\tau$$
$$= P(\omega) Q(\omega), \qquad\qquad (6.85)$$

where $P(\omega)$ is the Fourier transform of $p(t)$. This is known as the *Fourier Convolution Theorem*, and can be written as

$$\mathcal{F}[p \otimes q] = P(\omega) Q(\omega)$$
$$= \mathcal{F}[p]\,\mathcal{F}[q]. \qquad\qquad (6.86)$$

Let's look at a specific example. Consider the two functions

$$p(t) = \begin{cases} 0, & t < 0, \\ 1, & 0 < t < 1, \\ 0, & t > 1, \end{cases} \quad \text{and} \quad q(t) = \begin{cases} 0, & t < 0, \\ 1-t, & 0 < t < 1, \\ 0, & t > 1. \end{cases} \qquad (6.87)$$

With some effort, we can find that

$$p \otimes q = \frac{1}{\sqrt{2\pi}} \int_{max\{0,t-1\}}^{min\{1,t\}} (1-\tau)\, d\tau$$

$$= \begin{cases} 0, & t < 0 \\ \dfrac{2t - t^2}{2\sqrt{2\pi}}, & 0 \le t \le 1 \\ \dfrac{4 - 4t + t^2}{2\sqrt{2\pi}}, & 1 \le t \le 2 \\ 0, & t > 2. \end{cases} \qquad (6.88)$$

EXERCISE 6.14

Verify, by direct integration, that $p(t)$, $q(t)$, and $p \otimes q$ satisfy the Convolution Theorem.

To a considerable extent, the FFT is simply a numerical approximation to the analytic Fourier transform. Previously we've seen this to be true, although we must be careful in choosing the range, sampling frequency, and number of points used in the transform to ensure the accuracy of the correspondence, as well as accounting for the differences in normalization. With these caveats, we anticipate that the same will be true with convolution.

EXERCISE 6.15

Explore the FFT version of the Convolution Theorem. In particular, investigate the effects of range, sampling frequency, and N on the "quality" of the approximation. For example, compare each of the functions to its discrete sampling, and its analytic Fourier transform to its FFT.

We can take the comparisons of this exercise one step further. Taking the inverse Fourier transform of Equation 6.86, we find

$$p \otimes q = \mathcal{F}^{-1}[P(\omega)Q(\omega)]. \tag{6.89}$$

That is, the original convolution is simply the inverse transform of the product of the individual input transforms.

EXERCISE 6.16

Evaluate the convolution of p and q by Equation 6.89. Because of the numerical efficiencies of the FFT, evaluating a convolution in this way is much faster than using Equation 6.81.

While there are numerous instances where we want the convolution, we are often more interested in the *deconvolution*. That is, if we know $p \otimes q$ and $q(t)$, can we find $p(t)$? If the physical situation is simple enough, the differential equations describing the system can be solved to find p, but more commonly the equations are not easily solved and such a direct determination is not possible. We can, however, use the Convolution Theorem. That is,

$$\mathcal{F}[p \otimes q] = \mathcal{F}[p]\,\mathcal{F}[q], \tag{6.90}$$

or

$$\mathcal{F}[p] = \frac{\mathcal{F}[p \otimes q]}{\mathcal{F}[q]}, \tag{6.91}$$

and hence

$$p(t) = \mathcal{F}^{-1}\left[\frac{\mathcal{F}[p \otimes q]}{\mathcal{F}[q]}\right]. \tag{6.92}$$

There are potential difficulties when implementing this with the FFT—what happens if $\mathcal{F}[q]$ has a zero in it? Still, with care, this expression can be useful.

EXERCISE 6.17

In a previous exercise, you verified the Convolution Theorem using p and q. Now write a computer program to perform this deconvolution. Compare your result to the known function $p(t)$.

We previously commented that convolutions arise when we try to predict the response of a physical system to a given input. For example, we might have an electronic device that detects and amplifies a voltage signal. Real devices—as opposed to hypothetical ideal ones—always have a certain amount of electrical resistance and capacitance. Let's characterize the device as simply as possible, having only a resistor and a capacitor, as in the circuit in Figure 6.6. The signal we *want* to observe is the one input on the left, associated with a "real" physical quantity—the signal we actually see, as a result of our detection, is output on the right as the voltage drop across the capacitor. How is "what we see" related to the "real physical quantity"? Consider what the response of the detector will be. Before the signal arrives, the output of the "detector" is zero; as it arrives, some of its energy goes to charge the capacitor so that the output signal *does not* exactly reproduce the input. Then, after the input signal has passed, the circuit will dissipate its stored energy into the output signal, and so a voltage will persist after the input signal has passed.

We can apply Kirchhoff's law to the circuit to find how the input and output signals are related. Assume the current is flowing in a clockwise direction. Then the current flowing into point b is just the potential difference across the resistor, divided by the resistance, $(V_a - V_b)/R$. The current flowing away from point b is the current that flows through the capacitor. Recall that in a capacitor the current is equal to the capacitance, C, multiplying the time rate of change of the potential difference,

$$I_{\substack{through \\ capacitor}} = C \frac{d(V_b - V_c)}{dt}. \tag{6.93}$$

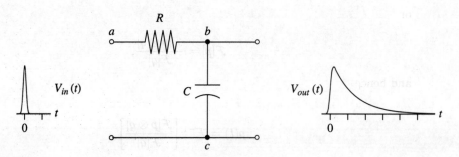

Figure 6.6   A simple electrical circuit having resistance R and capacitance C. The response of the circuit to a finite duration input pulse is illustrated.

The continuity of the current thus tells us that

$$\frac{V_a - V_b}{R} = C \frac{d(V_b - V_c)}{dt}. \tag{6.94}$$

For convenience, we can set $V_c = 0$. Then V_a is simply the input voltage, V_{in}, and V_b is the output voltage, V_{out}. Equation 6.94 becomes

$$\frac{V_{in} - V_{out}}{R} = C \frac{dV_{out}}{dt}, \tag{6.95}$$

or

$$\frac{dV_{out}}{dt} + \frac{V_{out}}{RC} = \frac{V_{in}}{RC}. \tag{6.96}$$

This is a linear first-order differential equation, and as such has the analytic solution

$$V_{out}(t) = e^{-t/RC} \left[\frac{1}{RC} \int_{-\infty}^{t} e^{\tau/RC} V_{in}(\tau) \, d\tau + c_1 \right], \tag{6.97}$$

where c_1 is a constant of integration, chosen so that the solution satisfies the initial conditions. Let's consider an example: How does this circuit respond to a unit impulse like $V_{in}(t) = \delta(t)$? Performing the integration, we find

$$V_{out}(t) = \begin{cases} 0, & t < 0 \\ \dfrac{1}{RC} e^{-t/RC}, & t \geq 0. \end{cases} \tag{6.98}$$

That is, even if the input—the actual physics, so to speak—is an instantaneous electrical impulse, the output of the circuit will be a signal that jumps from zero to a maximum determined by the properties of the circuit (R and C), followed by an exponential decay. The larger the product RC, the larger the maximum and the more rapid the decay, but any real circuit will be unable to exactly reproduce (or transfer) the actual voltage applied to it. We will denote this response of the system to a unit impulse as $r(t)$,

$$r(t) = \begin{cases} 0, & t < 0 \\ \dfrac{1}{RC} e^{-t/RC}, & t \geq 0. \end{cases} \tag{6.99}$$

But what does all this have to do with convolution? Imagine that there is a string of pulses, arriving one after another in rapid succession. The output at any given instant will then be a combination of the responses to the individual input pulses— since the system is *linear*, the combination is simply a sum! That is, the output at a given instant is equal to the sum of the responses to the pulses that have arrived at all previous times. This situation is portrayed in Figure 6.7.

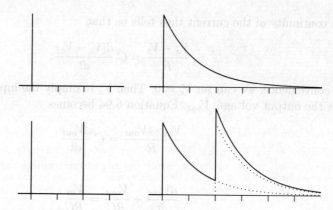

Figure 6.7   Response of the RC circuit to delta function inputs. As the delta functions arrive closer in time, the output becomes complicated.

Of course, as we consider more and more pulses arriving at smaller and smaller time separations, we pass to the continuous case. In fact, we can always write a continuous function as an integral over delta functions,

$$f(t) = \int_{-\infty}^{\infty} f(\tau)\delta(t-\tau)\,d\tau, \tag{6.100}$$

or in our case,

$$V_{in}(t) = \int_{-\infty}^{\infty} V_{in}(\tau)\delta(t-\tau)\,d\tau. \tag{6.101}$$

Then, the output voltage, the "sum" of the responses, must simply be

$$
\begin{aligned}
V_{out}(t) &= e^{-t/RC}\frac{1}{RC}\int_{-\infty}^{\infty} e^{\tau/RC}\,V_{in}(\tau)\,d\tau \\
&= \int_{-\infty}^{\infty}\left[\frac{1}{RC}e^{\tau-t/RC}\right]V_{in}(\tau)\,d\tau \\
&= \int_{-\infty}^{\infty} V_{in}(\tau)\,r(\tau-t)\,d\tau \\
&= V_{in}\otimes r.
\end{aligned}
\tag{6.102}
$$

Thus the output of the system is the *convolution* of the input signal with the response of the system to a delta function input. As illustrated in Figures 6.6 and 6.7, the detection tends to broaden features and to smear the input signal—this physical distortion of the input is mathematically described as the convolution.

Of course, if we know (have measured?) $V_{out}(t)$, and have determined (either by measurement or calculation) the response $r(t)$, then we can determine $V_{in}(t)$ by deconvolution. That is,

$$V_{in}(t) = \mathcal{F}^{-1}\left[\frac{\mathcal{F}[V_{out}(t)]}{\mathcal{F}[r(t)]}\right]. \tag{6.103}$$

EXERCISE 6.18

The file Vout.dat contains voltage output data for the RC circuit we've been discussing, with $RC = 1$. Using the response function $r(t)$, evaluate $\mathcal{F}[r(t)]$ analytically, and sample it appropriately in order to determine the input signal $V_{in}(t)$. (Note: The file contains data at every 0.01 second. You may not need data at this fine a scale.)

While the usual application of convolution is the interaction of a signal with an instrument, *correlation* provides a measure of how much one signal is similar to another. Mathematically, it's defined as

$$p \odot q = \frac{1}{\sqrt{2\pi}} \int_{-\infty}^{\infty} p^*(\tau) q(t+\tau)\, d\tau. \tag{6.104}$$

We note that *correlation* involves a complex conjugation of one of the functions, while *convolution* does not. If the two functions p and q are entirely different and unrelated, $p \odot q = 0$, they are said to be *uncorrelated*.

Consider the two functions $p(t)$ and $q(t)$, as before. To evaluate the correlation $p \odot q$, q is displaced a distance t relative to p, and their product integrated over all τ. This operation is shown in Figure 6.8, in which the evaluation of the correlation at two different times is depicted. The integrals themselves are not difficult, but the limits of integration are not obvious. For $p(\tau)$ to be non-zero, we must have

$$0 \le \tau \le 1.$$

And for $q(t+\tau)$ to be non-zero, we must have

$$0 \le t + \tau \le 1,$$

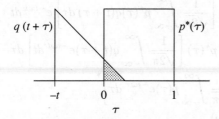
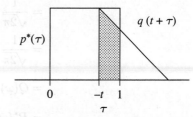

Figure 6.8   Graphical representation of correlation. The function q is shifted relative to p^* and the product of the two functions is integrated over all τ to yield the correlation at time t. Note that $q = 1$ at $\tau = -t$.

or

$$-t \le \tau \le 1 - t.$$

Taken together, the only region for which both functions are non-zero is

$$max\{0, -t\} \le \tau \le min\{1, 1 - t\},$$

which are then the limits of the integration. We thus find

$$p \odot q = \frac{1}{\sqrt{2\pi}} \int_{max\{0,-t\}}^{min\{1,1-t\}} (1 - t - \tau)\, d\tau$$

$$= \begin{cases} 0, & t < -1 \\ \dfrac{1 - t^2}{2\sqrt{2\pi}}, & -1 \le t \le 0 \\ \dfrac{(t-1)^2}{2\sqrt{2\pi}}, & 0 \le t \le 1 \\ 0, & t > 1. \end{cases} \qquad (6.105)$$

Unlike convolution, for which the order of the functions is immaterial, correlation depends upon the order—$p \odot q$ is not the same as $q \odot p$.

EXERCISE 6.19
Evaluate the correlation $q \odot p$ of the functions described, analytically.

As with convolution, correlation is included in our discussion of Fourier analysis because of the unique character of its Fourier transform,

$$\mathcal{F}[p \odot q] = \frac{1}{\sqrt{2\pi}} \int_{-\infty}^{\infty} [p \odot q] e^{-i\omega t}\, dt$$

$$= \frac{1}{\sqrt{2\pi}} \int_{-\infty}^{\infty} \left[\frac{1}{\sqrt{2\pi}} \int_{-\infty}^{\infty} p^*(\tau) q(t + \tau)\, d\tau \right] e^{-i\omega t}\, dt$$

$$= \frac{1}{\sqrt{2\pi}} \int_{-\infty}^{\infty} p^*(\tau) \left[\frac{1}{\sqrt{2\pi}} \int_{-\infty}^{\infty} q(t + \tau) e^{-i\omega t}\, dt \right] d\tau$$

$$= Q(\omega) \left[\frac{1}{\sqrt{2\pi}} \int_{-\infty}^{\infty} p(\tau) e^{-i\omega \tau}\, d\tau \right]^*$$

$$= P^*(\omega)\, Q(\omega), \qquad (6.106)$$

where $Q(\omega)$ and $P(\omega)$ are the Fourier transforms of $q(t)$ and $p(t)$, respectively. Clearly, the similarity with convolution is obvious. However, the presence of the complex conjugation makes the correlation a distinctly different operation.

To become better acquainted with correlation, we need to explore the relationship between the numerical approximation, obtained with the FFT, and the actual correlation.

EXERCISE 6.20

Explore the relations between $p(t)$, $q(t)$, $p \odot q$ and their Fourier transforms with their numerical approximations obtained with the FFT. In particular, investigate the effects of range, sampling frequency, and N on the "quality" of the approximation. For example, compare each of the functions to its discrete sampling, and its analytic Fourier transform to its FFT.

As an alternative to Equation 6.104, the correlation can be evaluated using the inverse Fourier transform of Equation 6.106,

$$p \odot q = \mathcal{F}^{-1} \left[P^*(\omega) Q(\omega) \right]. \tag{6.107}$$

EXERCISE 6.21

Evaluate the correlation of p and q using Equation 6.107. Compare your numerical result to the known correlation function, Equation 6.105.

In many instances the functions being correlated are not of finite duration. In this case, the integrands don't vanish as $t \to \pm\infty$, and the integral of Equation 6.104 need not exist. In these situations we define an *average correlation function* as

$$[p \odot q]_{average} = \lim_{T \to \infty} \frac{1}{T} \int_{-T/2}^{T/2} p^*(\tau) q(t + \tau) \, d\tau. \tag{6.108}$$

In the particular case that p and q are periodic with period T_0, this reduces to

$$[p \odot q]_{average} = \frac{1}{T_0} \int_{-T_0/2}^{T_0/2} p^*(\tau) q(t + \tau) \, d\tau. \tag{6.109}$$

Let's write the functions $p(\tau)$ and $q(\tau)$ as

$$p(\tau) = \langle p \rangle + \delta_p(\tau) \quad \text{and} \quad q(\tau) = \langle q \rangle + \delta_q(\tau), \tag{6.110}$$

where $\langle p \rangle$ and $\langle q \rangle$ are the mean values of the functions and δ_p and δ_q are the deviations of the functions from their means. Then the correlation of the two functions is

$$p \odot q = \lim_{T \to \infty} \frac{1}{T} \int_{-T/2}^{T/2} [\langle p \rangle + \delta_p(\tau)]^* [\langle q \rangle + \delta_q(t+\tau)] \, d\tau$$

$$= \langle p \rangle^* \langle q \rangle + \langle p \rangle^* \lim_{T \to \infty} \frac{1}{T} \int_{-T/2}^{T/2} \delta_q(t+\tau) \, d\tau + \langle q \rangle \lim_{T \to \infty} \frac{1}{T} \int_{-T/2}^{T/2} \delta_p^*(\tau) \, d\tau$$

$$+ \lim_{T \to \infty} \frac{1}{T} \int_{-T/2}^{T/2} \delta_p^*(\tau) \delta_q(t+\tau) \, d\tau. \tag{6.111}$$

Since δ_q has been defined as the deviation of q from its mean value, the integral

$$\lim_{T \to \infty} \frac{1}{T} \int_{-T/2}^{T/2} \delta_q(t+\tau) \, d\tau$$

must be zero, and likewise for the integral of δ_p^*. Let's now specify that the functions are (in some sense) independent of one another—in particular, that the variations in p are unrelated to the variations in q. Then the remaining integral is

$$\lim_{T \to \infty} \frac{1}{T} \int_{-T/2}^{T/2} \delta_p^*(\tau) \delta_q(t+\tau) \, d\tau = 0. \tag{6.112}$$

This specification serves to define what we mean by two functions being *uncorrelated*, in which case we have

$$p \odot q = \langle p \rangle^* \langle q \rangle. \tag{6.113}$$

As a consequence, if the mean value of either p or q is zero, then the correlation will also be zero.

Of particular interest is the correlation of a function with itself, the *autocorrelation*. Consider, for example, our favorite function

$$p(t) = \begin{cases} 0, & t < 0 \\ 1, & 0 \le t \le 1 \\ 0, & t > 1. \end{cases} \tag{6.114}$$

EXERCISE 6.22

Calculate the autocorrelation function of $p(t)$, analytically. Compare to your numerical results obtained via the FFT.

If a function is periodic then it should exhibit a pronounced autocorrelation, since shifting the function by one period will simply shift the function onto itself. For example, the autocorrelation of $\sin t$ is

$$\frac{1}{2\pi} \int_{-\pi}^{\pi} \sin \tau \, \sin (t+\tau) \, d\tau = \frac{1}{2} \cos \tau. \tag{6.115}$$

The autocorrelation of a periodic function thus has oscillations in it, the various maxima occurring whenever the function has been shifted in time by an integral number of periods.

Another example of particular interest to us is at the far extreme from periodic functions—functions that are "random." There are numerous sources of random noise in real experiments, all characterized as being uncorrelated, at least for sufficiently long times. (All signals relating to real physical situations are continuous and so are necessarily correlated for short times. As larger time increments are considered, the extent of correlation diminishes.) For long times, then,

$$p \odot p = |\langle p \rangle|^2. \tag{6.116}$$

A rather common occurrence is the presence of a random signal, e.g., *noise*, superimposed upon a signal that we're trying to detect. That is, we might want to observe the signal $s(t)$, but actually be measuring $p(t) = s(t) + n(t)$, where $n(t)$ is random noise. If the *signal-to-noise ratio* is unfavorable, it might be very difficult to observe the signal. For example, the detected signal might appear as in Figure 6.9. While a certain periodicity to the signal can clearly be discerned, the random scatter of the data makes straightforward analysis difficult.

In contrast, let's evaluate the autocorrelation function,

$$p \odot p = s \odot s + s \odot n + n \odot s + n \odot n. \tag{6.117}$$

Since the signal and the noise are uncorrelated, we have

$$s \odot n = n \odot s = \langle s \rangle \langle n \rangle. \tag{6.118}$$

Thus, for long times we find

$$p \odot p = s \odot s + 2\langle s \rangle \langle n \rangle + |\langle n(t) \rangle|^2, \tag{6.119}$$

so that the autocorrelation of the signal, $s \odot s$, is found on a constant background due to the noise. For example, if $s(t) = \sin t$ then

$$p \odot p = \frac{1}{2} \cos t + |\langle n(t) \rangle|^2. \tag{6.120}$$

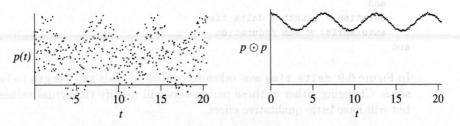

$p(t)$

$p \odot p$

Figure 6.9   On the left, a scatter plot of "typical" noisy data. On the right, its autocorrelation.

This autocorrelation function is also plotted in Figure 6.9. While the noise present in $p(t)$ masks its sinusoidal identity, the autocorrelation clearly exhibits the periodicity in the signal.

The data presented in this figure was simulated, i.e., generated by the computer, by the code

```
...
delta_time = ...
for i= 1: ...
  time = time + delta_time;
  p(i) = sin(time) + 4.0*rand;
end
```

This fills the array p with data that ranges from 0 to 5. (Using a uniform distribution of random numbers, such as provided by the function rand is not particularly realistic, but suffices for our illustration. A Gaussian distribution of random numbers would be more appropriate in simulating actual experiments.) The autocorrelation function is then approximated by the integral

$$p \odot p \approx \frac{1}{T} \int_0^T p^*(\tau)p(\tau + t)\, d\tau, \tag{6.121}$$

which we compute by a simple trapezoid rule. The autocorrelation function is then evaluated by the following code.

```
%
%Compute the autocorrelation for different 'lag' times
%
for shift = 1: ...
    lag_time = shift * delta_time
%For this particular 'lag_time':
%
    Sum = 0.0
    for i = 1: length + 1
        Sum = Sum + p(i) * p(i+shift) * delta_time
    end
    duration = length * delta_time
    auto(shift) = Sum / duration
end
```

In Figure 6.9, delta_time was taken to be 0.05 seconds and length to be 200 time steps. Changing either of these parameters will modify the actual values obtained but will have little qualitative effect.

EXERCISE 6.23

Reproduce Figure 6.9. The data, $p(t)$, is provided for you—you just need to evaluate $p \odot p$. Note that the limited data set will restrict the number of lag times you may consider.

Note that we find

$$\mathcal{F}[p \odot p] = |P(\omega)|^2. \tag{6.122}$$

We recognize the right side of this equation as the power spectrum—Equation 6.122 is the *Wiener-Khintchine Theorem*: The Fourier transform of the autocorrelation function is the power spectrum.

EXERCISE 6.24

Evaluate the power spectrum of the noisy data of the previous exercise.

A final word of warning: Convolution and correlation are extremely important operations in very diverse physical situations. As a result, different definitions and conventions have arisen in different areas. For example, there is no single, universally accepted symbol representing either convolution or correlation. The ubiquitous factor of 2π, or perhaps $\sqrt{2\pi}$, wanders about. And in some applications, the signals being investigated are always real, so that the complex conjugation is superfluous, and not used—unfortunately, this leads to the possibility of a definition, perfectly appropriate in one discipline, being used inappropriately outside that particular area. There is even disagreement on basic terminology: energy spectrum, power spectrum, power spectral density, and so on, are all used to refer to the same entity. When working in a particular area, you should of course use the standards and definitions of that area—but be aware that they may be slightly different from what you first learned. i her times, the randomness of

6.8 Ranging

The use of correlation is important to many areas of experimental physics and has significant technological applications. One such example is in SONAR or RADAR ranging. By measuring the time delay between the transmission of the signal and the reception of its echo, and knowing the speed of the wave, the distance to the object that reflected the signal can be determined. However, the intensity of the returned echo is often quite low—the intensity falls off as $1/r^4$—and the detected signal will likely be corrupted by extraneous noise. Rather than looking for the echo directly in the received signal, the echo is sought in the correlation between a reference signal (a copy of the original transmitted signal) and the received signal. This *cross correlation* will be large at the lag time associated with the time duration of the

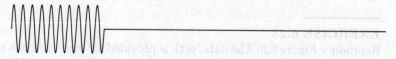

Figure 6.10 This is the transmitted signal, as used in the example. The pulse lasts for 10 periods of the sine wave.

signal to the the reflecting object and its return; at other times, the randomness of the noise in the signal should make the correlation integral vanish (or nearly so).

As an example, let the signal pulse be a simple sine wave lasting over several cycles, as illustrated in Figure 6.10. We'll simulate the returned signal by adding random numbers, e.g., noise, to the original signal. If the signal is large compared to the noise, then there's little difficulty in detecting the signal and hence determining the distance to the target. But if the noise and the signal are of comparable intensity, the signal is harder to identify. This example is depicted in Figure 6.11, where we've taken the magnitudes of the signal and noise to be the same.

Can you see the "signal" in this data? If you look closely, the presence of the signal is barely discernible, but it would be rather difficult to make a reliable distance estimate from the data as it is presented. In contrast, let's consider the cross correlation between the original reference signal and the echo.

The echo has two components: the original signal, equivalent to the reference $r(t)$, but delayed in time, and the noise $n(t)$. Thus

$$e(t) = \alpha r(t - \Delta) + n(t), \tag{6.123}$$

where α (< 0) represents the attenuation of the signal and Δ is the time delay. The cross correlation is then

$$\begin{aligned} r(t) \odot e(t) &= r(t) \odot [\alpha r(t - \Delta) + n(t)] \\ &= \alpha r(t) \odot r(t - \Delta) + \alpha r(t) \odot n(t). \end{aligned} \tag{6.124}$$

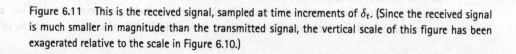

Figure 6.11 This is the received signal, sampled at time increments of δ_t. (Since the received signal is much smaller in magnitude than the transmitted signal, the vertical scale of this figure has been exaggerated relative to the scale in Figure 6.10.)

But $r(t)$ and $n(t)$ are uncorrelated, and for the particular signal pulse of our example, $\langle r(t) \rangle = 0$. Thus the cross correlation between the reference signal and its echo is just the autocorrelation of the reference signal, multiplied by α. *The noise itself does not contribute to the cross correlation!* This is a truly amazing thing— by taking the cross correlation between the reference signal and the noisy received signal, the noise has been eliminated!

We can easily evaluate the ideal cross correlation function for our example. We'll take the reference function to be

$$r(t) = \begin{cases} \sin(t), & 0 < t < 20\pi \\ 0, & |t - 10\pi| \geq 0. \end{cases} \tag{6.125}$$

Then the ideal cross correlation is just a multiple of the autocorrelation function, $r \odot r$, as plotted in Figure 6.12.

In practice, the effects of the noise are usually not totally removed, although the results are still quite dramatic. To illustrate, let's further explore the example we've been considering. Let's store the reference signal in the array `ref(i)` and the echo in `echo(i)`. To evaluate the cross correlation, we need to evaluate the integral

$$r(t) \odot e(t) = \frac{1}{\sqrt{2\pi}} \int_0^T r(\tau)e(t+\tau)\, d\tau. \tag{6.126}$$

If this integral were evaluated "perfectly," then the noise would be totally eliminated. In any real situations, however, the evaluation will be less than exact. Often this integration is done with analogue electronic circuitry—basic LRC circuits with appropriately chosen time constants designed so that the output of the circuit is the time integral of the input signal. The integration might also be done digitally, in which case the signals have been sampled at discrete time intervals, such as we are

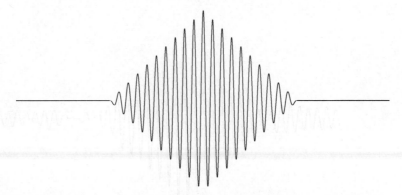

Figure 6.12   Ideal cross correlation between the reference signal and the returned signal, obtained analytically.

simulating. In either case, integration errors will be introduced. In our example, the integral might be evaluated by the simple trapezoid rule, as in the autocorrelation example discussed earlier. Error is thus introduced by the fundamental inaccuracy of the integration method itself. Statistical error is also introduced, in that the function is being sampled only a finite number of times. For example, we have argued that

$$\frac{1}{T} \int_0^T n(t)\, dt = 0. \tag{6.127}$$

However, if we evaluate this integral by a finite sum we will find that the integral is not identically zero, although we would expect that the sum approaches zero as we take a sufficiently large number of function evaluations. (This, of course, is a statement that you can easily verify for yourself. As more terms are included in the summation, how rapidly does the sum approach zero?)

The cross correlation obtained for our example problem is displayed in Figure 6.13. Clearly, the noise present in the received signal displayed in Figure 6.11 has been dramatically reduced. Its effect on the cross correlation is to give a "jitter" to the baseline, a jitter that could be reduced if we worked harder at evaluating the integral.

Although this cross correlation could certainly be used to determine distance, it would be easier if the correlation were more localized. (This is particularly so if the received signal contains echoes from multiple objects.) This could be done by making the initial signal pulse shorter in duration, but then the energy transmitted— and more importantly, the energy received—would be decreased, while the magnitude of the noise would not be affected. Hence the end result would be to decrease the signal-to-noise ratio. Another approach is to find a reference signal that has a more localized autocorrelation function. The premier example of such a signal is the chirped pulse,

$$r(t) = \sin \omega t, \tag{6.128}$$

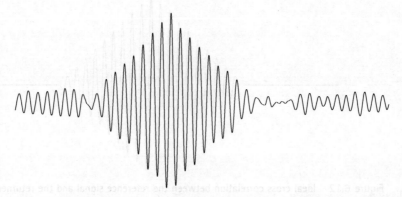

Figure 6.13   Calculated cross correlation between the reference signal and the returned signal.

in which the frequency ω is itself time-dependent. That is, the frequency changes as a function of time, like a bird's chirp. The simplest such time variation is a linear one, and we have for example

$$\omega = \omega_0 + ct, \qquad (6.129)$$

where c governs how rapidly the frequency changes.

EXERCISE 6.25

Write a computer code to evaluate the cross correlation of our simulated signal and reference, for a chirped signal pulse. For comparison to our example, take ω_0 to be 1, and investigate the correlation for values of c in the range $0 < c < 0.05$.

An important reason for wanting the autocorrelation function to be as localized as possible is to acquire the ability to discriminate between two different objects. That is, the received signal might contain echoes from two or more reflectors, not just one. If the correlation is broad, then the correlation due to one reflector can overlap the correlation due to the other, hiding the fact that there are two reflectors. By having a localized autocorrelation signature, echoes from objects that are located close to one another will generate correlations that don't overlap, so that the objects can more easily be resolved. If the autocorrelation is sufficiently narrow, different reflectors can be resolved even though the echoes themselves overlap in time.

EXERCISE 6.26

Add a second reflector to the simulation, and investigate the ease with which it is resolved as a function of c.

6.9 Spectrum Analysis

Insight into experimental data can often be gained by analyzing the data in frequency space rather than in time. That is, an experiment might generate data as a function of time. We can take this time sequence of data, use the FFT to find its Fourier Transform, and examine the resulting data as a function of frequency. We might find, for example, that the data is much easier to understand in terms of its frequency content, rather than its time series.

Let's assume that the experiment is interfaced to a computer, takes the data, and writes it to a file. Thus, it's necessary to read a file.

MATLAB can easily do this. For example, perhaps we have a file with the following data in it:

```
Simple data
1 2.5
```

    2 7.6
    3 8.8

Clearly, the first line is a description of the contents, and the next three lines contain two numbers per line. This data could be read by the script

```
Rows   = 2;
Cols   = 3;
id     = fopen('data.dat','r')          % Open the file named data.dat
info   = fgetl(id);                     % Get a line of descriptive data
data   = fscanf(id,'%f', [Rows, Cols]); % Read formatted data from file
                                        %  as a Rows x Cols array
status = fclose(id);                    % Close the file
data   = transpose(data);
```

Consider a particular example: Using a computer equipped with a sound sensor, a tuning fork can be struck and the time and voltage signal from the sensor can be recorded, say in the file `tuning_fork.dat`.

EXERCISE 6.27
Use a text editor to look at the file and determine how to read it. Write a simple script to read the file, and plot the voltage as a function of time. Select the data to use, then apply the FFT to the data and find the frequency of the tuning fork. That is, plot $|g(\omega)|$ versus ω, and find the largest value of $|g(\omega)|$.

Of course, tuning forks and violins don't sound alike—but why? The sound of a note when first struck is considerably different from its sound while it's being sustained. But just comparing the middle of the note, the sustained part, the ear clearly distinguishes between a simple tuning fork and the violin. Part of that difference is the frequency components present in the note. As seen in the just completed exercise, the tuning fork has an overwhelming amount of its energy being put into a single frequency. The violin, on the other hand, "sounds different" because it *is* different.

Imagine that we had audio files containing a musical note played by different instruments. MATLAB actually has the ability to play such files, as well as retrieve numerical data from them. Thus we could both *hear* the note, and analyze it for its frequency components. The program might look a bit like

```
% Play_Analyze.m
% Script to play a .wav file, calculate its FFT, and display.
%
function Play_Analyze
% To hear the notes, turn your sound on---suggest you use
```

```
%      external speakers.
Nf=4;              % number of files to read
WavFile(1,:)='Sine.wav';        % A computer generated sine curve
WavFile(2,:)='TuningFork.wav'; % Tuning fork
WavFile(3,:)='Piano.wav';       % Piano
WavFile(4,:)='Violin.wav';      % Violin

for i=1:Nf
    clear y;                        % reset y
    [y,fq]=wavread(WavFile(i,:));   % read the WAV file
                                    %   (y = data, fq = sampling rate)
    wavplay(y,fq);                  % Play the WAV file
%  Get the data
    Nc=length(y);                   % actual data length read
    k=fix(log2(Nc));
    N = 2^k;
    dat=y(1:N);

%  Evaluate the Fourier transform
    ...
%  Plot |fft|
    figure
    ...
end
```

EXERCISE 6.28

Develop a program to play and analyze notes from various instruments.

New insights can be gained by the application of FFT's to experimental data—by converting data obtained as a function of time to data expressed in terms of frequency. However, such an analysis can be just as useful in understanding the physical content of *synthetic data*, such as produced by a numerical calculation.

As an example, let's reconsider the van der Pol oscillator. Previously, we saw that a phase–space diagram was a useful tool in understanding the oscillator's behavior. Now, we'll see that Fourier analysis, via the FFT, will complement that understanding.

We'll want to integrate the van der Pol equation for some time before we begin storing the data. That is, we don't start taking data immediately-nonlinear oscillators tend to wander around for awhile, depending upon their initial conditions. But we're interested in their long-term behavior, so we wait some period of time to allow for the transients to disappear. We can then start taking data; say, 512 points at time increments of 0.1 seconds. This data is presented in Figure 6.14. Clearly, it's periodic but not sinusoidal.

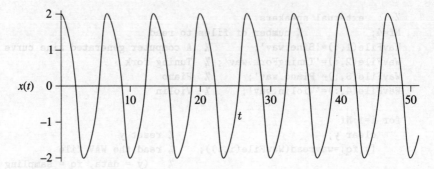

Figure 6.14   Position versus time for the van der Pol oscillator using $\Delta t = 0.1$ seconds and 512 points.

This data, taken in the time domain, can then be Fourier transformed to the frequency domain. Since the data is real, plotting the positive frequencies is sufficient. The frequency spectrum $|g(\omega)|$ is plotted in Figure 6.15.

Clearly, there is a main peak near $\omega = 1$, and a second peak a little short of 3. (There might also be a third peak between 4.5 and 5, but it's hard to be sure.) One way to enhance the spectrum in order to make small features more visible is to plot the data on a logarithmic scale rather than on a linear one. The same data as is plotted in Figure 6.15 is also presented in Figure 6.16—not only is the third peak visible, but a 4th and 5th as well! Still, the "background noise" is pretty high, and the resolution is pretty low.

Why are there so many peaks? Recall that the van der Pol oscillator is very stable, so that its period is very regular. *But it's not a simple harmonic oscillator*—we can

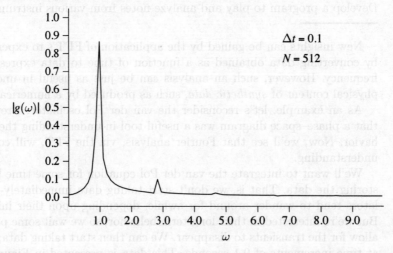

Figure 6.15   The frequency spectrum $|g(\omega)|$ of the van der Pol oscillator, using $\Delta t = 0.1$ seconds and 512 points.

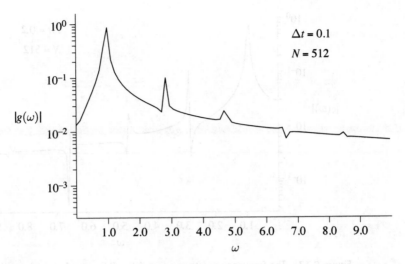

Figure 6.16   The same spectrum as in Figure 6.15, but plotted on a logarithmic scale to enhance the smaller features that might be present.

see that in Figure 6.14! More than one harmonic of the fundamental frequency is required to describe its relatively complicated motion. And that's what the extra peaks are, the harmonics. Note that the peaks appear at approximately odd integer multiples of the fundamental—but not at even multiples.

If we want to improve the frequency resolution of the spectrum, the total observation time must be increased. This can be done either by increasing Δt, or by increasing N. The Nyquist frequency for $\Delta t = 0.1$ seconds is 31.416 sec^{-1}, but the spectrum shows that the contributions from the higher frequencies are not significant. So we can double Δt, thereby halving the Nyquist frequency, without fear of undersampling, while at the same time doubling the frequency resolution. This new spectrum is plotted in Figure 6.17. The higher harmonics are much more apparent in this figure, and the "background" is somewhat reduced. Overall, the spectrum is better than the previous one. Still, the peak is rather broad—is this *real*, or an artifact of the approach?

Let's reexamine the original time–domain data, as presented in Figure 6.14. We see that the observation time is not an integer number of periods. That is, the sampling period is not commensurate with the period of the oscillator—Δt was chosen at our convenience, and is not related to the physics of the problem. The reason for the broad peaks in these spectra is due to *leakage*. While we could improve the resolution by further increasing the observation time, choosing a commensurate sampling rate will probably have a greater impact upon the quality of the spectrum. From the data of Figure 6.14, we find that the period of an oscillation is 6.66338 seconds. Thus, if we were to sample at $\Delta t = 0.208231$ seconds, 16 complete

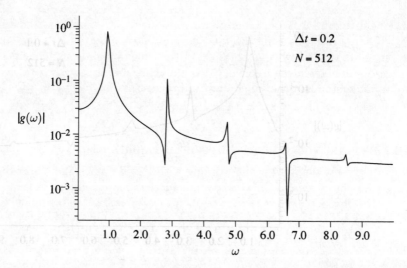

Figure 6.17   The frequency spectrum using $\Delta t = 0.2$ seconds, on a logarithmic scale.

cycles of the oscillator would be sampled with 512 data points. Sampling at this rate, we obtain the spectrum of Figure 6.18.

The difference between this spectrum and the previous ones is astounding. Here the peaks have narrowed to nearly delta functions, and the background has diminished by several orders of magnitude. This spectrum is clearly superior to the

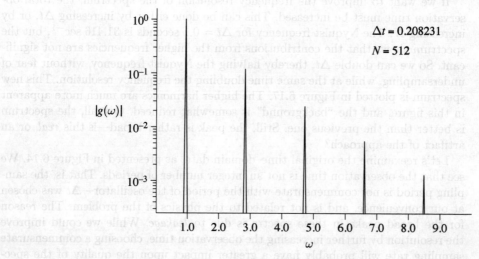

Figure 6.18   The frequency spectrum obtained by using a sampling period commensurate with the oscillator. (Again, on a logarithmic scale.)

one of Figure 6.17, although it was obtained with essentially the same amount of effort—a result of using the knowledge we have to better our understanding. It also suggests that knowledge obtained in the time domain complements that obtained, or obtainable, in the frequency domain. They are, in fact, two different approaches to understanding the same physical processes.

6.10 Chaos in Non-Linear Differential Equations

In previous chapters, while working with logistic maps and the solutions of differential equations, you have encountered the ideas of stable fixed points and limit cycles in phase space. You'll recall that a stable fixed point might be reached, independent of the initial conditions of the problem. Sometimes, as in the case of a damped harmonic oscillator, the system loses energy as it continues to move and ultimately the phase space evolves to a point, or in the case of the logistic map, the system evolves (again) to a single point. The limit cycle refers to the stable orbit to which a system evolves in phase space—once such an orbit is reached, the system will remain in that orbit forever. Both the fixed point and the limit cycle are examples of attractors.

A particularly interesting situation arises when an external periodic driving force is added to the problem. Consider the van der Pol oscillator, for example, which van der Pol investigated in the 1920s:

$$\ddot{x} = -x - \epsilon(x^2 - 1)\dot{x} + f_o \cos \Omega t. \qquad (6.130)$$

The presence of the external force has the effect of adding energy to the system. There are actually two frequencies in this problem, the frequency of the self-oscillation determined by ϵ and the frequency of the periodic forcing, Ω. van der Pol was interested in this oscillator because of its stability characteristics—the oscillator tends to "lock" into a frequency, and to be stable. The frequencies that could be locked into were simple multiples of the driving frequencies (or ratios of integers), and for the most part were not affected by small changes in the parameters. Not surprisingly, the asymptotic behavior of the oscillator is a limit cycle, as depicted in Figure 6.19. (In all that follows, we are interested in the long-time behavior, and hence ignore any transients associated with starting the oscillator.)

EXERCISE 6.29

Solve the van der Pol equation, Equation 6.130, with $f_o = 5$, $\Omega = 1.788$, and $\epsilon = 2.70$ and 2.80. For each ϵ, find the frequency of the limit cycle in the asymptotic time limit and compare to the results in Figure 6.19a. Note that the initial conditions are (or should be) irrelevant.

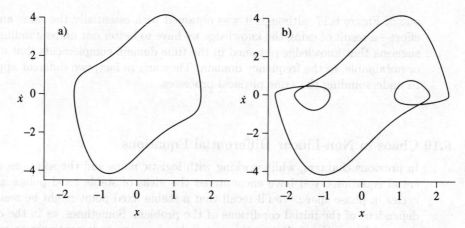

Figure 6.19   The van der Pol oscillator, with $f_o = 5$, the driving frequency $\Omega = 1.788$, and a) $\epsilon = 2.75$ and b) $\epsilon = 3.25$. The difference in the orbits is obvious, particularly when you note that the vertical scales ($\dot{x}$) differ by a factor of two. In a) the response of the oscillator is to oscillate at the same frequency as the driving frequency Ω, while in b) it oscillates at 0.596, one third the driving frequency.

However, if ϵ is sufficiently different, an entirely different mode of oscillation is encountered, as in Figure 6.19b. Furthermore, the frequency of this new mode of oscillation is quite different; in this case, exactly $\Omega/3$. Again, the mode is stable with respect to small changes in the parameters.

EXERCISE 6.30

Solve the van der Pol equation, Equation 6.130, with $f_o = 5$, $\Omega = 1.788$, and $\epsilon = 3.20$ and 3.30. For each ϵ, find the frequency of the limit cycle in the asymptotic time limit and compare to the results in Figure 6.19b.

Now, somewhere between $\epsilon = 2.75$ and $\epsilon = 3.25$ something rather dramatic must occur. (van der Pol himself inserted a telephone receiver into the circuit, and reported hearing "irregular noises" as the period of the system jumped from one value to the next.) The phase space plot for the oscillator with $\epsilon = 3.0$ is shown in Figure 6.20. Clearly, there is no limit cycle, nor any "regular" behavior. The motion of the oscillator is, well, *chaotic*.

It's difficult, if not impossible, to make much sense of Figure 6.20. So instead, we'll use the Poincaré section, introduced in Chapter 5. We will sample the phase space at the period of the applied force, $T_\Omega = 2\pi/\Omega$. The Poincaré sections corresponding to the "well-behaved" cases of Figure 6.19 are shown in Figure 6.21. In a), the oscillator is moving on the limit cycle at the same frequency as the applied force. Hence the oscillator is at the same point in phase space every time it's sampled, and the Poincaré section consists of a single point. (For different initial conditions,

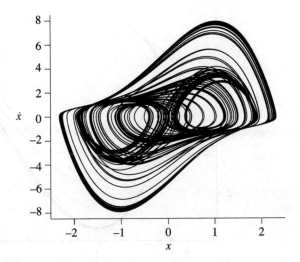

Figure 6.20   A trajectory in phase space for the van der Pol oscillator, with $f_o = 5$, $\Omega = 1.788$, and $\epsilon = 3.00$.

the oscillator would reach the same limit cycle, but its location on the limit cycle would be different. That is, the Poincaré section might be a *different* point, but it would still be a *single* point.) In Figure 6.21b, the phase space is sampled three times for every orbit through phase space, since the period is three times longer, and hence three points are present in the Poincaré section.

Now, let's look at the Poincaré section for the oscillator when it's chaotic, Figure 6.22. If the motion were truly random, you'd expect that the oscillator would be

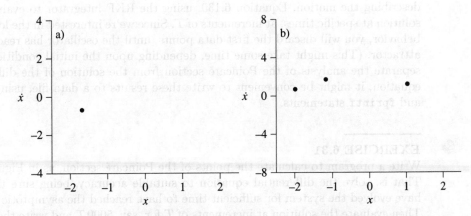

Figure 6.21   The Poincaré sections associated with phase space orbits of the van der Pol oscillator, as depicted in Figure 6.19. Rather large dots have been used to mark the points.

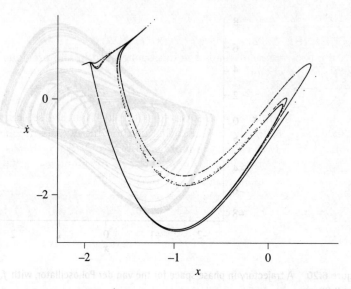

Figure 6.22   The Poincaré section for the trajectory in phase space of Figure 6.20.

found anywhere in phase space. But clearly, that's not the case—while the oscillator is not confined to a point, or even a finite number of points, its location is not arbitrary, either. We have discovered a new type of *attractor*, the so-called *strange attractor*. What makes it strange is that the dimensionality of the attractor is fractional.

To calculate the Poincaré section, we need only to solve the differential equation describing the motion, Equation 6.130, using the RKF integrator to evaluate the solution at specific times, at increments of T. Since we're interested in the long-time behavior, you will discard the first data points, until the oscillator has reached the attractor. (This might take some time, depending upon the initial conditions.) To separate the analysis of the Poincaré section from the solution of the differential equation, it might be convenient to write these results to a data file, using `fopen` and `fprintf` statements.

EXERCISE 6.31
Write a program to calculate the points of the Poincaré section, as in Figure 6.22. That is, solve the differential equation to suitable accuracy, being sure that you have evolved the system for sufficient time to have reached the asymptotic regime. Then evaluate the solution at increments of T for, say, $5000\,T$ and write the results to a data file.

EXERCISE 6.32

Write a program that reads the data generated in the previous exercise, and plots the Poincaré section.

The fractal dimension associated with the Poincaré section of Figure 6.22 can be calculated using the box-counting method introduced in Chapter 1. Recall that the basic idea is to count the number of boxes, $\mathcal{N}(s^{-1})$, that is required to cover a geometrical object as a function of the scale of the boxes, s. The fractal dimension D_F is then the slope of the line of $\log \mathcal{N}(s^{-1})$ versus $\log s^{-1}$.

Perhaps the most critical part of the fractal dimension calculation is the box counting itself. But as we'll see, it's really not that difficult. We'll assume that the data is available in arrays x and y. The boxes are all initialized to zero, indicating that they're empty. Then each point in the Poincaré section is examined, the indices of the box containing the point determined, and the value of the box set to one, indicating that it's occupied. This process is repeated for all the points. Afterward, the number of occupied boxes are counted, logarithms calculated, and the values returned. The code might be

```
function [logInvScale,logBoxes] = BoxCounter(x,y,Number)
%
%   Input:  x, y        location of points in Poincare section
%           Number      Number of division in each dimension. That is,
%                           the total number of 2D boxes is Number*Number.
%
% Output:  logBoxes     log of the number of occupied boxes
%          logInvScale  log of (1/s)
%
x0 = min(x); x1 = max(x); y0 = min(y); y1 = max(y);

XRange = x1-x0;
YRange = y1-y0;
box    = zeros(Number);     % box is Number by Number array
dx     = XRange/Number;
dy     = YRange/Number;

for i=1:length(x)
    xbox = (x(i)-x0)/dx;
    ybox = (y(i)-y0)/dy;
    box( 1+floor(xbox), 1+floor(ybox) ) = 1;  %  box set to 1 if occupied
end

Boxes       = sum(sum(box));    % double sum adds boxes in 2D
logBoxes    = log(Boxes);
logInvScale = log(Number);
```

Since the scale is essentially `dx`, `Number` is an adequate stand in for s^{-1}. The function returns the logarithms of the inverse scale and the number of Boxes required to cover the object, ready to be plotted, and the fractal dimension extracted.

EXERCISE 6.33

Calculate the fractal dimension of the Poincaré section of van der Pol's oscillator with $f_o = 5$, $\Omega = 1.788$, and $\epsilon = 3.00$, as depicted in Figure 6.22. Plot `logBoxes` versus `logInvScale`, as in Figure 6.23, and determine the best linear fit to the data. From the slope, determine D_F.

The fractal nature of the Poincaré section is a geometrical measure of the chaos in the system. There is also a dynamic measure, the *Lyapunov exponent*. (Recall that we encountered the Lyapunov exponent in Chapter 1. At that time, we looked at the growth of a quantity as a function of the number of iterations. Here, we'll consider growth as a function of the continuous variable t.) Consider a point on the attractor, $\vec{r}_o = (x_o, y_o)$, and a nearby point $\vec{r} = \vec{r}_o + \vec{d}_o$. As these two points evolve through time, they may grow apart exponentially. Actually, in a two-dimensional phase space, there will be two Lyapunov exponents, one negative and one (maybe) positive—a positive exponent is indicative of chaos. Let's imagine that we've oriented $\vec{d}_o$ to be aligned with the direction of greatest growth. Then

$$d_1 = d_o \, e^{\lambda t}, \tag{6.131}$$

where $\vec{d}_1$ is the distance between the two paths some small time t later, and λ is the largest of the Lyapunov exponents. In fact, since it's the largest exponent that's

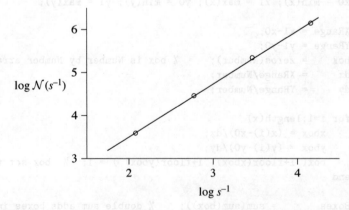

Figure 6.23   The log-log plot of occupied boxes versus scale factor, and the best linear fit to the data. The slope of the line is D_F.

associated with chaos, it's often referred to as *the* Lyapunov exponent. It can be evaluated as

$$\lambda = \frac{1}{t}\ln\frac{d_1}{d_o}. \qquad (6.132)$$

In practice, this quantity varies greatly with $\vec{r}$, and so a long time average should be taken to evaluate it. This is consistent with allowing the oscillator to sample a large amount of the phase space available to it, and averaging.

A relatively easy way to evaluate this exponent is to modify the RKF integrator to calculate a second trajectory for each time step. After the first trajectory, the actual solution to the problem, is calculated, a second solution with slightly different initial conditions is also calculated. This difference in initial conditions, denoted Ly_delta in the computer code, is reset for each time step. In general, Ly_delta will have components in both the growing and shrinking coordinates—by aligning with the direction of growth, after a few iterations Ly_delta will be aligned with the direction of maximum growth, for which Equation 6.131 holds. That is, this realignment is necessary in order to "isolate" the largest Lyapunov exponent. Within the overall calculational loop, we simply added the code necessary to evaluate the second trajectory, evaluate λt, and add to the running accumulation:

```
    ...
    if( hnew >= h )
%   The error is small enough, so this step is acceptable.
%
%%%%%%%%%%%%%%%%%%%%%%%%%%%%%%%%%%%%%%%%%%%%%%%%%%%%%%%%%%%%%%%%%%%%%%%%%%
%                                                                       %
%   Before actually moving the solution forward, calculate a SECOND     %
%   solution, to be used for the calculation of the Lyapunov exponent.  %
%   Ly_delta is the vector pointing to the nearby point. Note that      %
%   NOTHING required for the FIRST solution is modified by this         %
%   additional code.                                                    %
%                                                                       %
%   Initialize SECOND solution...                                       %
%                                                                       %
    SS0 = [S0(1)+Ly_delta(1);S0(2)+Ly_delta(2)];                        %
    f0=  derivs(t0,SS0);                                                %
    t = t0 + a1*h;                                                      %
    SS = SS0 + b10*h*f0;                                                %
    f1 = derivs(t,SS);                                                  %
    t = t0 + a2*h;                                                      %
    SS = SS0 + b20*h*f0 + b21*h*f1;                                     %
    f2 = derivs(t,SS);                                                  %
    t = t0 + a3*h;                                                      %
    SS = SS0 + h*(b30*f0+b31*f1+b32*f2);                                %
    f3 = derivs(t,SS);                                                  %
    t = t0 + a4*h;                                                      %
```

```
            SS = SS0 + h*(b40*f0+b41*f1+b42*f2+b43*f3);        %
            f4 =  derivs(t,SS);                                %
            t = t0 + a5*h;                                     %
            SS = SS0 + h*(b50*f0+b51*f1+b52*f2+b53*f3+b54*f4); %
            f5 = derivs(t,SS);                                 %
            SShat = SS0 + h*(c0*f0+c2*f2+c3*f3+c4*f4+c5*f5);   %
            Ly_d1 = sqrt( (Shat(1)-SShat(1))^2 + (Shat(2)-SShat(2))^2 );  %
            Ly_delta=[Ly_d0*(SShat(1)-Shat(1))/Ly_d1;          %
                      Ly_d0*(SShat(2)-Shat(2))/Ly_d1 ];        %
            XPONENT = XPONENT + log(Ly_d1/Ly_d0);              %
%                                                              %
%                                                              %
%%%%%%%%%%%%%%%%%%%%%%%%%%%%%%%%%%%%%%%%%%%%%%%%%%%%%%%%%%%%%%%%%
%
            t0 = t0 + h;
            S0 = Shat;
            ...
```

Clearly, XPONENT was initialized to zero elsewhere. The final evaluation of the Lyapunov exponent is then simply

```
            Lyapunov = XPONENT/t0;
```

which yields the time averaged exponent.

EXERCISE 6.34
Evaluate the Lyapunov exponent of Exercise 6.33, and compare to the value of 0.1932 given by Sprott in *Chaos and Time-Series Analysis*. (See Figure 6.24.)

The van der Pol oscillator is primarily stable; it's only in certain narrow regions that chaos reigns. Another such region, in addition to the one we've been investigating, is centered on the parameters

$$\epsilon = 3.16,$$
$$f_o = 13.1,$$
$$\Omega = 3.79, \tag{6.133}$$

originally studied by Shaw (R. Shaw, "Strange Attractors, Chaotic Behavior, and Information Flow," Zeitschrift für Naturforschung, 36a:80–112, 1981).

EXERCISE 6.35
Create the Poincaré section for the van der Pol oscillator using the Shaw parameters. From that data, evaluate its fractal dimension.

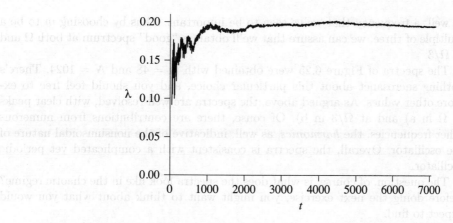

Figure 6.24 The convergence of the Lyapunov exponent with time. Note that there's considerable fluctuation in λ as calculated over *any* short time span—it's only in the long time limit that the result converges.

EXERCISE 6.36

Evaluate the Lyapunov exponent associated with the van der Pol oscillator with the Shaw parameters.

As with the unforced van der Pol oscillator, we can learn much about the system by investigating the frequency spectrum of the oscillator, using the FFT. As discussed earlier, finding that combination of sampling rate and number of points in the transform greatly affects the spectrum obtained, and we should be willing to experiment some to find a suitable combination. In the present case, however, we understand that the frequency of the driving force, Ω, is central to the problem, at least for the range of parameters we've been studying. That suggests that we look at the system for an integer number of periods of the driving force, which we've denoted as

$$T_\Omega = \frac{2\pi}{\Omega}. \tag{6.134}$$

The longer the total time, T, the more finely resolved is the frequency, since for the FFT

$$\Delta\omega = \frac{2\pi}{T}. \tag{6.135}$$

Thus we'll let

$$T = mT_\Omega, \tag{6.136}$$

where m is an integer of our choosing. But there's another consideration: If T were an integer multiple of $3T_\Omega$, then it would be commensurate with the frequency $\Omega/3$

as well, a frequency that we've seen to be important. Thus by choosing m to be a multiple of three, we can assure that we'll obtain a "good" spectrum at both Ω and at $\Omega/3$.

The spectra of Figure 6.25 were obtained with $m = 48$ and $N = 1024$. There's nothing sacrosanct about this particular choice, and you should feel free to explore other values. As argued above, the spectra are well-resolved, with clear peaks at Ω in a) and at $\Omega/3$ in b). Of couse, there are contributions from numerous other frequencies, the *harmonics*, as well, indicative of the nonsinusoidal nature of the oscillator. Overall, the spectra is consistent with a complicated yet periodic oscillator.

The question, of course, is what does the spectra look like in the chaotic regime? Before doing the next exercise, you might want to think about what you would expect to find.

EXERCISE 6.37
Calculate the spectrum of the van der Pol oscillator for $\epsilon = 3$, $\Omega = 1.788$, and $f_o = 5.0$.

Another interesting case is *Duffing's oscillator*, described by the differential equation

$$\ddot{x} + k\dot{x} + x^3 = f_o \cos \Omega t. \tag{6.137}$$

This is clearly a nonlinear oscillator, and admits a wide range of possible behaviors. In fact, it can be periodic, or its motion can be so complicated as to be seemingly unpredictable. Although the motion is certainly *deterministic*, it's another example of *chaos*.

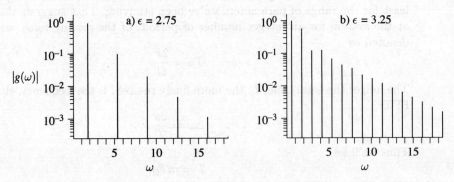

Figure 6.25   The spectra of the van der Pol oscillator with $f_o = 5$, $\Omega = 1.788$, and a) $\epsilon = 2.75$ and b) $\epsilon = 3.25$. 1024 points were used in the FFT, over a range in time of 48 T_Ω.

Consider Duffing's oscillator with the parameters

$$k = 0.1,$$
$$f_o = 40.0,$$
$$\Omega = 1.0. \qquad (6.138)$$

The Poincaré section is shown in Figure 6.26. It certainly *appears* that it might be a strange attractor.

EXERCISE 6.38
Determine the fractal dimension of the Poincaré section of Figure 6.26. Recall that D_F is a measure of the chaos—the further from integer, the more chaotic.

EXERCISE 6.39
The second measure of chaos is the Lyapunov exponent—the larger it is, the more chaotic the system. Calculate the Lyapunov exponent associated with Duffing's oscillator with the parameters of Equation 6.138.

EXERCISE 6.40
Calculate the frequency spectrum of Duffing's oscillator with the parameters given in Equation 6.138.

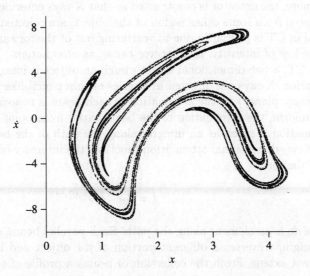

Figure 6.26   Duffing's oscillator Poincaré section with $k = 0.1$, $f_o = 40.0$, and $\Omega = 1.0$.

6.11 Computerized Tomography

Fourier analysis is commonplace throughout physics, particularly in areas of "applied" physics. In some areas, such as modern optics, it can be argued that Fourier analysis is truly *fundamental* to the field. Such widespread applicability of Fourier methods certainly warrants its study in computational physics, although we cannot begin to devote the space it justifies. Rather, we shall present only a single example—but one that has revolutionized modern medicine.

When Wilhelm Roentgen discovered X-rays in 1895, its importance to the practice of medicine was quickly recognized. Within months, the first medical X-ray pictures were taken. For his efforts, Roentgen was awarded the first Nobel Prize in Physics in 1901. In the 1960s and '70s, another revolution occurred as X-rays were employed to obtain detailed internal images of the body, using computerized tomography. Today, CAT scans are an important and commonly used tool in the practice of medicine. In 1979, Cormack and Hounsfield were awarded the Nobel Prize in Medicine for their efforts. Our interest in computerized tomography is simple—CT is fundamentally based upon Fourier transforms.

As a beam of X-rays passes through a uniform slab of material, the intensity of the beam decreases in a regular pattern. If we measure that intensity, we find the intensity to be

$$I = I_0 e^{-\lambda d}, \tag{6.139}$$

where I_0 is the initial intensity, d is the thickness of the slab, and λ is an appropriate coefficient. λ is often called an absorption coefficient, but there are actually many processes occurring that diminish the intensity of the beam. In particular, the detector is arranged to measure the intensity of the beam that passes straight through the object, so that any X-rays that are *scattered* will not be detected. (Furthermore, the detector is constructed so that X-rays entering at an angle, and hence scattered from some other region of the object, are rejected.) The reduction of the signal in CT is primarily due to scattering out of the forward direction. We'll refer to the loss of intensity, to whatever cause, as *attenuation*.

In CT, a two-dimensional slice through an object is imaged. In its simplest configuration, X-rays are directed in a series of thin pencil-like parallel beams through the image plane, and the attenuation of each beam is measured. Since the object is nonuniform, the attenuation of the beam varies from point to point, and the total attenuation is given as an integral along the path of the beam. That is, if $f(x, y)$ is the two-dimensional attenuation function, the intensity of each of the beams will be of the form

$$I = I_0 e^{-\int f(x,y)\, d\eta}, \tag{6.140}$$

where $d\eta$ is an element along the path. Each parallel beam, offset a distance ξ from the origin, traverses a different portion of the object and is thus attenuated to a different extent. From the collection of beams a profile of the object can be built.

More to the point, the *projection at* ϕ can be obtained by evaluating the logarithm of the measured I/I_0 ratio,

$$p(\xi; \phi) = -\ln\left(\frac{I}{I_0}\right) = \int f(x, y)d\eta. \tag{6.141}$$

(See Figure 6.27.) Our goal is to reconstruct $f(x, y)$ from the various projections $p(\xi; \phi)$ obtained at different angles ϕ.

Consider the coordinate systems in Figure 6.27. Associated with the object being scanned are the "fixed" xy-coordinates. We have a second coordinate system aligned with the X-ray beams, with coordinate η along the beam path and ξ perpendicular to them. The angle ϕ is simply the angle between $+x$ and $+\xi$ (and between $+y$ and $+\eta$). These coordinates are related by the familiar relations

$$\xi = x\cos\phi + y\sin\phi \tag{6.142}$$

and

$$\eta = -x\sin\phi + y\cos\phi. \tag{6.143}$$

The projection can be thought of as a function of ξ obtained at the particular angle ϕ.

Let's look at the Fourier transform of $f(x, y)$, which is simply

$$\mathcal{F}[f(x, y)] = F(k_x, k_y) = \frac{1}{2\pi}\iint_{-\infty}^{\infty} f(x, y)e^{i(k_x x + k_y y)}\, dx\, dy, \tag{6.144}$$

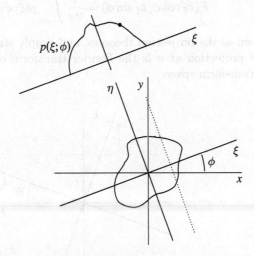

Figure 6.27 CAT scan geometry. The path of a typical beam is shown by the dotted line; its attenuation is represented by a single point in the projection $p(\xi; \phi)$.

and write the transform in terms of the $\xi\eta$−coordinate system. In transform space, k_ξ and k_η are rotated with respect to k_x and k_y in exactly the same fashion as ξ and η are rotated with respect to x and y, as seen in Figure 6.28. Thus

$$k_\xi = k_x \cos\phi + k_y \sin\phi \qquad (6.145)$$

and

$$k_\eta = -k_x \sin\phi + k_y \cos\phi. \qquad (6.146)$$

We easily find that the exponential factor appearing in the Fourier integral can be written as

$$e^{i(k_x x + k_y y)} = e^{i(k_\xi \xi + k_\eta \eta)}. \qquad (6.147)$$

To this point, we have been perfectly general. But now we're going to restrict ourselves. First, we fix ϕ in both coordinate and transform space. Then, instead of evaluating the Fourier transform *everywhere* in the $k_x k_y$-plane, we're only going to evaluate the transform on one line in the plane—the k_ξ axis. (Note that this line is coincident with the radial coordinate of a polar coordinate system, but extends from $-\infty$ to $+\infty$.) Since $k_\eta = 0$ along this line, we have

$$F(k_\xi \cos\phi, k_\xi \sin\phi) = \frac{1}{2\pi} \iint_{-\infty}^{\infty} f(x,y) e^{ik_\xi \xi} \, d\xi \, d\eta, \qquad (6.148)$$

where we've replaced the element of area $dx\,dy$ by the equivalent $d\xi\,d\eta$ in the integration. But with reference to Equation 6.141, we see that *the η integral is simply the projection* $p(\xi; \phi)$, so that

$$F(k_\xi \cos\phi, k_\xi \sin\phi) = \frac{1}{2\pi} \int_{-\infty}^{\infty} p(\xi; \phi) e^{ik_\xi \xi} \, d\xi. \qquad (6.149)$$

This is known as the projection theorem, and simply states that the Fourier transform of the projection at ϕ is the Fourier transform of the attenuation function along ϕ in transform space.

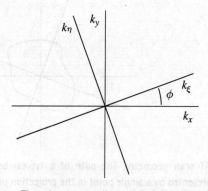

Figure 6.28   The relevant coordinate systems in transform space.

Let's review: What we *want* is $f(x,y)$, which is a representation of the object being scanned. If we had its Fourier transform, $F(k_x, k_y)$, we could obtain $f(x,y)$ by taking its inverse transform. What we *have* are projections $p(\xi; \phi)$, whose Fourier transforms are F at specific points on a polar grid.

By measuring the projections $p(\xi; \phi)$ at several different angles, the Fourier transform of the attenuation function can be acquired throughout the two-dimensional plane, one radial line at a time. In principle, the attenuation function could be obtained by evaluating the inverse Fourier transform. There is, however, a substantial obstacle to this straightforward approach—the points at which the transform is known are not the same as those needed for the inverse transform.

In building the Fourier transform from the projections, knowledge of the transform was acquired along the radial coordinate at different angles, as illustrated in Figure 6.29. But the grid points of a polar coordinate system do not coincide with the grid points of a Cartesian system, although these are precisely where they're needed if the Fourier transform is to be evaluated by the FFT. Increasing the number of grid points in a projection, or the number of projections, does not help solve the problem since the points still will not be where they are needed. Ultimately, interpolation must be used. A high-order interpolation will require extensive calculations, in addition to the two-dimension FFT needed to obtain the attenuation function in coordinate space. Any interpolation introduces additional error, and interpolation in transform space is particularly tricky—the error at one grid point, when transformed back to coordinate space, is spread over the entire plane. The image thus obtained is the sum of the true image plus error contributions from every interpolated point in transform space. As a result of these difficulties, direct inversion is rarely used. Rather, so-called *back projection* methods are employed. In effect, these methods perform the (necessary!) interpolation in *coordinate space* rather than in transform space.

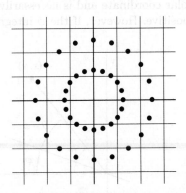

Figure 6.29   The Fourier transform is known on the polar grid, indicated by the black dots, while the straightforward FFT requires the data to be known on a Cartesian grid.

To see how this works, let's begin by writing the attenuation function as

$$f(x,y) = \frac{1}{2\pi} \iint_{-\infty}^{\infty} F(k_x, k_y) e^{-i(k_x x + k_y y)} \, dk_x \, dk_y. \tag{6.150}$$

With reference to Figure 6.30, we can write x and y in terms of the polar coordinates r and θ, and k_x and k_y in terms of ρ and ϕ, to find

$$k_x x + k_y y = \rho \cos \phi \, r \cos \theta + \rho \sin \phi \, r \sin \theta = \rho r \cos(\theta - \phi). \tag{6.151}$$

Then $f(x,y)$ becomes

$$
\begin{aligned}
f(r\cos\theta, r\sin\theta) &= \frac{1}{2\pi} \int_0^\infty \int_0^{2\pi} F(\rho\cos\phi, \rho\sin\phi) e^{-i\rho r \cos(\theta-\phi)} \, \rho \, d\phi \, d\rho \\
&= \frac{1}{2\pi} \int_0^\infty \int_0^{\pi} F(\rho\cos\phi, \rho\sin\phi) e^{-i\rho r \cos(\theta-\phi)} \, \rho \, d\phi \, d\rho \\
&\quad + \frac{1}{2\pi} \int_0^\infty \int_{\pi}^{2\pi} F(\rho\cos\phi, \rho\sin\phi) e^{-i\rho r \cos(\theta-\phi)} \, \rho \, d\phi \, d\rho \\
&= \frac{1}{2\pi} \int_0^\infty \int_0^{\pi} F(\rho\cos\phi, \rho\sin\phi) e^{-i\rho r \cos(\theta-\phi)} \, \rho \, d\phi \, d\rho \\
&\quad + \frac{1}{2\pi} \int_0^\infty \int_0^{\pi} F(-\rho\cos\phi, -\rho\sin\phi) e^{+i\rho r \cos(\theta-\phi)} \, \rho \, d\phi \, d\rho \\
&= \frac{1}{2\pi} \int_0^{\pi} \left(\int_0^\infty F(\rho\cos\phi, \rho\sin\phi) e^{-i\rho r \cos(\theta-\phi)} \, \rho \, d\rho \right. \\
&\quad \left. + \int_0^\infty F(-\rho\cos\phi, -\rho\sin\phi) e^{+i\rho r \cos(\theta-\phi)} \, \rho \, d\rho \right) d\phi. \tag{6.152}
\end{aligned}
$$

In the last integral, we might be tempted to make the substitution $\rho \to -\rho$. But ρ is the radial polar coordinate and is necessarily positive—to avoid confusion, we should leave it positive. However, if the ϕ integral is done last, the angle is fixed

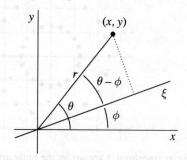

Figure 6.30   Geometry relating (x,y) and (r,θ) to ξ.

while the ρ integral is performed. And at fixed ϕ, ρ is simply $+k_\xi$. Thus, in the next-to-last integral we make the substitution $\rho \to k_\xi$, while in the last we use $\rho \to -k_\xi$ and reverse the limits of integration. By our definition of these coordinate systems, we also have that $r\cos(\theta - \phi) = \xi$. Thus we find

$$f(r\cos\theta, r\sin\theta) = \frac{1}{2\pi}\int_0^\pi \left(\int_0^\infty F(k_\xi\cos\phi, k_\xi\sin\phi)e^{-ik_\xi\xi}\, k_\xi\, dk_\xi \right.$$
$$\left. + \int_{-\infty}^0 F(k_\xi\cos\phi, k_\xi\sin\phi)e^{-ik_\xi\xi}\,(-k_\xi)\, dk_\xi \right)d\phi$$
$$= \frac{1}{2\pi}\int_0^\pi \int_{-\infty}^\infty F(k_\xi\cos\phi, k_\xi\sin\phi)e^{-ik_\xi\xi}\,|k_\xi|\, dk_\xi\, d\phi$$
$$= \int_0^\pi \tilde{p}(\xi; \phi)\, d\phi, \tag{6.153}$$

where

$$\tilde{p}(\xi; \phi) = \frac{1}{2\pi}\int_{-\infty}^\infty F(k_\xi\cos\phi, k_\xi\sin\phi)e^{-ik_\xi\xi}\,|k_\xi|\, dk_\xi \tag{6.154}$$

is the *modified projection at* ϕ.

Again, let's review what we've done. Taking the Fourier transform of the projections, we find the Fourier transform of the attenuation function on a polar grid in transform space. To recover the function in coordinate space, we need to perform the inverse transform, but this is easily done *only* in Cartesian coordinates. To avoid interpolation in transform space, the inverse transform is written in terms of polar coordinates. Then, instead of integrating from 0 to 2π, we integrate from 0 to π and extend the "radial integration" to negative values. In this way, we're still integrating over the entire two-dimensional plane, but the "radial" integral now has the limits of a Cartesian coordinate. The price we pay is the presence of the factor $|k_\xi|$ in the integrand—but the integral has the form of an inverse Fourier transform and can be evaluated by the FFT!

What, then, are the actual steps to be taken to reconstruct the image? One possible scheme is the following:

0. Initialize everything. Zero the entries of the image. The outermost loop will integrate over the various angles.

1. Obtain the projection $p(\xi; \phi)$ at a new angle ϕ. The projection will be known (measured) at the points ξ_i.

2. Using the FFT, obtain $F(k_\xi\cos\phi, k_\xi\sin\phi)$ via Equation 6.149.

3. Using the inverse FFT, evaluate $\tilde{p}(\xi; \phi)$ via Equation 6.154. This modified projection will be known at the same points ξ_i as the original projection.

4. Evaluate the contribution to the image from this one projection.

4a. For a particular xy coordinate, determine ξ from Equation 6.142.

4b. Approximate the modified projection at ξ by interpolation of the $\tilde{p}(\xi_i; \phi)$. (Linear interpolation is usually sufficient.)

4c. Add this contribution to the ϕ integral to the image array, Equation 6.153. Note that this contribution depends only upon ξ and is independent of η.

4d. Repeat Steps 4a, 4b, and 4c for all xy coordinates in the image array.

This step is the essence of the "back projection." Every pixel in the image is given a value that depends *only* upon ξ, not η, so that even points where $f(x, y) = 0$ will receive a contribution.

5. Display the image obtained thus far. (Optional.) **NOTE:** Because of the spurious contributions from the back projection step, it's a good idea to examine the range of pixel values in the reconstructed image. In particular, large values are associated with pixels that have many contributions, while small values are an indication that they were spurious. Thus it's reasonable to set a non-zero minimum value to be required before that particular pixel is given weight.

6. Repeat Steps 1–5 for all angles in the ϕ integration.

With this outline as a guide, construction of a computer program is made easier. But first, we need to obtain the projections. In practice, of course, this is the data that would be obtained from the CT scanning device. For our purposes, we supply two functions to provide this information. The first is `Unknown(filename)`. This function retrieves the file and does some internal processing with the data in preparation for calculating the projections. The second is the function `CT_Projection(N,phi)`, which returns the N elements of the projection at the angle ϕ. Together, these simulate the interaction with an actual CT scanning device. The first test image, the data for which is provided in `CT1.dat`, is an L-shaped object and a circle, as shown in Figure 6.31. (That is, these objects will attenuate any X-ray beams traversing the region.) Note that the entire image is contained within a circle of unit radius, and hence the coordinate range for all spacial dimensions is $[-1, 1]$.

Since the numerical values in the image are obtained by interpolation, the size of the image is independent of the number of points in the projection. To emphasize this point, we'll make the image 100×100, a size that produces an adequate image and is incommensurate with any of the other parameters of the problem. A sketch of the computer program would look like the following:

```
%  CT.m
%  CT performs image reconstruction by computerized tomography.
%  In principle, it's a fairly complicated problem, but when
%  broken down and attacked piece by piece, it's not so bad.
%
%  Typical Usuage: CT CT1.dat
```

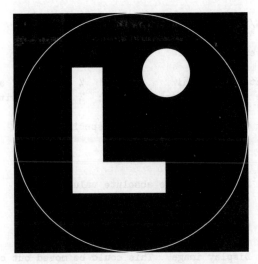

Figure 6.31 A test image to explore computerized tomography. A unit circle has been added to indicate the allowed extent of the object being imaged—it is not present in the datafile provided to you.

```
%            Output: a reconstruction of the original image.
%
%  As presently constructed, the image is updated as the contribution
%  from each separate angle is obtained.
%
%  Requires additional functions "Unknown", and "CT_Projection".
%
function CT

% STEP 0: Initialize things, get the data, zero the image

File=input(' Enter an input data file: ','s'); %  Get the data file
if(isempty(File)), ...
    disp(' ERROR: Need a data file name ... ') ; return; end
%
Unknown(File);                % This initializes the "scanning device"
CTdimension = 100;            % Initialize CTimage to zero
CTimage     = zeros(CTdimension,CTdimension);
colormap(gray);               % Gray scale replaces the default colors.
%
NumPhi = 20;
m = 5;
N = 2^m;
delta_x = 2.0/N;
```

```
halfN = N/2;

% Loop over Steps 1-5:

for icount = 1: NumPhi                    %  The "0.5" avoids phi being
    Phi = (icount-0.5)*pi/(NumPhi);       %  aligned with x,y axes...

% STEP 1: Get the projection at a specific Phi

% STEP 2: Evaluate the FFT

% STEP 3: Multiply by the absolute value of k
%         and take the inverse FFT

% STEP 4: Update CTimage

% STEP 5: Display image...This could be moved out of the loop, but
%         it's kind of impressive to see the image being reconstructed.

% STEP 6: Repeat Steps 1-5

    end
```

Let's look at this in more detail. In Step 0, the user is asked for the name of the file containing the data, such as CT1.dat. The function Unknown is called upon to read the file and initialize whatever is required to evaluate the projections. The program then enters a loop over the angle ϕ. To avoid anything "special" associated with the x and y axes, ϕ is chosen to avoid them. (This would not be a problem with "real" images, but arise with "artificial" images such as the test image used here.)

The first step is to obtain the total projection at ϕ, done by simply calling CT_Projection(N,phi). The data (e.g., the original image) is assumed to be totally contained within a unit circle, so that $-1 < \xi < 1$. The determination of the appropriate ξ at which to evaluate the projection is performed with the function, based upon the value of N. With these considerations, Step 1 might look something like

```
% STEP 1: Get the projection at a specific Phi

        projection = CT_Projection(N,Phi);
```

We then move on to Step 2, Fourier transforming the projection. There are two crucial considerations to be made here, the first being the number of points to be used in the Fourier transform. We have already decided to use 32 points in the transform, as the code now stands, but this should be regarded as a provisional decision. Since the image lies entirely within the unit circle, we can be sure to have adequately sampled the *range* of the projection, but it is possible that we haven't sampled often enough. And of course, we also need to consider the range and resolution of k_ξ in transform space.

The second consideration regards the manner of storage. The FFT expects—no, *requires!*—the data to be in a specific order: the first entry corresponds to the coordinate being zero, e.g., $\xi = 0$, and increases. But the data is also periodic, so that the last entry in the array corresponds to $\xi = -\Delta\xi$. This is not the order in which the projection data is obtained (and stored), however. There are several remedies for this data mismatch, the easiest of which is to simply reorder the projection data. That is, the data is scuffled into a different array to be used in the FFT subroutine. Then we can complete Step 2, Fourier transform the data stored in temporary.

```
%  STEP 2: Evaluate the FFT

    for i=1:halfN
        temporary(  i  ) = complex(projection(i+halfN),0.);
        temporary(i+halfN) = complex(projection(  i  ),0.);
    end
    t2 = fft(temporary);
```

Step 3 is straightforward, if we remember that the data is stored in transform space in the same periodic manner as it is in coordinate space. Thus multiplication by $|k_\xi|$ is accomplished by

```
% STEP 3: Multiply by the absolute value of k

    delta_k = 2*pi/(N*delta_x);
    for i=1:halfN
        k = (i-1)*delta_k;          %  k = (i-1)*delta_k;
        t2(i)=k*t2(i);              %  absolute value trivial
%
        k = i*delta_k;              %  k = -i*delta_k;
        t2(N+1-i)=k*t2(N+1-i);      %  absolute value accounted for
    end
```

Note that we took the absolute value "manually." The inverse transform, provided by the MATLAB function ifft, then yields the modified projection, in the wraparound storage scheme. It will be helpful to return the data to its original ordering,

```
temporary = ifft(t2);
for i=1:halfN
    projections(  i  ) = real(temporary(i+halfN));
    projections(i+halfN) = real(temporary(  i  ));
end
```

We can now evaluate the contribution from this projection to the image, i.e., to all the pixels in the xy-image plane. Cycling over all the CTdimension×CTdimension elements of the image, Step 4 might look like

```
% STEP 4: Update CTimage
        big =0;
        for i=1:CTdimension
            xx = -1.+(i-1)*2.0/(CTdimension-1);
            for j=1:CTdimension
                yy = -1.+(j-1)*2.0/(CTdimension-1);
                xi = (xx*cos(Phi)+yy*sin(Phi));
                if( xi >= -1.0  & xi <= 1.0)
                    xi = (xi-(-1.0))*halfN+1;
                    ii = fix(xi);
                    if( ii > N-1 ), ii=N-1; end
                    alpha = xi-ii;                 % linear interpolation:
                    CTimage(i,j)= CTimage(i,j)+...
                        projections(ii)*(1.-alpha)+alpha*projections(ii+1);
                    if(CTimage(i,j) > big)big = CTimage(i,j);end;
                end
            end
        end
```

Anticipating the need for knowing the largest element of the array, big is evaluated.

It's not necessary to display the image after every additional projection. However, it's interesting to see the image build in this way, and so let's do it at least this once.

```
%  STEP 5:  Display image...This could be moved out of the loop, but
%          it's kind of impressive to see the image being reconstructed.

        minimum = 0.25 * big;
        imagesc(CTimage,[minimum big]);  % Scale image data and display
        shading interp
        axis image              % square aspect ratio
        pause(0.05)
```

The data contained in the array CTimage is scaled and displayed, such that values less than minimum are painted black and the largest values are painted white, with intermediate values an interpolated shade of gray.

EXERCISE 6.41
Using the outline provided, write a program to reconstruct the test image, using CT1.dat.

Depending upon the computer you are using, the reconstructed image might appear rather small. After all, 100×100 pixels is not a very large area. Or, the image might be displayed at a larger scale, but be severely pixelated.

EXERCISE 6.42
Increase the number of points used in the image to, say, 400×400. Note that this modification is independent of both the number of points in a single projection and the number of projections.

While this last exercise yields a larger, less pixelated image, little (if any?) of the "fuzziness" that was present in the original reconstruction has been eliminated. Simply by virtue of its increased size, more detail is visible—but is the detail real, or an artifact of the reconstruction? (Since we know what the image is supposed to be, Figure 6.31, we in fact know that it's an artifact.) We can try to improve the image by replacing the simple linear interpolation with something more sophisticated. Perhaps cubic interpolation would help....

EXERCISE 6.43
Modify the reconstruction program by using cubic interpolation to obtain the specific value of the modified projection at ξ.

Regardless of the results of the last exercise, even more improvement can be obtained. There are at least three further variables at your disposal for improving the quality of the image: the number of points in each projection, the range of the projections, and the number of projections used. That improvement can come with increasing the number of points shouldn't be a surprise. But recall that the range of the projection determines the resolution in transform space, so that a greater range might also lead to improvement of the image. We chose the range to be 2 (from -1 to 1), based on the physical requirement that the object being imaged lie entirely within the region being imaged. But the range could be extended, to larger and smaller values, simply by padding the array with zeros. One of the "secrets" of Fourier analysis is that regions in which the function is zero are just as important as those regions in which it isn't!

EXERCISE 6.44
Investigate improvements in the image quality by modifying these variables. Does the quality "stabilize" at some point?

The real test of your understanding of computerized tomography is in construct-ing an image of an unknown object, of course. In addition to CT1.dat, you have been provided with CT2.dat, associated with an "unknown object."

EXERCISE 6.45

Construct an image of the "unknown object" from the data in CT2.dat.

Astrophysicists face a problem remarkably similar to computerized tomography when they attempt to create images from the interference patterns obtained by radio telescopes. There are additional complexities, but the basic similarity exists: The signal that is measured is related via Fourier transforms to the source of the signals. Radar imaging, either terrestrial or planetary, also involves the manipu-lation of data and its Fourier transforms. These applications are computationally intensive and require considerable computer power. But as more powerful comput-ers become available we can expect such applications to increase both in number and in complexity.

6.12 References

Fourier Analysis is an extremely valuable tool in physics, applied physics, and engineering. As a result, it's discussed in many texts on the subject, such as

> H. J. Weber and G. B. Arfken, *Mathematical Methods for Physicists, Sixth Edition*, Elsevier Academic Press, Burlington, MA, 2005.

> Mary L. Boas, *Mathematical Methods in the Physical Sciences, Third Edition*, John Wiley & Sons, New York, 2006.

> Sadri Hassani, *Foundations of Mathematical Physics*, Allyn and Bacon, Needham Heights, MA, 1991.

There are also a wide variety of excellent references devoted exclusively to Fourier Analysis. One of the very best for physical scientists is

> C. C. Champeney, *Fourier Transforms and Their Physical Applications*, Academic Press, New York, 1973.

There's also considerable literature on the FFT, such as the book

> E. Oran Brigham, *The Fast Fourier Transform*, Prentice-Hall, Englewood Cliffs, NJ, 1974.

And there are applications of Fourier analysis to specific areas of physics, such as

J. D. Gaskill, *Linear Systems, Fourier Transforms, and Optics,* John Wiley & Sons, New York, 1978.

E. G. Steward, *Fourier Optics: An Introduction,* John Wiley & Sons, New York, 1987.

References to RADAR are also quite extensive. An excellent place to begin is

M. I. Skolnik, *Introduction to Radar Systems,* McGraw-Hill, New York, 1980.

In addition to the references to chaos provided in Chapter 1, chaos is discussed in

J. C. Sprott, *Chaos and Time-Series Analysis*, Oxford University Press, Oxford, 2003.

G. R. Fowles and G. L. Cassady, *Analytical Mechanics, 7th Edition,* Thomson, Brooks/Cole, Belmont, CA, 2005.

S. T. Thornton and J. B. Marion, *Classical Dynamics, 5th Edition,* Thomson, Brooks/Cole, Belmont, CA, 2004.

P. Hamill, *Intermediate Dynamics,* Jones and Bartlett, Sudbury, MA, 2010.

J. Thijssen, *Computational Physics, Second Edition,* Cambridge University Press, Cambridge, 2007.

The topic of computerized tomography can be quite complicated, and is not usually presented at an introductory level. If you want to study it more, you might consider the following:

R. H. T. Bates and M. J. McDonnell, *Image Restoration and Reconstruction,* Clarendon Press, Oxford, 1986.

F. Natterer, *The Mathematics of Computerized Tomography,* John Wiley & Sons, New York, 1986.

Image Reconstruction from Projections, edited by G. T. Herman, Springer-Verlag, Berlin, 1979.

Partial Differential Equations

As we consider the "more advanced" topics of physics, such as advanced classical mechanics, electromagnetic theory, and quantum mechanics, we find a profusion of *partial differential equations* used to describe the physical phenomena. There are times when these equations can be simplified, or perhaps special cases considered, so that the problem is reduced to one involving ordinary differential equations, which are generally easier to solve. More generally, however, a numerical approach is called for.

Earlier, we saw that derivatives can be approximated by differences, and differential equations thus transformed into difference equations. In this chapter the finite difference method, introduced in Chapter 5, will be extended to the multidimensional case appropriate for partial differential equations. We'll also investigate a radically different method of solution, one that utilizes the FFT with dramatic efficiency for certain problems.

• 7.1 Classes of Partial Differential Equations

As noted above, many of the interesting equations of physics are partial differential equations. That is, the physical problem involves two or more independent variables, such as an x-coordinate and time, and is described as having specific relationships existing between various derivatives. For example, we have the *wave equation*

$$\frac{\partial^2 u}{\partial t^2} - c^2 \frac{\partial^2 u}{\partial x^2} = 0 \tag{7.1}$$

in one spatial dimension, where c is the velocity of the wave. The equation simply states that the second derivatives of the "solution" are proportional to one another, with proportionality constant c^2.

Other equations express different relationships between the derivatives. For example, if only the first derivative with respect to time appears, we have the *diffusion equation,*

$$\frac{\partial u}{\partial t} - k\frac{\partial^2 u}{\partial x^2} = 0. \tag{7.2}$$

This is also known as the *heat equation*, as it describes the flow (diffusion) of heat through a conductor. (In this case, k is the thermal conductivity—its reciprocal, R, is the thermal resistivity, or resistance, e.g., the insulation quality of a material.) If the boundaries of an object are held constant, eventually the object will reach a steady-state distribution of temperature such that the temperature is no longer changing, i.e., the time derivative is zero. This is the *Laplace equation,*

$$\frac{\partial^2 u}{\partial x^2} = 0 \tag{7.3}$$

in one dimension. More interesting is the three-dimensional case, for which Laplace's equation becomes

$$\nabla^2 u = \frac{\partial^2 u}{\partial x^2} + \frac{\partial^2 u}{\partial y^2} + \frac{\partial^2 u}{\partial z^2} = 0, \tag{7.4}$$

where ∇^2 is called the *Laplacian*. Laplace's equation states that the Laplacian is everywhere zero—*Poisson's equation* states that the Laplacian exhibits a specific spatial dependence,

$$\nabla^2 u - f(x, y, z) = 0. \tag{7.5}$$

This allows for the introduction of heat "sources" and "sinks" into the problem. Like Laplace's equation, the solutions to Poisson's equation are independent of time.

Another equation of common interest, not too unlike Poisson's equation, is the *Helmholtz equation,*

$$\nabla^2 u + \lambda u = 0. \tag{7.6}$$

Last in our brief list, but certainly not least in importance, is the *Schrödinger equation,*

$$\left[-\frac{\hbar^2}{2m}\nabla^2 + V(x, y, z) \right] u - i\hbar\frac{\partial u}{\partial t} = 0. \tag{7.7}$$

(We note that the Schrödinger equation is also a diffusion equation, although complex. As such, it also allows for oscillatory solutions, which the real valued diffusion equation does not. Its fundamental importance to Quantum Mechanics warrants its special mention.)

Let's consider a general (linear) second order partial differential equation in two variables, say x and t, such as

$$A\frac{\partial^2 u}{\partial x^2} + B\frac{\partial^2 u}{\partial x \partial t} + C\frac{\partial^2 u}{\partial t^2} + D\left(x, t, u, \frac{\partial u}{\partial x}, \frac{\partial u}{\partial t}\right) = 0, \tag{7.8}$$

where A, B, and C are functions of x and t and D is a function of u and the derivatives $\partial u/\partial x$ and $\partial u/\partial t$ as well as x and t. Now, we might try to introduce new variables such that the terms involving mixed derivatives vanish. In so doing, we would find that the discriminant $B^2 - 4AC$ plays an important role. This same quantity appears in the analysis of conic sections—that is, the shape of the curve resulting from the intersection of a plane with a cone. In that case, there are three distinct possibilities: the hyperbola, the parabola, and the ellipse. By analogy, we employ the same terminology here. That is, if

$$B^2(x_0, t_0) - 4\,A(x_0, t_0)\,C(x_0, t_0) > 0 \qquad (7.9)$$

at (x_0, t_0), then the partial differential equation is said to be *hyperbolic at the point* (x_0, t_0). If the equation is hyperbolic at all points in the domain of interest, then it is said to be a *hyperbolic equation*. For example, since the velocity c is a real number the wave equation, Equation 7.1, is a hyperbolic equation. If

$$B^2(x_0, t_0) - 4\,A(x_0, t_0)\,C(x_0, t_0) = 0, \qquad (7.10)$$

the equation is *parabolic at the point* (x_0, t_0). The diffusion equation is an example of a parabolic partial differential equation. And finally, if

$$B^2(x_0, t_0) - 4\,A(x_0, t_0)\,C(x_0, t_0) < 0, \qquad (7.11)$$

the equation is *elliptic at the point* (x_0, t_0)—Laplace's and Poisson's equations are examples of elliptic equations.

7.2 The Vibrating String... Again!

As our first example of a physical problem described in terms of partial differential equations, we'll investigate the motion of waves on a string. We'll begin with an *ideal* string, one that's perfectly elastic, offers no resistance to bending, and is stretched between two immovable supports. We'll further assume that the mass density of the string is uniform, that the tension in the string is far greater than the weight of the string—so that we can ignore the effect of gravity—and that the amplitude of the string's motion is very small. We thus have a naive model of a violin string, for example.

We'll consider a small element of that string, as in Figure 7.1, and apply Newton's Second Law to it. There are two forces acting on the element, the tension at x and at $x + \Delta x$. The vertical component of the net force is simply

$$F_y = -T(x)\sin\alpha + T(x + \Delta x)\sin\beta. \qquad (7.12)$$

If the displacement of the string is small, the angles α and β are small, so that the *sine* of an angle can be replaced by the *tangent* of the angle,

$$\sin\alpha \approx \tan\alpha \quad \text{and} \quad \sin\beta \approx \tan\beta. \qquad (7.13)$$

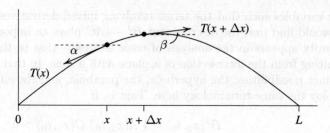

Figure 7.1   A vibrating string.

But, of course, the tangent of the angle is just the slope of the curve, the derivative $\partial u/\partial x$, so that

$$F_y = -T(x) \left. \frac{\partial u}{\partial x}\right|_x + T(x+\Delta x) \left.\frac{\partial u}{\partial x}\right|_{x+\Delta x}. \qquad (7.14)$$

For our problem, the tension in the string is the same everywhere so that $T(x) = T(x+\Delta x)$. Expressing the derivative at $x + \Delta x$ in a Taylor's series about x, we have

$$F_y = -T \left.\frac{\partial u}{\partial x}\right|_x + T\left[\left.\frac{\partial u}{\partial x}\right|_x + \Delta x \left.\frac{\partial}{\partial x}\frac{\partial u}{\partial x}\right|_x + \cdots\right]$$

$$\approx T\Delta x \frac{\partial^2 u}{\partial x^2}. \qquad (7.15)$$

Of course, Newton's Second Law tells us that the net force produces an acceleration, $\mathbf{F} = m\mathbf{a}$. If μ is the mass density of the string, then $\mu \Delta x$ is the mass of an element of the string and

$$\mu\,\Delta x \frac{\partial^2 u}{\partial t^2} = T\,\Delta x \frac{\partial^2 u}{\partial x^2}. \qquad (7.16)$$

Canceling the length element, we arrive at the wave equation

$$\frac{\partial^2 u}{\partial t^2} = \frac{T}{\mu} \frac{\partial^2 u}{\partial x^2}. \qquad (7.17)$$

Comparing to Equation 7.1, we conclude that the velocity of a wave on the string is

$$c = \sqrt{\frac{T}{\mu}}. \qquad (7.18)$$

7.3 Finite Difference Equations

We'll devise a numerical approach to the solution of the wave equation using finite difference approximations to the derivatives. We've already used finite differences for problems involving one independent variable—it works the same with two (or more). Recall that the second derivative can be approximated by

$$\frac{d^2 f(x)}{dx^2} = \frac{f(x+h) - 2f(x) + f(x-h)}{h^2} + O(h^2). \tag{7.19}$$

In two dimensions, we impose a rectangular grid in space and time such that

$$\begin{aligned} x_i &= ih_x, \quad i = 0, 1, \ldots, N_x, \\ t_j &= j\delta_t, \quad j = 0, 1, \ldots, N_t. \end{aligned} \tag{7.20}$$

The finite difference approximation to the wave equation is then

$$\frac{u_i^{j+1} - 2u_i^j + u_i^{j-1}}{\delta_t^2} - c^2 \frac{u_{i+1}^j - 2u_i^j + u_{i-1}^j}{h_x^2} = 0, \tag{7.21}$$

where we've introduced the notation

$$u_i^j = u(x_i, t_j). \tag{7.22}$$

Solving for u_i^{j+1}, we find

$$u_i^{j+1} = \frac{\delta_t^2 c^2}{h_x^2} \left(u_{i+1}^j + u_{i-1}^j \right) + 2 \left(1 - \frac{\delta_t^2 c^2}{h_x^2} \right) u_i^j - u_i^{j-1}. \tag{7.23}$$

This equation tells us that if we know u at all x_i at the times t_j and t_{j-1}, then we can immediately determine u at all x_i at the next time step, t_{j+1}. It is said to be an *explicit* method for determining the solutions.

7.4 Stability

Until now, our concern with the size of the finite differences has been with *accuracy*—that is, as we make h_x (or any other difference) smaller, how does the accuracy of the result change? But here we're faced with a different challenge, as we'll soon see: What about the *stability* of the result?

To be specific, consider the equation

$$\frac{\partial u}{\partial t} = c \frac{\partial u}{\partial x}, \quad u(x, 0) = u_o(x). \tag{7.24}$$

Consider a simple differencing scheme leading to the equation

$$\frac{u(x, t + \delta_t) - u(x, t)}{\delta_t} = c \frac{u(x + h_x, t) - u(x, t)}{h_x}, \tag{7.25}$$

or

$$u(x, t + \delta_t) = u(x, t) + \frac{c\delta_t}{h_x} \left[u(x + h_x, t) - u(x, t) \right]. \tag{7.26}$$

Let's start at $t = 0$, so that $u(x, 0) = u_o(x)$. From the discussion of the last chapter, we know that $u_o(x)$ could be written as a Fourier series, or transform. We'll consider just one of those components, and let

$$u_o(x) = e^{ikx}. \tag{7.27}$$

(Since the differential equation is linear, the full solution can be obtained by summing over all the Fourier components, so that what we're doing here is perfectly general.) Then

$$
\begin{aligned}
u(x, \delta_t) &= e^{ikx} + \frac{c\delta_t}{h_x}\left[e^{ik(x+h_x)} - e^{ikx}\right] \\
&= \left[1 + \frac{c\delta_t}{h_x}(e^{ikh_x} - 1)\right]e^{ikx} \\
&= G(k)e^{ikx} \\
&= G(k)u(x, 0).
\end{aligned} \tag{7.28}
$$

In this expression, $G(k)$ is a growth factor. After n time steps, the solution has grown by a factor of G^n. If $|G| > 1$, our solution has "blown up."

Let's look at the worst case scenario: if $kh_x = \pi$, then

$$G(k) = 1 - 2\frac{c\delta_t}{h_x}. \tag{7.29}$$

In order to keep $|G| < 1$, we must require that

$$\lambda \equiv \left|\frac{c\delta_t}{h_x}\right| \leq 1, \tag{7.30}$$

where we've introduced the *Courant number*, λ. Here, then, is a new requirement we must meet. In addition to choosing h_x and δ_t to be small enough to yield accurate results, yet large enough for the calculation to proceed in a timely manner, we must meet the requirement that $\lambda \leq 1$ in order to ensure the stability of the solution, i.e., that the solution is meaningful.

Returning to our original differential equation,

$$\frac{\partial^2 u}{\partial t^2} = c^2 \frac{\partial^2 u}{\partial x^2}, \tag{7.31}$$

we might realize that this can be written in an array form as

$$\frac{\partial}{\partial t}\begin{bmatrix} \dfrac{\partial u}{\partial t} \\ c\dfrac{\partial u}{\partial x} \end{bmatrix} = \begin{bmatrix} 0 & c \\ c & 0 \end{bmatrix}\frac{\partial}{\partial x}\begin{bmatrix} \dfrac{\partial u}{\partial t} \\ c\dfrac{\partial u}{\partial x} \end{bmatrix}. \tag{7.32}$$

This, of course, we recognize as a vector version of Equation 7.24. A detailed analysis of this equation leads to the same requirement,

$$\lambda \equiv \left| \frac{c\delta_t}{h_x} \right| \leq 1, \tag{7.33}$$

which must be met when using Equation 7.23.

7.5 Back to the String...

There is a small difficulty in starting the solution since we usually won't know u at two successive times. Rather, we might know $u(x_i, 0)$ and the derivative $\partial u(x_i, 0)/\partial t$ at all x_i. Then we have

$$\left. \frac{\partial u(x_i, t)}{\partial t} \right|_{t=0} = \frac{u_i^1 - u_i^{-1}}{2\delta_t} \tag{7.34}$$

or

$$u_i^{-1} = u_i^1 - 2\delta_t \left. \frac{\partial u(x_i, t)}{\partial t} \right|_{t=0}. \tag{7.35}$$

With this expression for u_i^{-1}, we can write the $j = 0$ case of Equation 7.23, i.e., the solution at the first time step, as

$$u_i^1 = \frac{\delta_t^2 c^2}{2h_x^2} \left(u_{i+1}^0 + u_{i-1}^0 \right) + \left(1 - \frac{\delta_t^2 c^2}{h_x^2} \right) u_i^0 + \delta_t \frac{\partial u(x_i, 0)}{\partial t}. \tag{7.36}$$

These equations are readily transformed into a suitable computer code. Perhaps the most straightforward way to proceed is to introduce one array to hold u at all x_i at the time t_j, a second array to hold all the u at the time t_{j-1}, and a third to hold the newly computed results at t_{j+1}. Then we loop through the code incrementing the time and shuffling the arrays appropriately. An outline of the subroutine might look like the following:

```
% string.m
% Fragment to calculate and observe the motion of a string.
clear;
% U_0 is the initial u at t=0, and dU_0 is the time derivative
%    evaluated at t=0, the initial conditions of the problem.
%
% These arrays must be initialized. This can be done
%    through an assignment statement, or by evaluating
%    appropriate functions inside a for-loop.
```

```
       Nt =                % number of time steps
  maxtime =                % maximum simulation time
       dt =                % time increment
        N =                % number of points in the x-grid
        L =                % string length
       dx =                % space increment
        x =                % x array
        T =                % tension
       mu =                % mass density
        c =                % wave velocity
  epsilon = (dt*c/dx)^2; % Needs to remain < 1 to ensure stability
  % See U(i) below
  ...
  % Initialize U and Uold. Let Uold = u(0), U = u(x,1 dt).
  time     = 0.0;          % Time t=0 initial condition
  U_0(1)   = 0.0;
  U_0(N)   = 0.0;
  dU_0     = zeros(1,N);
  Uold     = U_0;
  % U(endpoints) are fixed, = 0.
  U(1) = 0.0;
  U(N) = 0.0;
  for i = 2: N-1     % If epsilon > 1, U(i) becomes unstable
      U(i)=0.5*epsilon*(U_0(i+1)+U_0(i-1))+...
           (1.0-epsilon) * U_0(i) + dt * dU_0(i);
  end
  %
  % Start main time loop
  while time < maxtime
      time     = time + dt;
      Unew(1) = 0.0;
      Unew(N) = 0.0;
      for i = 2: N-1
              Unew(i) = epsilon * ( U(i+1) + U(i-1) ) + ...
                  2.d0 * (1.0-epsilon) * U(i) - Uold(i);
      end
      % Shuffle arrays, and animate ...
      Uold=U;
      U=Unew;
      clf        % Animation Step 1: clear the screen
      plot(x,U)  % Animation Step 2: plot the new data
      pause(0.01);
  end
```

This computer code can be used to "solve" the problem—that is, to generate a large amount of data over many time steps. But data in such a form is nearly impossible to comprehend. On the other hand, a visual representation of the data is readily understood. So, we've added a primitive level of animation by erasing the screen and redrawing the solution at the new time. By so doing, the motion of the wave is vividly displayed.

The program we've developed can be applied to a variety of problems. Let's start with a meter length of string, stretched with a tension of 10 Newtons and having a mass of 1 gram. Initially, we'll deform the string so that it has a "bump" in the middle,

$$u(x,0) = \begin{cases} 0, & x = 0, \\ e^{-100(x-0.5)^2}, & 0 < x < 1, \\ 0, & x = 1. \end{cases} \tag{7.37}$$

and is motionless at time $t = 0$. Take $h = 1$ cm, and $\delta_t = 0.0001$ seconds.

EXERCISE 7.1
Use the computer code outlined above, with the parameters discussed, to calculate and observe the motion of the string for 20 time steps.

EXERCISE 7.2
Before proceeding, it might be a good idea to investigate the behavior of the solution as δ_t is changed. In particular, choose δ_t such that $\lambda > 1$, to see what is meant by "unstable."

You probably observed a rather curious result—the bump "fell apart" into two bumps, moving in opposite directions. This is a very general result. Solutions to the wave equation are *waves*—depending upon the initial conditions, the general solution to the equation is a combination of one waveform moving to the right and a second waveform moving to the left. If, as we required, the initial time derivative is zero and the initial waveform is symmetric, then the waveform has no choice but to evolve as it did. To demonstrate, write

$$u(x,t) = f(x+ct) + g(x-ct), \tag{7.38}$$

where f and g are the waveforms moving to the left and right, respectively. Then

$$\begin{aligned}\frac{\partial^2 u(x,t)}{\partial t^2} &= \frac{\partial}{\partial t}\left[\frac{\partial}{\partial t}(f(x+ct)+g(x-ct))\right] \\ &= \frac{\partial}{\partial t}\left[c\frac{df(x+ct)}{dt} - c\frac{dg(x-ct)}{dt}\right] \\ &= c^2\frac{d^2f}{dt^2} + c^2\frac{d^2g}{dt^2}\end{aligned} \tag{7.39}$$

and

$$\frac{\partial^2 u(x,t)}{\partial x^2} = \frac{\partial}{\partial x}\left[\frac{\partial}{\partial x}\left(f(x+ct)+g(x-ct)\right)\right]$$

$$= \frac{\partial}{\partial x}\left[\frac{df(x+ct)}{dx}+\frac{dg(x-ct)}{dx}\right]$$

$$= \frac{d^2 f}{dx^2}+\frac{d^2 g}{dx^2}. \tag{7.40}$$

Clearly then, our guess of Equation 7.38 is a solution to the wave equation of Equation 7.1, and we've shown that the general solution of the wave equation is a linear combination of two counter-propagating waves.

Let's see if we can construct a wave that is moving to the left. To do this, we need a function that depends upon the particular combination $x + ct$, such as

$$u(x,t) = \begin{cases} 0, & x = 0, \\ e^{-100(x+ct-0.5)^2}, & 0 < x < 1, \\ 0, & x = 1. \end{cases} \tag{7.41}$$

The time derivative of this function is

$$\left.\frac{\partial u}{\partial t}\right|_{t=0} = -200c(x-0.5)e^{-100(x+ct-0.5)^2}, \quad 0 < x < 1, \tag{7.42}$$

and zero at the rigid endpoints.

EXERCISE 7.3

Incorporate this new boundary condition at $t = 0$ into your computer code and verify that this function represents a wave moving to the left, by following the time evolution for 20 time steps.

We can, of course, easily observe the phenomena of constructive and destructive interference of waves. Let the displacement of the string be written as

$$u(x,t) = \alpha f(x,t) + \beta g(x,t) \tag{7.43}$$

where $f(x,t)$ is initially centered at $x = 0.75$ and moving to the left,

$$f(x,0) = e^{-100(x-0.75)^2}, \tag{7.44}$$

$$\left.\frac{\partial f}{\partial t}\right|_{t=0} = -200c(x-0.75)e^{-100(x-0.75)^2}, \quad 0 < x < 1, \tag{7.45}$$

and $g(x,t)$ is initially centered at $x = 0.25$ and moving to the right,

$$g(x,0) = e^{-100(x-0.25)^2}, \tag{7.46}$$

$$\left.\frac{\partial g}{\partial t}\right|_{t=0} = +200c(x - 0.25)e^{-100(x-0.25)^2}, \quad 0 < x < 1. \tag{7.47}$$

EXERCISE 7.4
Show that constructive interference occurs when α and β have the same sign, while the waves interfere destructively if they have opposite signs.

Thus far, the wave has been kept away from the ends, where it is rigidly supported. But the interaction of the wave with the supports is very important—in particular, the support will *reflect* the wave.

EXERCISE 7.5
Follow the wave disturbance for a longer time, say 500 time steps.

You observed, of course, the phenomena of *phase reversal* as the wave was reflected from the rigid support. What happens if the support is not rigid? Let's imagine that the string is free at $x = 0$. The vertical component of the force on the end of the string is

$$F_y = -T(0)\sin\alpha \approx -T(0)\left.\frac{\partial u}{\partial x}\right|_{x=0}. \tag{7.48}$$

But there's no physical support to provide the force, so the force must be zero! Hence

$$\left.\frac{\partial u}{\partial x}\right|_{x=0} = 0. \tag{7.49}$$

In terms of a difference equation, we have

$$\frac{u_1^j - u_0^j}{h} = 0, \tag{7.50}$$

or simply

$$u_0^j = u_1^j, \quad \text{for all } j. \tag{7.51}$$

To treat a free end we simply replace our fixed boundary condition, that $u_0^j = 0$, by this one.

EXERCISE 7.6

Modify your program to treat the string as free at $x = 0$, and repeat the previous exercise.

That the supports of real strings move is not a trivial observation. In fact, virtually all stringed musical instruments use this feature to generate sound. With a violin, for example, the sound doesn't emanate from the vibrating string—it comes from the vibrating violin, set in motion by the string. That is, the vibration of the string is coupled to the vibration of the violin box to generate the sound. If the string supports were truly rigid, the box would not vibrate, and the sound we recognize as the violin would not be generated.

The supports for real strings, such as found on musical instruments, lie somewhere between being perfectly rigid and being free. One way we can at least begin to consider real strings is by modeling the support as having mass: the free end corresponds to zero mass, and the rigid end corresponds to infinite mass. Real supports lie between these extremes.

We've already calculated the force on the string, Equation 7.48. We now apply Newton's second law to the support to find

$$M\frac{\partial^2 u}{\partial t^2}\bigg|_{x=0} = T\frac{\partial u}{\partial x}\bigg|_{x=0}, \tag{7.52}$$

where M is the effective mass of the support. Our finite difference expression for the condition at the boundary is then

$$u_0^{j+1} = \left(2 - \frac{T\delta^2}{Mh}\right)u_0^j - u_0^{j-1} + \frac{T\delta^2}{Mh}u_1^j. \tag{7.53}$$

EXERCISE 7.7

Modify your program so that the support at $x = 0$ has an effective mass $M = 0.001$ kg. How does the behavior of the system compare to the behavior of the system with the end fixed? With the end free?

We could continue to make our description of supports, and hence our boundary conditions, more realistic. For example, we could model the support as being a mass on a spring, damped by the loss of energy to the support (and the soundboard). Then the force might be modeled as

$$M\frac{\partial^2 u}{\partial t^2}\bigg|_{x=0} + R\left.\frac{\partial u}{\partial t}\right|_{x=0} + Ku(0,t) = T\frac{\partial u}{\partial x}\bigg|_{x=0}, \tag{7.54}$$

where K is a spring constant, or stiffness, and R is a damping coefficient. Real musical instruments, such as a violin, are further complicated by the presence of a large number of vibrational modes in the instrument itself. These modes couple to one another, and to the string, providing a richness that is both complicated to describe mathematically, and pleasing to the ear.

7.6 The Steady-State Heat Equation

In Chapter 5 we used the finite difference method to solve a two-point boundary value problem in one dimension. However, the real importance of these methods lies not in one dimension, but in their application to multidimensional problems, e.g., partial differential equations. For example, the heat flow in a homogeneous body is governed by the heat equation

$$\nabla^2 u(x, y, z, t) = \frac{1}{c^2} \frac{\partial u(x, y, z, t)}{\partial t}, \quad c^2 = \frac{K}{\sigma \rho}, \qquad (7.55)$$

where u is the temperature, K is the thermal conductivity, σ is the specific heat, and ρ is the density. If we consider a thin metal plate, the problem reduces to two dimensions, and the steady-state distribution of temperature in the plate will then satisfy the two-dimensional Laplace equation

$$\frac{\partial^2 u}{\partial x^2} + \frac{\partial^2 u}{\partial y^2} = 0. \qquad (7.56)$$

Of course, we must know something of the boundary conditions before we can solve the problem. Suppose, for example, that we know the temperature at all points on the boundary of the plate. This is a common situation, known as *Dirichlet boundary conditions*, and allows us to determine a unique solution to the problem.

After having solved the two-point boundary value problem in one dimension, the plan of attack for this two-dimensional problem is rather obvious: we replace the partial derivatives by their finite difference approximation, and solve the resulting finite difference equations by the method of successive over-relaxation. Recall that the second derivative can be approximated by

$$\frac{d^2 f(x)}{dx^2} = \frac{f(x+h) - 2f(x) + f(x-h)}{h^2} + O(h^2). \qquad (7.57)$$

For a rectangular plate of dimension $a \times b$ we introduce a grid such that

$$x_i = ih_x, \quad i = 0, 1, \ldots, N_x,$$
$$y_j = jh_y, \quad j = 0, 1, \ldots, N_y. \qquad (7.58)$$

We then easily find the finite difference equation

$$\frac{u_{i+1,j} - 2u_{i,j} + u_{i-1,j}}{h_x^2} + \frac{u_{i,j+1} - 2u_{i,j} + u_{i,j-1}}{h_y^2} = 0, \qquad (7.59)$$

where we've introduced the notation $u_{i,j} = u(x_i, y_j)$. Solving for $u_{i,j}$, we find

$$u_{i,j} = \frac{h_x^2 h_y^2}{2h_x^2 + 2h_y^2} \left[\frac{u_{i+1,j} + u_{i-1,j}}{h_x^2} + \frac{u_{i,j+1} + u_{i,j-1}}{h_y^2} \right]. \qquad (7.60)$$

Of course, if $h_x = h_y$ the expression takes on the much simpler form

$$u_{i,j} = \frac{1}{4} \left[u_{i+1,j} + u_{i-1,j} + u_{i,j+1} + u_{i,j-1} \right]. \qquad (7.61)$$

The manner of solution is exactly as for the two-point boundary value problem; that is, by iteration, except that we now loop over both x and y coordinates. For example, the code to solve the heat equation on a 33 by 33 grid might be patterned after the following:

```
% heat2d.m
% This fragment implements Successive Over-Relaxation
% to solve the 2D Heat equation on a 33 x 33 grid.
clear;
N       = 33;
hx      = ...
hy      = ...
alpha   = ...
maxiter = ...              % maximum number of iterations
tol     = 5.e-5;           % tolerance level
% Initialize u(i,j) --- to help keep things straight,
%                       i will always refer to the x-coordinate,
%                       j will always refer to the y-coordinate.
u = ...
% Initialize values on the boundaries
u(1,1:N) = ...
...
%
% Iteration starts here...
%
count = 0;
figure('Name','Temperatures on a Square Plate');  % Initialize FIGURE
done = false;
while ~done
    done  = true;                     % <----- LOOK HERE
    count = count + 1;
    if (count >= maxiter), error( Too many iterations!'); end
    % These loops do the SOR, using the relaxation parameter alpha.
    for i = 2: N-1
        for j = 2: N-1
                        % "u(i,j)" is the old value,
            uu =        % "uu" is the latest iterate.
            if(abs((uu-u(i,j))/uu) > tol), done = false; end
```

```
            u(i,j) = uu + alpha * ...;     % SOR iterate
         end
      end
%
% Write the temperatures to a Figure, dynamically changing their values
%   as the calculation proceeds...
%
      clf;
      axis image;                 axis([0 1 0 1]);
      set(gca,'xtick',[],'ytick',[])
      set(gcf,'Color',[1 1 1]);
      rectangle('EdgeColor','b');
      str = cat(2,'Temperature Distribution after Iteration # ',num2str(count));
      title(str);
      set(gca,'xcolor','b','ycolor','b','FontSize',8);
      for j = 1:4:N                    % Display every 4th value
         xj = (j-1)*hx;
         for i = 1:4:N                 % Display every 4th value
            yi = (i-1)*hy;
            str = num2str(u(i,j),'%4.1f');     % Write a temperature
            text(xj,yi,str,'FontSize',7);     %   to the screen.
         end
      end
      pause(0.05);
   end
% SOR finished
```

The functioning of this code fragment should be pretty clear. Various quantities are initialized before the iteration loop, as well as the function itself. Note that *every* value of the function should be initialized, not just the ones on the boundary.

While we could have written the results to the usual MATLAB screen, we've chosen to display them as text in a `figure`. (To avoid cluttering the screen, only every 4th value is displayed.) This permits us to see the temperatures changing dynamically, as the calculation unfolds. (A substantial amount of "real" time is expended in this effort, so for a larger problem you would want to limit the frequency of this writing, i.e., only every 10th iteration.)

When we first introduced Successive Over Relaxation (SOR) in Chapter 5, we indicated that there was an optimum value of α for every situation, dictated by the structure of the problem. As discussed in several numerical analysis texts, the optimum value can be derived analytically in certain cases and can be estimated in others. The optimal value for the relaxation parameter in situations using the second order central difference approximation in two Cartesian coordinates is given as

$$\alpha = \frac{4}{2 + \sqrt{4 - \left[\cos\frac{\pi}{N_x} + \cos\frac{\pi}{N_y}\right]^2}} - 1. \tag{7.62}$$

EXERCISE 7.8

Solve the two-dimensional heat equation for a 1 square meter plate (i.e., let $a = b = 1$ m) using a 33 by 33 grid, subject to the following boundary conditions:

i) Along the left and bottom edges, the temperature is held fixed at 100°C.

ii) Along the right and top edges, The temperature is held fixed at 0°C.

These boundary conditions admit a relatively simple solution, which can also be found analytically.

7.7 Isotherms

While the numerical output you've generated is correct and useful, it's rarely easy to recognize patterns in a collection of numerical results. Computational physics is moving away from purely numerical outputs toward presenting data, or results of calculations, in a graphical manner—scientific visualization. The state-of-the-art is far beyond the scope of this book, but surely we can do better than presenting a pile of numbers. For the heat problem, one possibility that comes to mind is to plot lines of constant temperature, or *isotherms*. Such contour plots are familiar to map readers everywhere. (*Isobars*, contours of equal barometric pressure, are often drawn on weather maps.) With a little practice, the interpretation of contour plots becomes fairly easy and a wealth of information becomes available.

The contouring algorithm we use is very simple—and always (?) works! (Some very sophisticated algorithms are known to produce erroneous contours in certain circumstances.) The function is described in the Appendix; to use it, simply modify your code to include the following:

```
% isotherms.m
% This fragment adds isothermal contours to the Successive Over
%   Relaxation solution of the 2D Heat equation on a 33 x 33 grid.
clear;
...
% SOR finished

% We next draw the contours using our function drawContours
xx(1) = x-coordinate of first grid line
xx(2) = x-coordinate of second grid line
...
yy(1) = y-coordinate of first grid line
yy(2) = y-coordinate of second grid line
...
contour(1) = temperature of contour 1;      % contour values desired
```

```
contour(2) = temperature of contour 2;
...
drawContours(xx, yy, u, contour, true, 'r');
```

EXERCISE 7.9

Modify your program so as to plot the isotherms after the calculation has been completed.

7.8 Irregular Physical Boundaries

It can happen, of course, that the physical plate doesn't match the grid very well. This can happen, for example, if we try to use a rectangular grid to investigate the temperature distribution in a circular plate. The best resolution of the difficulty is to use a grid more suitable to the problem. In the case of the circular plate, a cylindrical coordinate system is a much more natural choice than a Cartesian one. However, there are times when the problem is more than simply a choice of coordinate system. Consider, for example, a triangular plate—there's no coordinate system that makes that problem nice. We must face up to the possibility, nay, probability, that we cannot always choose our grid points to lie on the boundary of the object. For this case, we must come up with an acceptable procedure.

Actually, it's not all that difficult, once the need for special treatment along the boundary has been recognized. Consider the example shown in Figure 7.2. The function is known all along the boundary; the difficulty is just that the boundary doesn't happen to lie on a grid line. The real problem is simply to express the second derivative in terms of the value at the boundary rather than at the node.

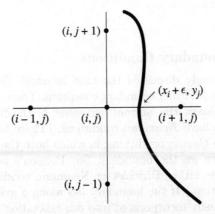

Figure 7.2   A boundary need not lie along a grid line.

As usual, we expand in a Taylor series about x_i:

$$f(x_i + \varepsilon) = f(x_i) + \varepsilon f'(x_i) + \frac{\varepsilon^2}{2} f''(x_i) + \frac{\varepsilon^3}{3!} f'''(x_i) + \cdots \tag{7.63}$$

and

$$f(x_i - h) = f(x_i) - h f'(x_i) + \frac{h^2}{2} f''(x_i) - \frac{h^3}{3!} f'''(x_i) + \cdots . \tag{7.64}$$

Eliminating $f'(x_i)$ from these two equations and solving for $f''(x_i)$, we easily find the finite difference approximation

$$f''(x_i) = \frac{h f(x_i + \varepsilon) - (h + \varepsilon) f(x_i) + \varepsilon f(x_i - h)}{h \varepsilon (h + \varepsilon)/2} + \frac{h - \varepsilon}{3} f'''(x_i) + \cdots . \tag{7.65}$$

This approximation to the second derivative can then be used in the expression for the Laplacian. We easily find that the analogue of Equation 7.61 is

$$u_{i,j} = \frac{\varepsilon}{2(h + \varepsilon)} \left[\frac{2h^2}{\varepsilon(h + \varepsilon)} u(x_i + \varepsilon, y_j) + \frac{2h}{h + \varepsilon} u_{i-1,j} + u_{i,j+1} + u_{i,j-1} \right]. \tag{7.66}$$

Depending upon how the physical boundary traverses the computational grid, appropriate finite difference approximations for various differential operators are easily obtained in a similar manner.

EXERCISE 7.10

Using a Cartesian grid, solve for the temperature distribution on a circular plate. The temperature along one quarter of the plate is held fixed at 100°C, while the remainder of the circumference is held at 0°C.

7.9 Neumann Boundary Conditions

So far, we've only discussed the case in which the *function* is known along the boundary, the *Dirichlet* boundary condition. There is an alternative boundary condition: If we know the *normal derivative* of the function at all points along the boundary, we have *Neumann* conditions. (There is yet another type of boundary condition, the *Cauchy* conditions, in which both the function and its normal derivative are known on the boundary. For Poisson's equation, Cauchy's condition is too restrictive—either Dirichlet or Neumann conditions are sufficient to generate a unique solution.) If the boundary lies along a grid line, the Neumann boundary condition is easily incorporated into our relaxation technique.

Let's reconsider our square metal plate. Only this time, instead of fixing the temperatures along the boundary, we'll fix the heat flow. That is, imagine that we are supplying heat to one edge, so there's a known flux of heat entering the plate along that edge. And let's further imagine that the heat flow out of the plate is different along the different edges, so that twice as much heat flows out the right edge as the top, and twice as much flows out the bottom as flows out the right. Since we are maintaining a steady-state temperature distribution, we must have that the total heat flowing into the square is equal to the amount flowing out—this is referred to as the compatibility condition. If this condition is not met, the plate cannot be in a steady-state and its temperature will either rise or fall.

Let's impose an $N \times M$ grid on the metal plate, and consider the left side of the computational boundary for which $i = 0$. (Figure 7.3.) Laplace's equation for the points along this boundary is

$$\frac{u_{1,j} - 2u_{0,j} + u_{-1,j}}{h_x^2} + \frac{u_{0,j+1} - 2u_{0,j} + u_{0,j-1}}{h_y^2} = 0. \tag{7.67}$$

But with Neumann conditions, we also know the derivative along the boundary,

$$\left.\frac{\partial u(x,y)}{\partial x}\right|_{x=0} = A_j \approx \frac{u_{1,j} - u_{-1,j}}{2h_x}, \tag{7.68}$$

where we've introduced A_j as the partial derivative at (x_o, y_j). We've also introduced $u_{-1,j}$ into these expressions, which isn't even on the grid! This point is introduced to help us think about the problem, but is never actually used. Eliminating it yields an expression for the temperature on the boundary explicitly involving the boundary condition:

$$u_{0,j} = \frac{h_x^2 h_y^2}{2h_x^2 + 2h_y^2} \left[\frac{2u_{1,j} - 2h_x A_j}{h_x^2} + \frac{u_{0,j+1} + u_{0,j-1}}{h_y^2} \right], \quad 0 < j < M-1. \tag{7.69}$$

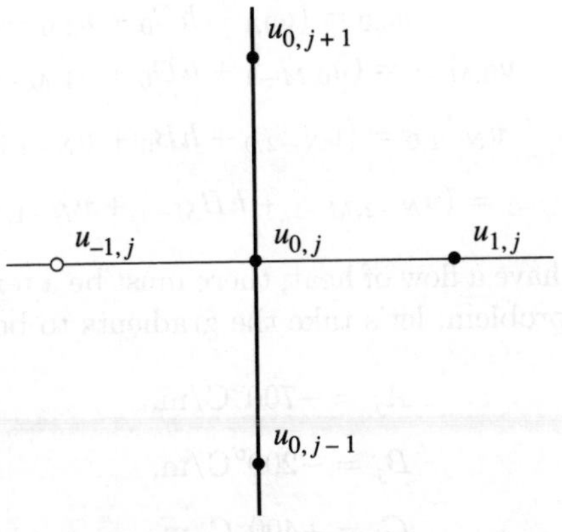

Figure 7.3 Applying Neumann conditions at a boundary. The open circle denotes a point off the computational grid.

If $h_x = h_y = h$, this expression simplifies to

$$u_{0,j} = \frac{2u_{1,j} - 2hA_j + u_{0,j+1} + u_{0,j-1}}{4}, \quad 0 < j < M - 1. \tag{7.70}$$

In like fashion, we have along the right side

$$B_j = \left.\frac{\partial u(x,y)}{\partial x}\right|_{x=x_{N-1}} = \frac{u_{N,j} - u_{N-2,j}}{2h}, \quad 0 < j < M - 1, \tag{7.71}$$

$$u_{N-1,j} = \frac{2u_{N-2,j} + 2hB_j + u_{N-1,j+1} + u_{N-1,j-1}}{4}; \tag{7.72}$$

along the bottom edge

$$C_i = \left.\frac{\partial u(x,y)}{\partial y}\right|_{y=y_o} = \frac{u_{i,1} - u_{i,-1}}{2h}, \quad 0 < i < N - 1, \tag{7.73}$$

$$u_{i,0} = \frac{u_{i+1,0} + u_{i-1,0} + 2u_{i,1} - 2hC_i}{4}; \tag{7.74}$$

and along the top edge

$$D_i = \left.\frac{\partial u(x,y)}{\partial y}\right|_{y=y_{M-1}} = \frac{u_{i,M} - u_{i,M-2}}{2h}, \quad 0 < i < N - 1, \tag{7.75}$$

$$u_{i,M-1} = \frac{u_{i+1,M-1} + u_{i-1,M-1} + 2u_{i,M-2} + 2hD_i}{4}. \tag{7.76}$$

The Laplacian at the corners of the computational grid will have two off-grid elements. Suitable approximations are found to be

$$u_{0,0} = (u_{0,1} - hC_0 + u_{1,0} - hA_0)/2, \tag{7.77}$$

$$u_{0,M-1} = (u_{0,M-2} + hD_0 + u_{1,M-1} - hA_{M-1})/2, \tag{7.78}$$

$$u_{N-1,0} = (u_{N-2,0} + hB_0 + u_{N-1,1} - hC_{N-1})/2, \tag{7.79}$$

$$u_{N-1,M-1} = (u_{N-2,M-1} + hB_{M-1} + u_{N-1,M-2} + hD_{N-1})/2. \tag{7.80}$$

In order to have a flow of heat, there must be a temperature gradient. (See Figure 7.4.) For our problem, let's take the gradients to be

$$A_j = -700°\text{C/m},$$

$$B_j = -200°\text{C/m},$$

$$C_i = +400°\text{C/m},$$

$$D_i = -100°\text{C/m}, \quad \text{for all } i \text{ and } j.$$

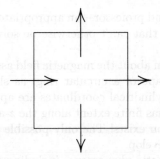

Figure 7.4   The direction of heat flow entering and leaving the square plate.

Note that if we evaluate the line integral of the *normal derivative* of the temperature around the perimeter of the square, we find that the net heat entering the plate is zero—the compatibility condition for a steady-state solution.

The astute reader will realize that we don't have enough information to determine the solution: we have only derivative information, which yields a family of solutions that satisfy both Laplace's equation and the Neumann Boundary condition. That is, we know how the temperature *changes* from point to point, but we don't know what the actual temperature is. To establish a unique solution to our problem, we need to know the steady-state temperature at some point: Let's imagine that a thermocouple on the lower left corner of the plate reads 750°C. This information is incorporated into the calculation by simply shifting all temperatures up (or down) so that the calculated temperature at the corner is correct. Mathematically, this shifting needs to be done only once, after the calculation has converged. However, you might want to shift with every iteration to help convey the progress the calculation is making toward convergence.

EXERCISE 7.11

Find the temperature everywhere on the plate. Plot isotherms at every 50°C to help visualize the temperature distribution.

7.10 A Magnetic Problem

Many, if not most, problems that you see as a student of Physics are far removed from the problems seen as a Physicist. This, of course, has a lot to do with the way we teach physics, the inherent difficulty of the subject, and the fact that *real* problems tax the abilities of PhDs and are simply not within the capabilities of an undergraduate student. However, the computer has a way of bridging the gulf between student and professor—an appropriate program can be used by the student to solve problems that can't otherwise be solved by anyone! The following is one such problem.

We want to learn about the magnetic field associated with a particular permanent magnet in the shape of a circular ring, as shown in Figure 7.5. Because of the magnet's shape, cylindrical coordinates are appropriate for the problem. However, since the magnet has finite extent along the z-axis, *the problem is not separable* and no analytic solution exists! The only possible solution is a numerical one, such as the one we now develop.

All electromagnetic phenomena, including the magnetic field produced by this magnet, are described by Maxwell's equations:

$$\nabla \cdot \mathbf{D} = \rho, \tag{7.81}$$

$$\nabla \times \mathbf{E} = -\frac{\partial \mathbf{B}}{\partial t}, \tag{7.82}$$

$$\nabla \cdot \mathbf{B} = 0, \tag{7.83}$$

and

$$\nabla \times \mathbf{H} = \frac{\partial \mathbf{D}}{\partial t} + \mathbf{J}. \tag{7.84}$$

Now, $\mathbf{H}$ and $\mathbf{B}$ are related by

$$\mathbf{B} = \mu_0(\mathbf{H} + \mathbf{M}), \tag{7.85}$$

where $\mathbf{M}$ is the magnetization of the material. That is, the magnetic field $\mathbf{B}$ is due to two factors: *macroscopic* currents and time-varying electric fields, which contribute to the magnetic intensity $\mathbf{H}$, and the inherent properties of the media, as manifest in $\mathbf{M}$. (We note that the permanent magnetism is due to the motion of subatomic particles on the *microscopic* scale within a magnetic domain.) For our purposes, we'll assume that the magnetization is homogeneous and is directed parallel to the axis of the magnet. For a steady-state problem, all the time derivatives vanish; there are no electric charges, so $\rho = 0$; and there are no currents, so that $\mathbf{J} = 0$. Thus

$$\nabla \times \mathbf{H} = 0. \tag{7.86}$$

Since the curl vanishes, we're naturally led to write

$$\mathbf{H} = -\nabla \Phi, \tag{7.87}$$

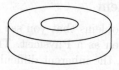

Figure 7.5   The Professor's magnet, used to affix loose pieces of paper to his metal filing cabinet.

where Φ is a scalar magnetic potential. From Equation 7.83 we then have that the potential satisfies

$$\nabla^2 \Phi = \nabla \cdot \mathbf{M}. \qquad (7.88)$$

Since we've assumed that the magnet is homogeneous, the divergence $\nabla \cdot \mathbf{M}$ is zero within the magnet. Outside the magnet, the magnetization and its divergence are also zero. There is, of course, a discontinuity at the boundary that must be considered. So, except at the surface of the magnet, the potential is described by Laplace's equation.

We will focus on the determination of Φ, the scalar magnetic potential. Note, however, that after Φ is known, we can calculate the magnetic field $\mathbf{B}$ from its gradient.

7.11 Boundary Conditions

From our studies of freshman Physics, we know that at the interface between two media we must have

$$\hat{\mathbf{n}} \times (\mathbf{H}_1 - \mathbf{H}_2) = 0, \qquad (7.89)$$

where $\hat{\mathbf{n}}$ is a unit normal vector at the interface. In terms of the scalar potential, we find that

$$\hat{\mathbf{n}} \times (\nabla \Phi_1 - \nabla \Phi_2) = 0. \qquad (7.90)$$

Integrating *along* the interface yields the condition that

$$\Phi_1 = \Phi_2. \qquad (7.91)$$

We also have a condition on the $\mathbf{B}$ field:

$$\mathbf{B}_2 \cdot \hat{\mathbf{n}} - \mathbf{B}_1 \cdot \hat{\mathbf{n}} = 0, \qquad (7.92)$$

which tells us that the *normal component* of $\mathbf{B}$ is continuous. In terms of the potential, we then find

$$(-\nabla \Phi_1 + \mathbf{M}_1) \cdot \hat{\mathbf{n}} = (-\nabla \Phi_2 + \mathbf{M}_2) \cdot \hat{\mathbf{n}},$$

or

$$(\nabla \Phi_1 - \nabla \Phi_2) \cdot \hat{\mathbf{n}} = (\mathbf{M}_1 - \mathbf{M}_2) \cdot \hat{\mathbf{n}}. \qquad (7.93)$$

This then is a condition on the gradient of the magnetic potential—as we cross the interface, the gradient changes so as to balance the change in the magnetization.

There is another boundary condition, that at infinity. Since the magnet is a dipole, the asymptotic form of the potential is

$$\Phi(\vec{r}) = -\frac{V}{4\pi} \mathbf{M} \cdot \nabla \left(\frac{1}{r} \right) = \frac{VMz}{4\pi r^3}. \qquad (7.94)$$

This boundary condition can be treated in several ways, the simplest of which is to simply take a large grid and set the potential to zero on its boundaries. In electrostatic problems, where the potential often *is* zero on the boundary, this is certainly correct. In the present context, however, it's not such a wise choice. We'll use the asymptotic values determined by Equation 7.94 to set the values at the boundary of our computational grid, and solve the finite difference equations on this grid. Then we'll repeat the calculation with a larger grid to ensure that the results are independent of the grid size.

7.12 The Finite Difference Equations

In circular cylindrical coordinates, the Laplacian is given as

$$\nabla^2 \Phi = \frac{1}{\rho} \frac{\partial}{\partial \rho} \left(\rho \frac{\partial \Phi}{\partial \rho} \right) + \frac{1}{\rho^2} \frac{\partial^2 \Phi}{\partial \phi^2} + \frac{\partial^2 \Phi}{\partial z^2}. \tag{7.95}$$

Our problem possesses cylindrical symmetry and does not depend upon the angle ϕ, so that the potential is independent of ϕ. This is, of course, a great simplification. The magnet we have in mind is of the short and squat ring variety, the type used to hold notes against metal file cabinets in Physics professors' offices, about 28 mm in diameter, 6 mm thick, and with a 10 mm hole in the middle. We will use a grid in ρ and z—for simplicity, let's choose the step size to be the same in both directions, and place the origin of the coordinate system at the geometrical center of the magnet. (Figure 7.6.) We then have

$$\nabla^2 \Phi \approx \frac{\Phi_{i+1,j} - \Phi_{i-1,j}}{2h\rho_i} + \frac{\Phi_{i+1,j} - 2\Phi_{i,j} + \Phi_{i-1,j}}{h^2} + \frac{\Phi_{i,j+1} - 2\Phi_{i,j} + \Phi_{i,j-1}}{h^2}, \tag{7.96}$$

where we've introduced the notation

$$\Phi_{i,j} = \Phi(\rho_i, z_j), \quad 0 \le i \le N_\rho, \quad 0 \le j \le N_z. \tag{7.97}$$

Because of the symmetry of the physical object, we shouldn't need to consider the potential other than in this quadrant. For a point not on the boundary of the

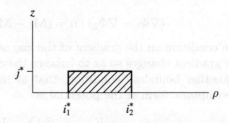

Figure 7.6   Cross section of the ring magnet in the first quadrant.

magnet and with neither ρ nor z equal to zero, Equation 7.88 reduces to Laplace's equation and, with the above approximation for the Laplacian, we find that

$$\Phi_{i,j} = \frac{1}{4}\left[\left(1 + \frac{h}{2\rho_i}\right)\Phi_{i+1,j} + \left(1 - \frac{h}{2\rho_i}\right)\Phi_{i-1,j} + \Phi_{i,j+1} + \Phi_{i,j-1}\right], \quad i,j \neq 0.$$
(7.98)

Along the symmetry axis of the magnet, where $\rho = 0$, we must exercise some care; for our problem, the Laplacian is of the form

$$\nabla^2 = \frac{\partial^2 \Phi}{\partial \rho^2} + \frac{1}{\rho}\frac{\partial \Phi}{\partial \rho} + \frac{\partial^2 \Phi}{\partial z^2}.$$
(7.99)

The second term looks like it could give some trouble as $\rho \to 0$. However, without a physical reason, you wouldn't expect a singularity in this problem. (Or any other problem, for that matter!) We thus suspect that there's an easy way out, and indeed there is, if we make the very plausible assumption that Φ is a continuous function of position. For constant z, the physical environment is the same in all directions as ρ approaches 0, so that Φ can't be changing; that is, the partial derivative with respect to ρ must go to zero as ρ goes to zero. Then we can use L'Hôpital's Rule to evaluate the term,

$$\frac{1}{\rho}\frac{\partial \Phi}{\partial \rho}\bigg|_{\rho=0} = \frac{\partial \Phi/\partial \rho}{\rho}\bigg|_{\rho=0} = \lim_{\rho \to 0} \frac{\frac{\partial}{\partial \rho}(\partial \Phi/\partial \rho)}{\frac{\partial}{\partial \rho}(\rho)} = \frac{\partial^2 \Phi}{\partial \rho^2}\bigg|_{\rho=0}.$$
(7.100)

The correct expression for the Laplacian is thus

$$\nabla^2 \Phi = 2\frac{\partial^2 \Phi}{\partial \rho^2} + \frac{\partial^2 \Phi}{\partial z^2}, \quad \rho = 0.$$
(7.101)

With this form for the Laplacian, the correct finite difference equation is found to be

$$\Phi_{0,j} = \frac{[4\Phi_{1,j} + \Phi_{0,j+1} + \Phi_{0,j-1}]}{6}.$$
(7.102)

The solution along $z = 0$ is even simpler. Our little magnet is a dipole, with a North end and a South end. Hence the solutions for $z < 0$ must be exactly opposite those for $z > 0$. That is, Φ must be an odd function of z, and so must be zero at $z = 0$. This is true at all points in the $z = 0$ plane,

$$\Phi_{i,0} = 0, \quad \text{for all } i.$$
(7.103)

We now move to the tougher boundary conditions, those at the physical surface of the magnet. The first thing to realize is that Laplace's equation is not valid here—the operative equation is Equation 7.88, which at the surface includes a consideration of the change of the magnetization. We first consider the cylindrical surfaces of the magnet at $\rho = 5$ and 14 mm. Since the magnetization has no component normal to the surface, Equation 7.93 tells us that the normal derivative is continuous. If the derivative just inside the surface is equal to the derivative just outside the surface, then the second derivative must be zero! The requirement is then

$$\frac{\partial^2 \Phi}{\partial \rho^2}\bigg|_{i^*} = 0,$$

or

$$\Phi_{i^*,j} = \frac{\Phi_{i^*+1,j} + \Phi_{i^*-1,j}}{2}, \qquad (7.104)$$

where i^* is a grid index for points lying on the cylindrical surface of the magnet.

Along the top edge, $z = 3$ mm, we must account for the sudden change in Equation 7.93

$$\frac{\partial \Phi}{\partial z}\bigg|_{inside} - M = \frac{\partial \Phi}{\partial z}\bigg|_{outside}. \qquad (7.105)$$

Using forward and backward formulas to express the derivative inside and outside the magnet (at the surface), we find

$$\frac{\Phi_{i,j^*} - \Phi_{i,j^*-1}}{h} - M = \frac{\Phi_{i,j^*+1} - \Phi_{i,j^*}}{h}, \qquad (7.106)$$

where j^* is the grid index for points lying on the physical surface. Solving for Φ_{i,j^*}, we find

$$\Phi_{i,j^*} = \frac{Mh + \Phi_{i,j^*+1} + \Phi_{i,j^*-1}}{2}. \qquad (7.107)$$

There remains one problem, that of determining Φ_{i^*,j^*}. Thus far, we have two expressions for these points, Equations 7.104 and 7.107, and they don't agree. Forsaking more rigorous avenues of attack, we simply retreat and employ the average of the two values available:

$$\Phi_{i^*,j^*} = \frac{Mh + \Phi_{i^*,j^*+1} + \Phi_{i^*,j^*-1} + \Phi_{i^*+1,j^*} + \Phi_{i^*-1,j^*}}{4}. \qquad (7.108)$$

These equations allow us to solve for the magnetic potential Φ; once Φ is known, $\mathbf{H}$ follows from Equation 7.87, and since $\mathbf{M}$ is specified, the magnetic field $\mathbf{B}$ follows immediately from Equation 7.85.

7.13 Another Comment on Strategy

The general idea of what we need to do is pretty clear. However, the implementation of that idea can spell the difference between success and failure. Before you read any further, take a few minutes and think about how you would program this problem.

Have any ideas? It is tempting to just start coding, one special case after another, one `for` loop at a time. But that's a dangerous approach, for many reasons: what happens when you change i^*? Debugging becomes a nightmare. Besides, when all the cases are *special*, then none of them are unusual, are they? Can we instead develop a general approach that allows for differences from point to point while maintaining an evenhanded treatment of them? Such an approach will surely work as well as a collection of special cases, and will certainly be easier to write, debug, and modify.

We accomplish this by the introduction of an auxiliary array of flags. As part of the initialization, the "uniqueness" of each point is characterized by an index in the array FLAG. For the present problem, six indices will suffice. These correspond to points where:

1. Laplace's equation holds, and the solution is given by Equation 7.98;

2. the point lies on the boundary of the computational grid, and the solution is fixed by boundary conditions;

3. $\rho = 0$, and the solution is given by Equation 7.102;

4. the point is on the cylindrical wall, the solution is given by Equation 7.104;

5. the point is on the top surface, with the solution given by Equation 7.107; and

6. the point is (i^*, j^*), the solution is given by Equation 7.108.

At initialization, these indices are stored in the flag array and the solution array is initialized, including boundary conditions.

You're almost ready to begin developing code to solve this problem, except for one obstacle that we've encountered before—units. Since the computer stores only numbers, and not units, it is imperative that you understand the units and dimensions of the problem, and that all variables and parameters are expressed correctly. These difficulties are particularly acute in magnetic phenomena, since many of us do not have an intuitive feel for the units that are commonly employed.

In SI units, $\mathbf{B}$ is given in Tesla, $\mathbf{H}$ and $\mathbf{M}$ in Ampere meter^{-1}, and μ_0 has the value $4\pi \times 10^{-7}$ Tesla Ampere^{-1} meter. (For reference, the Earth's magnetic field is on the order of 6×10^{-5} Tesla. The Gauss, $1G = 10^{-4}T$, is often a more convenient unit for the magnetic field.) Typical values of the magnetization for permanent magnets are in the $10^5 - 10^6$ range, so we'll take the magnetization of our magnet to be 10^5 Ampere meter^{-1}. Now, as long as we remember to express all distances in meters, we should be ready to continue.

You're now ready to start developing a computer code to solve this problem. Begin with the initialization; where better to start than the beginning? Assume that the solution is sought on a 25 by 25 grid at 1 mm spacing, so that $i_1^* = 6$, $i_2^* = 15$, and $j^* = 4$. Not having any particular insight at this point, initialize the grid to unity. Then initialize the solution array for distances far from the magnet, using Equation 7.94, and for all other "special" places. As you sweep through the array, initialize both the flag and the solution arrays so that the connection between the two is clear. For example, as you set the solution matrix to its asymptotic value along the far right boundary, set the corresponding element in the flag array to "2" indicating that it shouldn't be allowed to relax, e.g., it's a fixed value.

After having put this effort into the initialization, the main relaxation code becomes relatively simple. We note the effort spent in organizing our approach and initializing the arrays is effort well spent—it will make the subsequent program much easier to write and to understand. The actual relaxation process is then clear cut: as we move through the solution array, we query the flag array to determine how that particular point is to be treated. The computer code for the problem might look something like the following:

```
% ring_magnet.m
% This fragment solves for the scalar potential in the
%   cylindrical magnet problem, by the method of SOR.
clear;
m = 1.0e5;        % Magnetization is in Ampere/meter; the magnetic
                  %   potential phi has units of m*distance = Amperes
% FLAG is an integer array that characterizes a point
%   in the grid. In particular, it is used to determine
%   which of various equations to use in determining the
%   solution, according to the following "code":
%
%   1. typical point, use Equation (7.98).
%   2. fixed value point, either on the boundary of the
%        computational grid or determined by symmetry.
%        NOT SUBJECT TO CHANGE!
%   3. along the axis of the magnet, use Equation (7.102).
%   4. on the cylindrical walls, use Equation (7.104).
%   5. on the top surface, use Equation (7.107).
%   6. at a corner, use Equation (7.108).
%
% Initialize variables:
h  = ...
Nx = ...
Ny = ...
...
% Initialize PHI and FLAG:
flag = ones(Nx,Ny);
phi  = zeros(Nx,Ny);
% Initialize all boundaries, points, etc.
...
for j = 2: jstar-1
    flag(istar1,j) = 4;
```

```
        flag(istar2,j) = 4;
end
...
% Use optimum alpha for 2D Cartesian coordinates.  Although not
%   optimum for this problem, it should be a reasonable guess.
alpha   = ...
maxiter = ...           % maximum number of iterations
tol     = ...           % tolerance level
% SOR iteration starts here...
count = 0;
done  = false;
while ~done
    done  = true;
    count = count + 1;
    if (count >= maxiter), error('Too many iterations!'); end
% The following for loops do the actual SOR, using the
%   relaxation parameter alpha:
%          "phi(i,j)" is the old value,
%          "current"  is the latest iterate.
    for i = 1: Nx
        for j = 1: Ny
            ...
            if (flag(i,j) == 1 )
                current = ...
            elseif(flag(i,j) == 2)
                current = ...
                ...
            else
                error(' Illegal value for flag!');
            end
            if(abs((current-phi(i,j))/current) > tol),done = false; end
            phi(i,j) = current + ...
        end
    end
end
% SOR finished, print final results
    ...
```

Note that the computer code contains all the documentation concerning the values of FLAG, so you understand how (and why) different points of the grid are to be treated. This variable treatment is handled in a very straightforward manner in the main SOR loop, which examines the value of FLAG(I,J) and acts upon PHI(I,J) accordingly. If we should later need to change the geometry, include a larger grid, or make other changes, the modifications can be made in a relatively easy manner. In order to continue to write updates to the screen as the calculation progresses, the format has been changed substantially—of course, *final results* can then be written in whatever format deemed appropriate. You might also want to display lines of constant potential, or even $|\mathbf{B}|$.

EXERCISE 7.12

Using a magnetization of 10^5 Ampere meter^{-1}, calculate the magnetic potential on the 25 by 25 grid we've been discussing. Final results should be displayed to 4 places. Then plot lines of constant magnetic potential Φ and constant magnitude $|\mathbf{B}|$.

7.14 Are We There Yet?

Having the computer supply us with numbers is not the same thing as having solved the problem, of course. The results of this calculation depend upon the size of the grid—after all, 2.5 centimeters is a long way from infinity. While the iterations continued until $\Phi_{i,j}$ was converged to 4 significant digits, this *does not* mean that the results are accurate to 4 places. We must still vary the size of the grid, and see how the results might change. We might also want to change the grid spacing. In general, all the parameters of the calculation need to be tested to ensure the convergence of the results.

EXERCISE 7.13

Vary the parameters of the calculation so as to achieve 5% accuracy in the calculation of the magnetic potential.

7.15 Spectral Methods

With finite difference methods, progress toward an approximate solution proceeds in a rather direct fashion. But sometimes there are advantages to being indirect. Previously, we've seen that the Fourier transform, particularly as implemented in the FFT algorithm, can be the basis of extremely accurate and efficient methods of solution. Let's see how it might be used here.

The basic idea of spectral methods is to *transform* the problem from its original description into one involving the Fourier transform of the solution. The motivation is that in many situations the solution in the transform space is much easier to obtain than is the solution in the original space. (Of course, if the solution isn't easier, we wouldn't be using this method!) The solution to the original problem is then obtained by evaluating the inverse Fourier transform of the solution found in transform space.

A simple example might we worthwhile. Consider the diffusion equation

$$\frac{\partial T}{\partial t} = \kappa \frac{\partial^2 T}{\partial x^2}, \tag{7.109}$$

which describes the temperature $T(x,t)$ in a long metal rod. We begin at time $t = 0$ knowing the initial distribution of temperature, $T(x,0)$. The problem is to find the temperature along the rod at later times. If $\tau(k,t)$ is the Fourier transform of $T(x,t)$, then

$$\tau(k,t) = \frac{1}{\sqrt{2\pi}} \int_{-\infty}^{\infty} T(x,t) e^{-ikx} \, dx \tag{7.110}$$

and we can write the temperature as

$$T(x,t) = \frac{1}{\sqrt{2\pi}} \int_{-\infty}^{\infty} \tau(k,t) e^{+ikx} \, dk. \tag{7.111}$$

Note that we are transforming between x and k at the same instant in time. Substituting this expression for the temperature into our diffusion equation, we find

$$\frac{\partial}{\partial t} \frac{1}{\sqrt{2\pi}} \int_{-\infty}^{\infty} \tau(k,t) e^{+ikx} \, dk = \kappa \frac{\partial^2}{\partial x^2} \frac{1}{\sqrt{2\pi}} \int_{-\infty}^{\infty} \tau(k,t) e^{+ikx} \, dk. \tag{7.112}$$

On the left side, the partial derivative operates on $\tau(k,t)$. But $\tau(k,t)$ is not a function of x, so that on the right side the derivative operates only on the exponential factor, to yield

$$\frac{1}{\sqrt{2\pi}} \int_{-\infty}^{\infty} \frac{\partial \tau(k,t)}{\partial t} e^{+ikx} \, dk = \kappa \frac{1}{\sqrt{2\pi}} \int_{-\infty}^{\infty} \tau(k,t) \left[-k^2\right] e^{+ikx} \, dk. \tag{7.113}$$

We now multiply both sides by $e^{-ik'x}$, and integrate over x to find

$$\frac{1}{\sqrt{2\pi}} \int_{-\infty}^{\infty} e^{-ik'x} \int_{-\infty}^{\infty} \frac{\partial \tau(k,t)}{\partial t} e^{+ikx} \, dk \, dx$$

$$= \kappa \frac{1}{\sqrt{2\pi}} \int_{-\infty}^{\infty} e^{-ik'x} \int_{-\infty}^{\infty} \tau(k,t) \left[-k^2\right] e^{+ikx} \, dk \, dx. \tag{7.114}$$

Exchanging the order of the integration and using the expression

$$\int_{-\infty}^{\infty} e^{i(k-k')x} \, dx = 2\pi \, \delta(k - k') \tag{7.115}$$

for the Dirac delta $\delta(k - k')$, we find

$$\frac{\partial \tau(k,t)}{\partial t} = -k^2 \kappa \tau(k,t). \tag{7.116}$$

In the original statement of the problem, Equation 7.109, we had two partial derivatives—we now find that in our "transform space," we have only one. Its solution is easily found to be

$$\tau(k,t) = e^{-k^2 \kappa t} \tau(k,0) \qquad (7.117)$$

where $\tau(k,0)$ is obtained by transforming the initial temperature distribution,

$$\tau(k,0) = \frac{1}{\sqrt{2\pi}} \int_{-\infty}^{\infty} T(x,0) e^{-ikx} \, dx. \qquad (7.118)$$

Having determined $\tau(k,t)$, we can use Equation 7.111 to perform the inverse transform to find the temperature,

$$T(x,t) = \frac{1}{\sqrt{2\pi}} \int_{-\infty}^{\infty} \tau(k,t) e^{+ikx} \, dk$$

$$= \frac{1}{\sqrt{2\pi}} \int_{-\infty}^{\infty} e^{-k^2 \kappa t} \tau(k,0) e^{+ikx} \, dk. \qquad (7.119)$$

We see, then, that the general approach consists of three steps: 1) transform the original partial differential equation, and the initial conditions, into transform space; 2) solve the (presumably simpler) equation in transform space; and 3) perform the inverse transform, so as to obtain the solution in terms of the original variables.

EXERCISE 7.14

Find the temperature in the long metal rod, and plot it, as a function of time. Take the initial temperature to be

$$T(x,0) = \begin{cases} 0, & |x| > 1\,\mathrm{m}, \\ 100°\mathrm{C}, & |x| \leq 1\,\mathrm{m}, \end{cases}$$

and $\kappa = 10^3 \, \mathrm{m^2/s}$.

Clearly, the advantage of the spectral approach is the ease with which the derivative can be treated in the transformed set of coordinates. For a number of problems, such as our diffusion example, this approach works very well. Of course, part of the reason it worked so well was that the equation was relatively simple—in transform space, our partial differential equation in two variables became a differential equation in one variable. In other cases, such a great simplification might not occur. In those instances, it might be advantageous to have the flexibility to treat part of the problem one way, and another part a different way.

7.16 The Pseudo-Spectral Method

Let's consider a different problem, the quantum mechanical scattering of a wavepacket from a step barrier. In many standard textbooks, this problem is discussed and figures are displayed that depict the time evolution of the wavepacket as it moves toward the barrier and interacts with it. But with the computer, we can calculate the relevant wavefunctions and watch the interaction. In one dimension, the Schrödinger equation is

$$i\hbar\frac{\partial\psi(x,t)}{\partial t} = -\frac{\hbar^2}{2m}\frac{\partial^2\psi(x,t)}{\partial x^2} + V(x)\psi(x,t)$$
$$= (\mathbf{T} + \mathbf{V})\psi(x,t), \tag{7.120}$$

where m is the mass of the particle, $\mathbf{T}$ is the kinetic energy term, and $\mathbf{V}$ is the potential. In quantum mechanics, both $\mathbf{T}$ and $\mathbf{V}$ are considered operators, although $\mathbf{T}$ is clearly a derivative operator—$\mathbf{T}\psi$ is obtained by taking the derivative of ψ— while $\mathbf{V}$ is simply a function that multiplies ψ.

We could, of course, solve this problem by finite differences. However, the discussion of the spectral method demonstrated that there is another, sometimes better, way to treat the derivative terms. In the present problem, the transform method would clearly enable us to treat the kinetic energy operator, but it would not help with the potential term. What we would really like to do is treat the derivative term one way and the potential term another. In particular, we would like to treat the potential term in coordinate space, where it's simply a function, and treat the derivative term in transform space where it's easily (and accurately) evaluated.

Let's return to the Schrödinger equation. With regard to its time dependence, we can immediately write a *formal solution* to the equation. (On a philosophical note, solutions that are easily written are almost never very useful. In this case, however, the formal solution will guide us to an excellent practical method for computationally solving the Schrödinger equation.) First we define the exponential of an operator as

$$e^{\mathbf{A}} = 1 + \mathbf{A} + \frac{1}{2!}\mathbf{A}\mathbf{A} + \frac{1}{3!}\mathbf{A}\mathbf{A}\mathbf{A} + \cdots. \tag{7.121}$$

This mathematical definition is valid for operators in general, including the kinetic and potential energy operators that we have. With this definition, a formal solution to Equation 7.120 is

$$\psi(x,t) = e^{-i(\mathbf{T}+\mathbf{V})(t-t_0)/\hbar}\,\psi(x,t_0). \tag{7.122}$$

EXERCISE 7.15

Using the definition of the exponentiation of an operator, verify that Equation 7.122 is a solution to the Schrödinger equation, Equation 7.120.

For convenience, we define $\delta_t = t - t_0$, so that the *time evolution* of the wavefunction is given by

$$\psi(x, t) = e^{-i(\mathbf{T}+\mathbf{V})\delta_t/\hbar}\, \psi(x, t_0). \tag{7.123}$$

This equation gives us a prescription for calculating $\psi(x, t)$ at any time t from knowledge of ψ at time t_0. Furthermore, the prescription involves the exponential of the sum of our two operators. It's *extremely tempting* to write

$$e^{-i(\mathbf{T}+\mathbf{V})\delta_t/\hbar} = e^{-i\mathbf{T}\delta_t/\hbar} e^{-i\mathbf{V}\delta_t/\hbar}. \tag{7.124}$$

Unfortunately, this expression is untrue! But if it were true, then we would have succeeded in splitting the time evolution operator into two terms, and could have treated each factor separately. As we will shortly see, while this equality is not valid, the decomposition can serve as a useful *approximation*. This technique of separating the evolution operator into two factors is generally termed the *split-operator approach*, and is more widely applicable than we have space to demonstrate.

Why is Equation 7.124 invalid? In general, derivatives and other operators yield different results when applied in a different order. For example, consider the operators $\mathbf{A} = x$ and $\mathbf{B} = d/dx$. Then

$$\mathbf{AB}\psi = x\frac{d\psi}{dx}, \tag{7.125}$$

but

$$\mathbf{BA}\psi = \frac{d}{dx}(x\psi) = \psi + x\frac{d\psi}{dx} = (\mathbf{AB} + 1)\psi. \tag{7.126}$$

Since the order of the operators *does* matter, the operators *do not commute*. The commutability of operators—or, as the case may be, lack thereof—is expressed by the *commutator* of $\mathbf{A}$ and $\mathbf{B}$. This is defined as

$$[\mathbf{A}, \mathbf{B}] = \mathbf{AB} - \mathbf{BA}, \tag{7.127}$$

and is evaluated by allowing it to act on an arbitrary function. (If the order of the operators is irrelevant, then the operators commute and the commutator is zero.) For our operators, we have

$$\left[x, \frac{d}{dx}\right]\psi = x\frac{d}{dx}\psi - \frac{d}{dx}x\psi = -\psi. \tag{7.128}$$

Since ψ is arbitrary, the commutator expresses a relationship between the operators x and d/dx independent of ψ; hence we write

$$\left[x, \frac{d}{dx}\right] = -1. \tag{7.129}$$

We are now prepared to consider the product of two exponentials, such as $e^{\mathbf{A}}e^{\mathbf{B}}$. Expanding each of the factors according to the definition of the exponential of an operator, we can verify that

$$e^{\mathbf{A}}e^{\mathbf{B}} = e^{\mathbf{C}} \tag{7.130}$$

if and only if

$$\mathbf{C} = \mathbf{A} + \mathbf{B} + \frac{1}{2}[\mathbf{A}, \mathbf{B}] + \cdots . \tag{7.131}$$

This is a statement of the famous Baker-Campbell-Hausdorff theorem.

EXERCISE 7.16
Find the next two terms of $\mathbf{C}$.

As an exact expression, the Baker-Campbell-Hausdorff theorem tells us that Equation 7.124 is invalid unless $\mathbf{T}$ and $\mathbf{V}$ commute—which they don't (usually)! But more than that, the theorem is extremely useful in developing approximations of known error. For example, we now know that Equation 7.124, which simply ignores the commutator, is accurate through $\mathcal{O}(\delta_t)$. A more accurate approximation is obtained by using a symmetric decomposition of the product, e.g., by using the expression

$$e^{-i(\mathbf{T}+\mathbf{V})\delta_t/\hbar} \approx e^{-i\mathbf{V}\delta_t/2\hbar}e^{-i\mathbf{T}\delta_t/\hbar}e^{-i\mathbf{V}\delta_t/2\hbar}, \tag{7.132}$$

which is accurate through $\mathcal{O}(\delta_t^2)$.

We are now ready to describe an efficient method of solving the quantum mechanical scattering problem, using a mixture of coordinate space and transform space techniques called the *pseudo-spectral method*. Let's imagine that we know $\psi(x, t_0)$—that is, we have an array containing $\psi_j = \psi(x_j, t_0)$ at the grid points x_j at the time t_0. Ultimately, we will use the FFT to evaluate the necessary transforms so that the number of points on the grid will be a power of two. Recall that the total range in x determines the grid spacing in k, and *vice versa*. ψ at time t is approximated by

$$\psi(x, t) \approx e^{-i\mathbf{V}\delta_t/2\hbar}e^{-i\mathbf{T}\delta_t/\hbar}e^{-i\mathbf{V}\delta_t/2\hbar}\psi(x, t_0). \tag{7.133}$$

Since V is a function it is easily evaluated at the x_j. We can define an intermediate quantity $\phi(x)$ as

$$\phi(x) = e^{-i\mathbf{V}\delta_t/2\hbar}\psi(x, t_0), \tag{7.134}$$

and evaluate it on the grid as

$$\phi(x_j) = e^{-iV(x_j)\delta_t/2\hbar}\psi(x_j, t_0).\tag{7.135}$$

This evaluation is perfectly straightforward: in coordinate space, it's a simple sequence of arithmetic operations. In fact, if δ_t is constant throughout the calculation, an array of these exponential factors can be evaluated once, stored, and used whenever needed without reevaluation.

The next step is to determine the result of the exponential of the kinetic energy operating on ϕ,

$$e^{-i\mathbf{T}\delta_t/\hbar}\phi(x_i).$$

In coordinate space, this is a troublesome term. In contains the second derivative operator, exponentiated! But in transform space, the derivative is easy to evaluate, as we've seen. To evaluate the term, we'll need $\Phi(k)$, the Fourier transform of $\phi(x)$,

$$\Phi(k) = \mathcal{F}[\phi(x)] = \frac{1}{\sqrt{2\pi}} \int_{-\infty}^{\infty} \phi(x)e^{-ikx}\, dx,\tag{7.136}$$

and the inverse relation

$$\phi(x) = \mathcal{F}^{-1}[\Phi(k)] = \frac{1}{\sqrt{2\pi}} \int_{-\infty}^{\infty} \Phi(k)e^{+ikx}\, dk.\tag{7.137}$$

Then

$$
\begin{aligned}
e^{-i\mathbf{T}\delta_t/\hbar}\phi(x) &= e^{-i\mathbf{T}\delta_t/\hbar} \frac{1}{\sqrt{2\pi}} \int_{-\infty}^{\infty} \Phi(k)e^{+ikx}\, dk \\
&= \left[1 + \frac{-i\mathbf{T}\delta_t}{\hbar} + \frac{(-i)^2\mathbf{T}\mathbf{T}\delta_t^2}{2!\hbar^2} + \cdots\right] \frac{1}{\sqrt{2\pi}} \int_{-\infty}^{\infty} \Phi(k)e^{+ikx}\, dk \\
&= \frac{1}{\sqrt{2\pi}} \int_{-\infty}^{\infty} \Phi(k)\left[1 + \frac{-i\mathbf{T}\delta_t}{\hbar} + \frac{(-i)^2\mathbf{T}\mathbf{T}\delta_t^2}{2!\hbar^2} + \cdots\right] e^{+ikx}\, dk
\end{aligned}
$$

$$= \frac{1}{\sqrt{2\pi}} \int_{-\infty}^{\infty} \Phi(k) \left[1 + \frac{-i}{\hbar} \frac{-\hbar^2 \delta_t}{2m} \frac{d^2}{dx^2} \right.$$

$$\left. + \frac{1}{2!} \left(\frac{-i}{\hbar} \frac{-\hbar^2 \delta_t}{2m} \right)^2 \frac{d^4}{dx^4} + \cdots \right] e^{+ikx} \, dk$$

$$= \frac{1}{\sqrt{2\pi}} \int_{-\infty}^{\infty} \Phi(k) \left[1 + \frac{-iT(k)\delta_t}{\hbar} + \frac{1}{2!} \left(\frac{-iT(k)\delta_t}{\hbar} \right)^2 + \cdots \right] e^{+ikx} \, dk$$

$$= \frac{1}{\sqrt{2\pi}} \int_{-\infty}^{\infty} \Phi(k) \left[e^{-iT(k)\delta_t/\hbar} \right] e^{+ikx} \, dk$$

$$= \frac{1}{\sqrt{2\pi}} \int_{-\infty}^{\infty} e^{-iT(k)\delta_t/\hbar} \Phi(k) e^{+ikx} \, dk$$

$$= \mathcal{F}^{-1} \left[e^{-iT(k)\delta_t/\hbar} \Phi(k) \right], \tag{7.138}$$

where we've introduced the kinetic energy term

$$T(k) = \frac{\hbar^2 k^2}{2m}. \tag{7.139}$$

The wavefunction at time t is then obtained by a final multiplication by the potential factor. The full propagation is thus given as

$$\psi(x, t) \approx e^{-iV(x)\delta_t/2\hbar} \mathcal{F}^{-1} \left[e^{-iT(k)\delta_t/\hbar} \mathcal{F} \left[e^{-iV(x)\delta_t/2\hbar} \psi(x, t_0) \right] \right]. \tag{7.140}$$

Although this seems a bit complicated, it has a certain elegance to it that is very attractive. The algorithm skips to and fro, to transform space and back again, weaving a solution from coordinate and transform space contributions. Yet the coding is very straightforward and easy to accomplish. And if the FFT is used to perform the Fourier transforms, it's extremely efficient and accurate as well. A general outline of the program will look like the following:

```
% wavepacket.m
% This fragment calculates the time evolution of a quantum
%   mechanical wavepacket by the pseudo-spectral method.
function wavepacket
% Initialize parameters
...
% Initialize the wavefunction:
...
psi=...
% Initialize some stuff:
dt = 5.0e-18; % time step in seconds
```

```
...
% Initialize the arrays ExpT and ExpV,
%   ExpT is an array of values exp(-i T delta_t /hbar)
%   ExpV is an array of values exp(-i V delta_t / 2*hbar)
...
% Loop over propagation steps until time > MaxTime:
time = 0.0;
MaxTime = ...
while time < MaxTime

    phi = ExpV.*psi;    % First Step: multiply by exponent of V:
                        % Second Step: multiply by exponent of T, by
    phi = fft(phi);     %     a) transform the wavefunction,
    phi = ExpT.*phi;    %     b) multiply by ExpT,
    phi = ifft(phi);    %     c) inverse transform,
    psi = ExpV.*phi;    % Third and final step: multiply by exponent
                        %     of V, again.

    % Plot psi**2
    ...
    time = time + dt;
end
```

That's all there is to it! Given that we're solving a rather difficult problem, the simplicity of the basic algorithm is rather amazing.

What should we use as an initial wavefunction? One particularly interesting example is the Gaussian function

$$\psi(x,0) = \frac{1}{\sqrt[4]{2\pi(\Delta x)^2}} e^{ik_0 x - \frac{(x-x_0)^2}{4(\Delta x)^2}}. \tag{7.141}$$

This is a plane wave, modulated by a Gaussian weighting function centered about $x = x_0$. The quantity Δx is related to the width of the function—if the width is small, the magnitude of the function quickly falls off away from x_0. (Remember that in quantum mechanics it's the square of the wavefunction that is physically meaningful. Δx is the half-width of the square of the wavefunction, as measured between the points at which it has fallen to $1/e$ of its maximum value.)

In general, Heisenberg's Uncertainty Principle states that

$$\Delta x \, \Delta p \geq \frac{\hbar}{2}, \tag{7.142}$$

or, since $p = \hbar k$, that

$$\Delta x \, \Delta k \geq \frac{1}{2}. \tag{7.143}$$

The Fourier transform of the Gaussian function of Equation 7.141 is easily found to be

$$\phi(k,0) = \frac{1}{\sqrt{2\pi}} \int_{-\infty}^{\infty} \psi(x,0) e^{-ikx} \, dx = \sqrt[4]{\frac{4(\Delta x)^2}{2\pi}} e^{-(\Delta x)^2 (k-k_0)^2}, \tag{7.144}$$

another Gaussian function. By comparing with Equation 7.141, we find that this function has a width of $\Delta k = 1/(2\Delta x)$, or that

$$\Delta x\, \Delta k = \frac{1}{2}. \tag{7.145}$$

That is, while the product is always greater than or equal to $1/2$, we find that the equality holds for the Gaussian wavefunction—this is the reason it's also known as the *minimum uncertainty wavepacket*.

Next, we need to initialize the arrays ExpV and ExpT. The first is not difficult; merely evaluate the potential at the specified grid points and fill the array appropriately. The second is more of a problem, although it's not all that difficult. δ_k and δ_x are related by

$$\delta_k = \frac{2\pi}{N\delta_x}. \tag{7.146}$$

With N points, k appears to range from 0 to $(N-1)\delta_k$. But recall from Chapter 6 that the Fast Fourier Transform algorithm imposes a periodicity to the functions, so that k's above the Nyquist frequency are actually negative. Since we need these k's in order to evaluate the kinetic energy, we must be a little careful. The array ExpT can be properly filled with the following code.

```
hbar2 = 0.076199682  % hbar^2, in units of (electron mass)*(eV)*(nm)^2
im    = complex(0.0, 1.0);
   ...
for i=1:N/2
%
% For k's between 0 and the Nyquist cutoff:
%
        k       = (i-1) * delta_k
%
%   KE is the Kinetic Energy in eV
%
        KE      = k * k * hbar2 / ( 2.0 * mass )
        ExpT(i) = exp( -im * KE * delta_t / hbar )
%
% K's above the Nyquist cutoff are actually negative:
%
        k           = -i * delta_k
        KE          = k * k * hbar2 / ( 2.0 * mass )
        ExpT(N+1-i) = exp( -im * KE * delta_t / hbar )
    end
```

7.17 A Sample Problem

Let's consider a specific example, a stationary wavepacket evolving in free space. That is, we'll set $k_0 = 0$ and $V(x) = 0$. As in Chapter 2, we'll find it convenient to use the parameter

$$\hbar^2 = 0.076199682 \; m_e \text{ eV nm}^2, \tag{7.147}$$

although we also know that $\hbar = 6.5821220 \times 10^{-16}$ eV-sec and may find this expression useful as well. We'll take the initial wavepacket to be a Gaussian function located at $x_0 = 0$ and having a width of $\Delta x = 0.1$ nm. As discussed in Chapter 6, the choices of grid spacing in the x and k coordinates and the number of points to be used in the calculation are not independent of one another. Let's tentatively choose the total range of the x-coordinate to be 2 nm, centered about $x = 0$, and use $N = 64$. This gives a grid spacing ≈ 0.03 nm, which should be adequate for a wavepacket this broad. With these parameters, we can propagate the wavefunction and find results such as presented in Figure 7.7.

Hint #1: Choose δ_x to be sufficiently small so that all the interesting detail of the wavefunction is adequately sampled.

For times less than about 6×10^{-16} seconds, we observe a standard characteristic of quantum mechanical wavepackets—as time evolves, they spread out in space. For simple cases such as this one, an analytic result can be obtained for Δx as a function of time, which we could verify if we choose. Of more immediate interest to us, however, is the behavior of the wavepacket at even longer times.

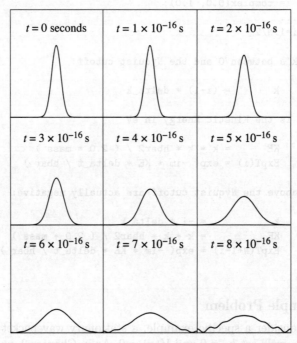

Figure 7.7   Time evolution of the stationary Gaussian wavepacket discussed in the text.

Physically, we would expect the wavepacket to continue to spread. Computationally, however, the wavepacket already nearly fills the calculational grid. Remember, the FFT imposes periodicity on the wavefunction—although we tend to view the solution as spreading toward $\pm\infty$, the computational reality is that the left and right extremes of the grid are the same point! Thus, as some portion of the wavepacket moves off the right edge of the grid, it *wraps around* and reappears on the left edge of the grid! But the wavefunction already exists at the left edge—the two contributions interact with one another and create an interference pattern. We should stress that this is NOT a physically meaningful result—our computational grid is *too small* to adequately describe the physical situation at these long times.

> Hint #2: *Always use a grid large enough so that the physics occurs far from any edge.*

The "cure" for this *wrap around problem* is to increase the size of the computational grid. However, δ_x shouldn't be increased, since this was chosen so as to adequately sample the wavefunction. The only parameter remaining for us to change is N.

EXERCISE 7.17

Use a time step of 5×10^{-18} seconds and replicate the results of Figure 7.7. Then try $N = 128$, to eliminate (or at least postpone until later times) the wrap around problem.

Now let's see if the wavefunction can be made to move. All the dynamics that actually cause the wavepacket to move are already present in the program, so that all that needs to be changed is the initial value of k_0. It's often convenient to use energy rather than wavenumber in specifying the initial conditions. For free particle motion, they're related through the relation

$$k = \sqrt{\frac{2mE}{\hbar^2}}. \tag{7.148}$$

EXERCISE 7.18

Let the initial kinetic energy be $E_0 = 150$ eV. Follow the evolution of the wavepacket for 100 time steps, with $\delta_t = 5 \times 10^{-18}$ seconds.

In addition to spreading, the wavefunction moves to the right. If not halted, it also wraps around, appearing at the left of the computational grid after moving off the right edge. Since the entire wavepacket is in motion, there's nothing for it to interfere with and so its shape is not distorted (beyond its natural spreading).

Still, a cautious program would halt and inform the user that the wavepacket is nearing an edge. Let's try this again, with a larger kinetic energy.

EXERCISE 7.19

Repeat the exercise, with $E_0 = 300$ eV. What happened?

So far, we've concentrated on the wavefunction in coordinate space. But it's just as valid to ask what the wavefunction is doing in k-space. And in this case, particularly illuminating. Modify the code so that the probability distribution in coordinate space and in k-space are displayed simultaneously, and repeat the previous two exercises. You should see that in Exercise 7.17, the k-space wavefunction is entirely contained within the range from 0 to the Nyquist frequency. But in Exercise 7.19, the wavefunction extends beyond the Nyquist limit. Those components of the wavefunction at large positive frequencies must be included in order to accurately describe this specific wavefunction, but as far as the FFT is concerned, frequencies above the Nyquist limit are *negative*. This is essentially another *wrap around problem*, this time in k-space.

> Hint #3: Choose the grid in k-space sufficiently large so that all the interesting physics is contained well within the Nyquist limit. (That is, choose δ_x to be sufficiently small. This is really just Hint #1 , expressed in different language.)

EXERCISE 7.20

Modify the code as indicated and repeat the previous two exercises.

We see that the use of the spectral method is not without its difficulties. In particular, we must be very aware of the wrap around problem, in both its disguises. On the positive side, however, it's a problem that is very easy to diagnose—when it's not working properly, the method yields results that are obviously incorrect when plotted. Wrap around is also easy to monitor: simply determine how much of the wavefunction is in the last, say, 5 percent of the computational grid in coordinate space, and within 5 % of the Nyquist limit in the reciprocal space. If the solution ever becomes appreciable in these regions, say more than 0.5%, a warning message can be printed and the execution of the program terminated. We emphasize that when the method is used properly and within its domain of validity, it works extremely well, yielding accurate results in a very timely manner. In these situations, virtually no other method is capable of producing results of such accuracy in a comparable amount of time.

7.18 The Potential Step Problem

Let's consider the behavior of a wavepacket at a step. Instead of being zero everywhere, the potential $V(x)$ is chosen to be

$$V(x) = \begin{cases} 0, & x \leq 0, \\ V_0, & 0 \leq x. \end{cases} \tag{7.149}$$

As before, we'll consider x on the range -2 nm $\leq x \leq 2$ nm, with $N = 128$. Let's take $E_0 = 100$ eV and $V_0 = 200$ eV. Initially, the wavepacket is centered at $x_o = -1.0$ nm with width $\Delta x = 0.1$ nm.

EXERCISE 7.21

Evolve the wavefunction for 50 time steps, $\delta_t = 5 \times 10^{-18}$ s, using these parameters.

As the wavepacket collides with the step, the reflected components interfere with the unreflected ones, giving rise to a probability distribution that resembles an interference pattern, as indicated in Figure 7.8. It is at times such as this that the grid size becomes particularly important—δ_x must be small enough to sample all the detail of the wavefunction, *particularly* when the wavefunction is rapidly changing. After sufficient time, all the components are reflected by the barrier and the wavepacket regains its initial shape.

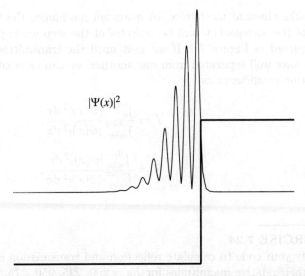

$|\Psi(x)|^2$

Figure 7.8   The probability distribution at some instant during the collision of the 100 eV wavepacket with the 200 eV step, on the range -1 nm $\leq x \leq 0.5$ nm. Note that the probability distribution extends *into* the step, a classically forbidden region.

We might want to increase the range, so that the evolution can be followed a bit longer in time. But if we increase the range and leave N the same, we are also increasing δ_x, which in turn decreases the range in k-space. Thus we need to increase N as well. A nice balance can be achieved by doubling N and increasing the range in x by $\sqrt{2}$. This has the effect of increasing the k range by a factor of $\sqrt{2}$ as well, while decreasing the grid spacing in both x and k coordinates.

EXERCISE 7.22

Evolve the wavefunction again, with -3 nm $\leq x \leq 3$ nm and $N = 256$.

According to classical mechanics, the particle can never be found in a region in which the potential energy is greater than the total energy. As seen in Figure 7.8, in quantum mechanics the particle's wavefunction doesn't vanish in these regions, but rather monotonically decays. (For a constant potential, the decay is exponential.) This is called an evanescent wave, and has an interesting analogue in optics. But what if the total energy *exceeded* the potential energy? If the particle were initially moving to the right and encountered such an obstacle, according to classical mechanics it would slow down, but continue moving to the right.

EXERCISE 7.23

Consider the 200 eV step again, but with $E_0 = 225$ eV.

Unlike classical mechanics, in quantum mechanics the wavepacket, or at least part of the wavepacket, will be *reflected* at the step while part of it is *transmitted*, as depicted in Figure 7.9. If we wait until the transmitted and reflected components have well separated from one another, we can calculate the transmission and reflection coefficients as

$$\mathcal{T} = \frac{\int_0^{max} |\psi(x)|^2 \, dx}{\int_{min}^{max} |\psi(x)|^2 \, dx}, \tag{7.150}$$

$$\mathcal{R} = \frac{\int_{min}^0 |\psi(x)|^2 \, dx}{\int_{min}^{max} |\psi(x)|^2 \, dx}. \tag{7.151}$$

EXERCISE 7.24

Modify your code to calculate reflection and transmission coefficients, and investigate their relative magnitudes for $E_0 = 200$, 225, 250, 275, and 300 eV.

It's interesting to note that we have reflection at a downward step as well. That is, if V_0 is negative, so that the kinetic energy of the wavepacket increases as it encounters the (negative) step.

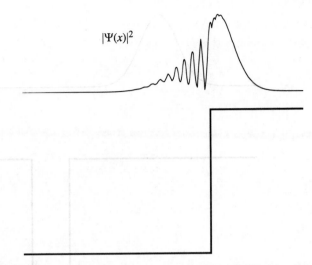

Figure 7.9   At 225 eV, the wavepacket's energy exceeds the 200 eV height of the step, yet we still observe interference-like behavior as a substantial portion of the wavepacket is being reflected.

EXERCISE 7.25
Investigate the reflection and transmission coefficients for the case of a negative step, $V_0 = -200$ eV, for $E_0 = 25$, 50, 75, and 100 eV.

7.19 The Well

One of the classic examples of these processes, often reproduced in textbooks, is a wavepacket traveling over a well. That is, on the potential

$$V(x) = \begin{cases} 0, & x \leq 0, \\ V_0, & 0 \leq x \leq a, \\ 0, & a \leq x, \end{cases} \qquad (7.152)$$

with V_0 negative, as shown in Figure 7.10. This example was originally discussed by Goldberg, Schey, and Schwartz, in "Computer-Generated Motion Pictures of One-Dimensional Quantum-Mechanical Transmission and Reflection Phenomena," *American Journal of Physics* **35**, 117 (1967). At the time, these were substantial calculations—but you can easily duplicate them, if you choose.

Goldberg *et al.* used arbitrary units, but we can approximate their parameters if we take $E_0 = 100$ eV, $V_0 = -200$ eV, and $a = 0.2$ nm. With $N = 256$ and -3 nm $\leq x \leq 3$ nm, you will find that the k-space wavefunction is not well confined below the Nyquist limit, so that you will need to change some of the parameters

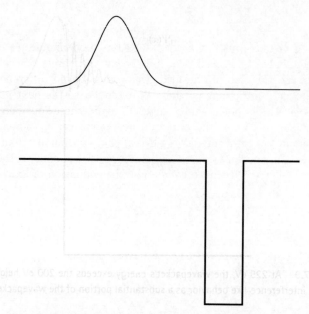

Figure 7.10   The wavepacket approaching a square well, with the parameters as discussed in the text.

in the calculation. The first change, of course, is to double the number of points—depending on how these points are distributed, the ranges of both x and k will change. Since the problem is in k-space, and not coordinate space, there is no reason to use a "balanced" approach, as we discussed earlier. Rather, you will want most of the extra range to appear in k-space. Let's allow a modest increase in the x range, say to -3.5 nm $\leq x \leq 3.5$ nm, thereby almost doubling the k range. (Actually, it will be increased by about 71%.)

We need one more change before we're ready to perform the calculations. For a free particle, i.e., the wavepacket away from the well, the energy is proportional to k^2. We've just argued that the range of k had to be increased, almost doubled, in order to adequately describe the wavepacket. That is, the range in *energy* has been almost quadrupled! But an indicator of the error in the pseudo-spectral method is the quantity $[V, T]\delta_t$—if T has been quadrupled and V unchanged, we need to reduce the time step by a factor of four!

> *Hint #4: Choose a time step that is consistent with the highest energies that appear in the problem. In particular, as the range of k space is increased the range of energies is also increased, and the time step must be decreased correspondingly.*

One more thing... Since the well will be sampled only a few times, e.g., the well is only a few δ_x wide, the way the grid points at each end of the well are treated can become very important. Such *end effects* are often troublesome, and should always be considered with some care. The difficulty stems from the fact that the physical well and the computational grid need not be commensurate with one another, so that the ends of the well need not lie on the points of the grid. If we were then to increase the size of the grid, we would see no difference in the computation whatsoever—until, that is, the well extended to the next grid point, and then we would have a discontinuous change. To avoid these spurious effects, instead of just using $V(x_i)$, let's use the potential averaged over δ_x. Then, as the parameters of the calculation are changed, we'll realize a continuous change in the results, thus avoiding the spurious effects associated with the ends of the grid. Using a simple weighted averaging, suitable code for the evaluation of ExpV is then

```
left  =   0.0;        % Start of the well
right =   0.2;        % End of the well
V0    = -200.0;       % Magnitude of well, in eV
for i=1:N
    if (x(i) <= left-delta_x/2)
        V = 0.0;
    elseif(x(i) > left-delta_x/2 & x(i) <=  left+delta_x/2)
        V = V0 * (x-(left-delta_x/2)) / delta_x;
    elseif(x(i) > left+delta_x/2 & x(i) <= right-delta_x/2)
        V = V0;
    elseif(x(i) > right-delta_x/2 & x(i) <= right+delta_x/2)
        V = V0 * (right+delta_x/2-x) / delta_x;
    else
        V = 0.0;
    end
    ExpV(i)=exp(-im * 0.5 * dt * V / hbar);
end
```

EXERCISE 7.26
Replicate the results of Goldberg *et al.*, with the parameters changed as we've discussed. Follow the evolution for about 3×10^{-16} seconds.

"Simple" systems like this are very helpful in gaining a better understanding of the process. After you've convinced yourself that the program is running correctly, *and that you understand the results it's generating*, you might want to try different collision energies. Certainly, you might expect that the reflection and transmission coefficients will vary with E_0, and that at sufficiently high energy the reflection will be small. But sometimes there are surprises along the way.

EXERCISE 7.27
Consider this scattering problem, with $E_0 = 150$ eV.

Can you explain the shape of the reflected wavepacket? The probability distribution in k space is also interesting, and might provide a clue. Essentially, what we have here is an exhibition of the *Ramsauer effect*—observed experimentally in the low-energy scattering of electrons from noble gasses—and we weren't even looking for it! Earlier, we found reflections from both a positive step and a negative one. What would you expect from the well? And how would you expect the two reflections to combine with one another?

7.20 The Barrier

Now, let's consider a barrier problem, that is, the potential given in Equation 7.152 with V_0 positive. You probably noticed in the exercises involving the positive step that the wavefunction penetrates into the "forbidden" region, e.g., the area where the potential is greater than the total available energy. If the barrier is sufficiently narrow, some of the wavefunction might "leak through" to the other side; that is, it might *tunnel* through the barrier. Goldberg *et al.* investigated this problem as well.

EXERCISE 7.28
With $E_0 = 100$ eV, $V_0 = +200$ eV, and $a = 0.2$ nm, replicate Goldberg's results for tunneling through a barrier.

Actually, with these parameters, there's not too much tunneling taking place—the barrier is just too high and too wide to allow the wavepacket through. A higher energy should permit more tunneling, of course.

EXERCISE 7.29
Try the tunneling problem with $E_0 = 200$ eV. The persistence of the wavepacket within the barrier is an interesting example of resonance in this physical situation.

7.21 Wavepackets in Two Dimensions

To develop an even better "feel" for the way quantum mechanical wavefunctions evolve in time, we can investigate the behavior of some simple wavepackets in two dimensions. (We could investigate this problem in three dimensions, although it would obviously require more computational time. Perhaps more important, the visual representation is much more difficult in three dimensions. We'll be content with two.)

While simple finite difference methods can be applied, it's just as convenient to apply the pseudo-spectral method we've developed. In particular, the generalization of Equation 7.140 is simply

$$\psi(x,y,t) \approx e^{-iV(x,y)\delta_t/2\hbar} \mathcal{F}^{-1} \left[e^{-iT(k_x,k_y)\delta_t/\hbar} \mathcal{F} \left[e^{-iV(x,y)\delta_t/2\hbar} \psi(x,y,t_0) \right] \right].$$

(7.153)

The important thing to realize is that factors like

$$e^{-iV(x,y)\delta_t/2\hbar} \psi(x,y,t_0)$$

(7.154)

are not matrix operations. That is, it's simply a scalar multiplication, evaluated at all the various points of the x-y grid, rather than a matrix product. The Fourier Transform (and its inverse) is two-dimensional, but is still quite fast if performed with the FFT. The end result is that the two-dimensional investigation is well within our computational capabilities.

Let's consider a simple free particle, moving in the x-y plane with an initial velocity in the x direction. As in the one-dimensional case, we'll take the initial wavefunction to be a Gaussian. In this case, we'll want the grid in the y direction to be large enough to account for the spread of the wavefunction, and the grid in the x direction to be larger by an amount equal to the distance the wavepacket will move while we're investigating it. But, as we've seen before, we also need to consider the size of the grid in transform space. Clearly, the range in transform space must be sufficient to represent the stationary wavefunction, say from $-k_\Psi$ to $+k_\Psi$. But there's more: Recall that the effect of the (initial) momentum is to shift the distribution in transform space. Thus the grid must represent the moving wavefunction up to $k_o + k_\Psi$, where $\hbar k_o$ is the initial momentum of the wavepacket. These considerations mean that the grid must be chosen with the maximum momentum in mind. To put numbers to this, for us to begin our investigation, let's take -10 nm $\leq x \leq 10$ nm, -5 nm $\leq y \leq 5$ nm, $x_o = -2$ nm, $y_o = 0$, and use 256 and 128 points in the x and y dimensions, respectively.

EXERCISE 7.30

Investigate this problem, with the electron having an initial kinetic energy of 10 eV. Is this sufficently low for this grid? Your computer code should graph the square of the wavefunction, so that you can watch it move.

We can also investigate some well-known "standard" problems, such as the single slit. That is, consider a potential that is $V = 0$ except at $x = 0$. Here, the potential should be much higher than the kinetic energy, say 400 eV, except at the location of the slit, where it's zero.

EXERCISE 7.31

Consider the wavepacket impinging upon a single slit of width 0.25 nm.

We can also investigate the double slit barrier. Consider the problem of two slits, each 0.25 nm in width, separated by a distance of 0.25 nm.

EXERCISE 7.32
Investigate the wavepacket encountering the double slit barrier.

7.22 And There's More...

This discussion of wavepackets is just an introduction to all that can be done with them, and all that can be learned from them in the pursuit of understanding quantum mechanics. The ability to calculate these wavepackets opens up avenues that simply were not available when the quantum theory was being developed. While the fundamental physics is all contained in the Schrödinger equation, quantum mechanics is so rich that much is hidden within it, only to be teased out as we ask the right questions. For example, what if....

7.23 References

The solution of partial differential equations, particularly with finite difference methods, is a standard topic in many texts, including those we've previously referenced. The spectral method, however, is relatively new, e.g., not a product of nineteenth-century mathematics. A definitive reference is

D. Gottlieb and S. A. Orszag, *Numerical Analysis of Spectral Methods: Theory and Applications,* SIAM–CBMS, Philadelphia, 1977.

Spectral methods are also discussed in some of the newer texts, such as

G. Strang, *Introduction to Applied Mathematics,* Wellesley–Cambridge Press, Wellesley, Massachusetts, 1986.

For an example of an important application, you might peruse

C. Canuto, M. Y. Hussaini, A. Quarteroni, and T. A. Zang, *Spectral Methods in Fluid Dynamics,* Springer–Verlag, New York, 1987.

C. A. J. Fletcher, *Computational Techniques for Fluid Dynamics,* Springer–Verlag, New York, 1988.

Although often used, the Baker-Cambell-Hausdorff theorem rarely receives the recognition it deserves.

J. E. Campbell, Proc. Lond. Math. Soc. **29**, 14 (1898); H. F. Baker, Proc. Lond. Math. Soc., Second Ser. **3**, 24 (1904); F. Hausdorff, Ber. Verh. Saechs. Akad. Wiss. Leipzig, Math.-Naturwiss. Kl. **58**, 19 (1906).

Appendix

- ## MATLAB

  MATLAB is a commercial software tool for the purpose of performing numerical computation and data visualization, and can be obtained from The MathWorks,

  http://www.mathworks.com/

  There are several versions available, including a student version for use in courses using MATLAB. (Details available on their website.) This textbook, for the most part, makes use of the numerical capabilities of the bare bones MATLAB, and was developed using MATLAB Version 7.7.0, release R2008b. (Some features may not be compatible with earlier versions.)

  The acronym MATLAB stands for matrix laboratory, and it is an array-based language whose basic variables are vectors, matrices, and n-dimensional arrays. MATLAB's power lies in the way it uses arrays to perform numerical tasks. There are also toolboxes available for needs beyond the textbook, but at an additional cost. MATLAB can be used in an interactive mode, simply entering commands into its "command window," or through the use of "scripts" or "M-files," which are stored on the computer. The command window accepts simple calculator-type commands, as well as much more complicated ones, which MATLAB's engine executes after the user presses Enter. The scripts are simple text documents that make use of MATLAB commands. In these notes, we provide some simple examples of how to run MATLAB and how to use and/or modify the fragments or scripts that accompany the text.

  The MathWorks has integrated extensive help and documentation into MATLAB, and provided a marvelous resource online detailing the use of their product, so to some extent this Appendix is superfluous. On the other hand, students are often stymied by the simple question: "Where to start." It's our hope that these notes will at least get you started in the right direction, with the knowledge that further help is available at the references at the end of this appendix as well as other tutorials available through web search engines.

Getting Started with MATLAB

Within its command window MATLAB's prompt, >>, indicates that the computer is ready to accept commands. Anything typed at the prompt is user input that MATLAB will try to act upon once the user presses Enter. MATLAB is case sensitive and allows for many different ways to define variables. (Older versions do not strictly enforce case sensitivity in all instances, but it's clearly the direction of future development.) For example, below we show a simple example of addition of three different variables.

```
>> a=2

a =

    2

>> B=3

B =

    3

>> b=4

b =

    4

>> a+b+B

ans =

    9
```

In this example, the variables were defined and then added. We could have added the three numbers in a single statement, such as

```
>> 2+3+4

ans =

    9
```

The results are equivalent, but the first case defined and named the variables, which can then be reused without retyping their numerical values. Such abstraction is a cornerstone of computer programming. Note that if a variable name is not supplied by the user, **ans** will be used.

MATLAB allows for comments, and we strongly encourage their use. These are preceded by the percent sign **%** and can be placed anywhere on a line. For example:

```
>> a=3   % defines a

a =

    3
```

We could have made the same definition and suppressed the output by placing a semicolon immediately after the command. Also, more than one command can be placed on the same line when separated by a comma or a semicolon. For example, the command

```
>> a=3; b=4;   % define a and b
```

produces no output, but defines the variables. This can be verified by looking at the defined variables:

```
>> who

Your variables are:

a  b
```

To check on the value of a variable, just type its name and press **Enter**. For example,

```
>> a

a =

    3
```

To clear the value of a variable, such as **a**, type **clear a** after the prompt. To clear all the variables, type **clear all** after the prompt. Typing **clear** also works, and typing **clc** and pressing **Enter** clears the command window itself. Typing **Ctrl-c** (press the **Ctrl** key while simultaneously pressing the **c** key) stops the execution of a script or a function. You may have noticed that MATLAB has a "workspace" that displays all the currently defined variables it recognizes. MATLAB's Graphic User Interface (GUI) is customizable, and the "workspace" can be easily added if it is not already present.

MATLAB was developed to make array manipulations easy. We can begin with defining a *row vector* c with components 1, 3, and 5, like this:

```
>> c=[2 4 7]

c =

    2    4    7
```

The same can be accomplished with the command line c=[2,4,7]—both the comma and the space are acceptable delimiters. While MATLAB is designed to work with the array as a whole, there are instances in which we might want to refer to a particular element. That is, we can refer to the second element of the array c as c(2):

```
>> c(2)

ans =

    4
```

Note that the counting begins at 1. (Some programming languages start at zero.)

Imagine that we want to create two arrays, one of the arguments x and the other $y = \sin x$. We've already seen that a row vector x could be created by explicitly entering all the elements of the array. Such a laborious task, however, is better suited to the computer, for which MATLAB supplies the "colon" operator,

```
>> x = 2 : 0.25 : 6;
```

This creates an array named x with elements $x = 2.0, 2.25, 2.50, \ldots, 6.0$. How useful! (By the way, the ; at the end of the statement suppresses the output, as mentioned earlier. If you want to see the output, simply omit the semicolon.) Now, to create the y array, we simply need to enter

```
>> y = sin(x);
```

MATLAB is *designed* to work with matrices, so that when you provide a function with an array variable, it knows to return an array of element-by-element function values. (Note that in other computer languages, this would be accomplished by a for loop, which can still be done in MATLAB, as we'll see.) This is another example of the "array orientation" that is present throughout MATLAB.

To define a *column vector* d with components 2, 4, and 7, separate the elements with semicolons,

```
>> d=[1;2;3]

d =
```

```
1
2
3
```

This is a common source of error: The elements of a *row vector* are separated by a space or a comma—the elements of a *column vector* are separated by a semicolon.

We can easily perform the matrix product of these two vectors according to the rules of matrices. For example c*d should produce a single element, a 1×1 matrix, but the product d*c should produce a 3×3 matrix. Let's see

```
>> c*d

ans =

    31

>> d*c

ans =

    2     4     7
    4     8    14
    6    12    21
```

We can take the transpose of this matrix as
```
>> (d*c)'

ans =

    2     4     6
    4     8    12
    7    14    21
```

or we could just type transpose(d*c) at the prompt. We can learn about the details of the stored variable by entering whos at the prompt:

```
>> whos
  Name     Size        Bytes  Class     Attributes

  ans      3x3            72  double
  c        1x3            24  double
  d        3x1            24  double
```

We can also ask for help at any time. For example, typing help at the MATLAB prompt gives a list of all help topics available. Typing help whos at the prompt outputs the description for the command whos and so on. Even more information is available with the doc command,

```
>> doc whos
```

which opens a new browser window and gives direct access to MATLAB's extensive documentation.

We've seen how easy it is to define and multiply vectors. The same is true for matrices. For example, we can define a square matrix, A:

```
>> A=[1 3 5;2 4 6; 7 9 1]

A =

    1    3    5
    2    4    6
    7    9    1
```

If we desired to square the matrix we could simply type

```
>> A^2

ans =

    42   60   28
    52   76   40
    32   66   90
```

which is the matrix product A*A. However, there are instances in which we want each element of the array to be squared. That is, an elementwise multiplication. This can be accomplished with the .* operation,

```
>> A.*A

ans =

    1     9    25
    4    16    36
   49    81     1
```

Clearly, this is most definitely *not* a matrix product. The usefulness of this feature in MATLAB is easily demonstrated. Reconsider our x and y arrays from earlier. If we wanted a new array, whose elements were $z = x \sin x$, we could simply enter

```
>> z=x.*y;
```

to multiply, element-by-element, the two arrays. (In this instance, the command

```
>> z=x*y;
```

would produce an error, since both x and y were defined as row vectors.)

Let's return to the subject of vectors for a moment. To consider a specific example, let's define the following vectors,

```
>> A=[1,2,3]

A =

    1    2    3


>> B=[4,5,6]

B =
    4    5    6
```

MATLAB provides the tools to evaluate the dot and cross products, so that

```
>> dot(A,B)

ans =

    32

>> cross(A,B)

ans =

    -3    6    -3
```

The angle between A and B is then simply

```
>> dot(A,B)/(sqrt(dot(A,A))*sqrt(dot(B,B)))

ans =

    0.9746
```

MATLAB has a full range of operations, including simple arithmetic operations (+, -, *, .*, ...), relational operations (>, <, ==, ~=, ...), logical operators (&&, || ...), and so on. Details of how to access these are described in the *Help and Documentation* section of these notes. These are important when typing MATLAB in a script or in a command window during a working session, and can be used in functions as well.

• Programming

Programming refers to devising a sequence of commands to be executed for the express purpose of performing a specific task, typically a numerical calculation.

This is made easier if the language provides commonly used functions, such as sine and cosine, and if a mechanism for user-defined functions is provided. Essential to practical programming is the ability to repetitively execute a sequence of commands, e.g., loops, and the ability to execute, or not to execute, a sequence of statements based on a well-defined condition, e.g., branching.

As an example, we could have created our earlier x and y arrays with

```
for i=1:1:17
   x(i)=2.0+0.25*(i-1);
   y(i)=sin(x(i));
end
```

In this example, the individual elements were accessed by referring to x(i), while the value of i was changed from 1 to 17 in units of 1 within the for loop. Clearly, this is more cumbersome than our earlier approach, but is ofttimes preferable. The point, of course, is that each element of the array can be accessed, and by looping over all the elements, the desired result is achieved.

This for construction is particularly useful when the loop is to be executed a specific number of times. Alternately, the while loop is useful when you want to loop until a specified condition has been met,

```
while   condition
      statements to be executed
  end
```

where *condition* is a logical expression. If the condition is evaluated as being true, all the statements within the loop are executed, and the condition is checked again, continuing to loop as long as the condition is true. Once the condition is evaluated as being false, the statements within the loop are no longer executed and the program skips over the block of code, past the end statement.

The basic conditional construction is of the form

```
if(  condition )
      statements to be executed
  end
```

where again the "condition" is a logical expression, the statements being executed if the condition is true, and skipped if not.

```
score=92;
if( score > 50)
   disp(' You scored greater than 50!')
end
```

results in a message being printed to your computer screen. (Note that we've used another MATLAB supplied function, disp, to display the message.) If the score had been 42, rather than 92, nothing would have been printed.

This construction can be enhanced by the else statement; for example,

```
score=92;
if( score > 50)
    disp(' You scored greater than 50!')
else
    disp(' You scored 50 points or less.')
end
```

Of course, there can be more than one statement executed, so that a large block of code is executed if the condition is true, and a totally different block of code executed if false. A further enhancement is achieved with the elseif statement,

```
score=92;
if( score > 90)
    disp(' You have earned an A.')
elseif ( score > 80)
    disp(' You have earned a B.')
elseif ( score > 70)
    disp(' You have earned a C.')
elseif ( score > 60)
    disp(' You have earned a D.')
else
    disp(' See you next semester!.')
end
```

Note that only a single end statement is required, matching the initial if. Also, the else statement acts as a default: The statements following else are executed only if none of the conditions were met.

You have now seen simple assignment statements, some elementary arithmetic operations, loops, and conditional execution statements. These are the basic elements of programming and significant, nontrivial programs can be written with just what you've seen. However, programming is made considerably more convenient by the use of modular code that is stored in files and reused, the topic of the next section.

Scripts, M-Files, Functions, Subfunctions, and Function Handles

If you've been typing in all our examples, you've probably wished that there was an easy way to save your work, so that you could edit and make changes without retyping the entire collection of commands. And indeed, there is!

MATLAB has a built-in text editor with which you can write, save, and edit files that contain MATLAB commands. Such a collection of commands is called a *script*. If the file is saved with the extension .m, then MATLAB can execute these commands, in the order in which they appear in the M-file. These files can (and should!) contain lines of comments as well as executable statements. (A comment is preceded by the % symbol, and can be placed at the end of a line of code or on a line by itself.) To execute the script stored in the M-file test.m, you simply need to type test at the MATLAB prompt within the command window. (The script must either be stored in the directory in which you're currently working, or in the command path.) The statements in the file will execute, just as if you had typed in each of the commands. Note that if you want to see the results of these executions, you need to either not suppress output, by leaving off the ; at the end of the statement, or by providing explicit output statements, using disp or fprintf, for example. Any errors in the script will be displayed in the command window, and can then be corrected with the text editor. This textbook contains many code fragments that can be modified using MATLAB's text editor and modified to become working programs.

(Note: MATLAB provides a convenient mechanism to save relatively simple scripts, the command diary. Simply typing diary test.m at the command prompt instructs MATLAB to "keep a diary" of all subsequent statements, until you enter the command diary off. These commands are stored in the file test.m, and the script can be executed from the command prompt by entering test, just as if you had created the file with the text editor.)

MATLAB supplies a large number of functions that you may use. Certainly, all the standard mathematical functions, such as sine, cosine, exponential, and logarithm, are included. Of more importance, perhaps, is that extensive documentation for these functions, and for MATLAB in general, is included in the basic MATLAB working environment. This is discussed in the *Help and Documentation* section.

In addition to MATLAB's supplied functions, users can write functions of their own. For example, suppose that we needed the numerical derivative of $\log(x)$. We could use an editor to create a file, which we could name dLog.m, such as

```
function [derivative] = dLog(x,del)
% dLog.m calculates the derivative of the logarithm function, log(x),
%    at x.    The derivative is calculated by the approximation
%
         derivative = ( log(x+del)-log(x-del) ) / (2*del);
```

The name of the file should be the name of the function, with the extension .m added. The function declaration in the first line *defines* this code to be a function, gives it a name so that it can be invoked through the MATLAB command window or through a line in a script file, and specifies what will be returned to the calling program. For example, suppose that we needed the derivative of $log(x)$ at $x = 5$. Assuming the above file is saved in the working directory, we could type the line dLog(5, 1.e-3) at the command prompt. The session would proceed as follows:

```
>> dLog(5, 1.e-3)

ans =

     0.2000
```

Furthermore, typing `help dLog` at the prompt produces the output:

```
% dLog.m calculates the derivative of the logarithm function, log(x),
%    at x.     The derivative is calculated by the approximation
```

which are just the comment lines immediately following the function declaration. (Actually, the first contiguous block of comments in the file will be printed.) In this case, we perhaps should have included the approximation used to evaluate the derivative in a comment, instead of just in the code itself. Thus it is important to write comments within functions to recall their usage.

A function file can contain functions within it; the functions inside the function file are known as *subfunctions*. They can only be accessed by the function or other subfunctions within the specified M-file. In contrast, a script *cannot* contain any function definitions, although it can access functions that are defined elsewhere. As a result, most M-files will in practice be written as functions.

An editor is not the only way to create functions. Another way is to create functions within a script with the help of the `inline` command. For example `f=inline('exp(x)')` defines the function $f(x) = e^x$ within a script. While it is common to invoke an inline defined function within a script file, the script file can't contain a standard function within it. In order to run a script that refers to a function, the function must exist in its own separate M-file.

Ultimately, functions are stored in memory within the computer. Normally, we have no need to know *where* functions are actually stored, but there are occasions when this knowledge, or at least indirect access to it, is useful. For example, imagine that we wanted to generalize the `dLog` function so that it could evaluate the derivative of an arbitrary function. How could we write this function to evaluate the derivative, if we don't know the name of the function itself?

The resolution of this problem is provided in MATLAB by a *function handle*—essentially, information about where the function is stored in memory. First, let's write the derivative function:

```
function [derivative] = Derivative(x,del,f)
% Derivative.m calculates the derivative of f(x), at x.
% The derivative is calculated by the approximation
%
%      derivative = ( f(x+del)-f(x-del) ) / (2*del).
%
derivative = ( f(x+del)-f(x-del) ) / (2*del);
```

For illustration, let's let $g(x) = \sin x$. Then

```
function [result] = g(x)
% g.m calculates the function g(x) = sin(x)
result = sin(x);
```

Note that this function can be named whatever is appropriate for it—if it was required to be named f, there would be no advantage—but being named g, it *must* be stored in the file g.m. The derivative of $g(x)$ is then evaluated, approximately, by

```
answer = Derivative( x, del, \@g);
```

The expression @g is the function handle, and informs the function Derivative where the function being differentiated can be found, e.g., in the file g.m. MATLAB refers to functions such as Derivative as *function functions*, since the argument of the function is a function itself.

• drawContours

In this section, we discuss the user-defined function, drawContours, which is used in the text to draw isotherms. Clearly, it can be used in other ways. As displayed, it works with data on a rectangular grid. With only minor modifications, it can work with polar data, as well.

```
function drawContours(xx, yy, data, contour, label, col)
% This function draws contour plots from given input data.  It is
% based on an article in the June 1987 issue of "BYTE" magazine by
% Paul D. Bourke and a subsequent comment in a following issue
% by Al Dunbar. Originally coded by Christopher J. Sweeney.
%
%                                    originally written: 2/ 2/88 cjs
%                                             modified: 1/ 1/93 pld
%          converted to Matlab, labeling and color added: 8/ 8/08 jeh
%
%          xx: array containing x-coordinates of grid lines
%          yy: array containing y-coordinates of grid lines
%        data: array containing data to be displayed with
%                        contour plots
%     contour: array containing contour values
%       label: true for labels, false for no labels
%         col: string value for a MATLAB color,
%                   i.e., 'r', 'b', 'k', etc
%
% ******************************************************************
%
nx = length(xx);
ny = length(yy);

for lines = 1:length(contour)
```

```
      counter = 0;
      target  = contour(lines);
      str     = cat(2,num2str(target,2));
      for jy = 1:ny-1
      for jx = 1:nx-1
```
%
% We now store the x, y, and data values of the four corners and an
% approximation to the center in some temporary arrays. The points
% are numbered as
%
%   4   3
%   5
%   1   2
%
```
         x(1) = xx(jx  );  y(1) = yy(jy  );  value(1) = data(jx  ,jy  );
         x(2) = xx(jx+1);  y(2) = yy(jy  );  value(2) = data(jx+1,jy  );
         x(3) = xx(jx+1);  y(3) = yy(jy+1);  value(3) = data(jx+1,jy+1);
         x(4) = xx(jx  );  y(4) = yy(jy+1);  value(4) = data(jx  ,jy+1);

         if(target >= min(value) & target <= max(value))

           x(5)     = 0.5 * (x(1)+x(2));
           y(5)     = 0.5 * (y(2)+y(3));
           value(5) = 0.25*(value(1)+value(2)+value(3)+value(4));
```

% Now we consider each of the 4 triangles, starting with 1-2-5 and
%   moving counterclockwise.

```
           v3 = 5;
           for v1 = 1:4
               v2 = v1+1;
               if(v1 == 4), v2 = 1; end
```

% At this point, we're considering one specific triangle. Arrange the
%   vertices of this triangle to be in increasing magnitude.

```
               [small,medium,large] = reorder(v1,v2,v3,value);
```

% Now we're ready to (maybe) draw some contours!
% But first, check to see if this contour value lies within this
%   particular triangle:

```
               if (value(small) < target) & (target < value(large))
```
%
% O.K., the value of the contour lies between the smallest and largest
%   values on this triangle -- we'll draw a contour! Now -- think about
%   this -- one side of the triangle MUST contain BOTH the smallest

```
%    and the largest vertices. Use inverse linear interpolation, INVL,
%    to find where the contour intersects that side.
%
            x1 = invl(x(small),value(small),x(large),value(large),target);
            y1 = invl(y(small),value(small),y(large),value(large),target);
    % And now find the other side...
            if (target > value (medium))
                x2 = invl(x(medium),value(medium),x(large),value(large),target);
                y2 = invl(y(medium),value(medium),y(large),value(large),target);
            else
                x2 = invl(x(small),value(small),x(medium),value(medium),target);
                y2 = invl(y(small),value(small),y(medium),value(medium),target);
            end
    % draw contour with a specific color
            line([x1,x2],[y1,y2],'Color',col);
            counter = counter + 1;
            if(label & mod(counter,100)==0)
    % label the contour
                        text((x1+x2)/2,(y1+y2)/2,str,'FontSize',7);
                end
            end
        end
      end
    end
   end
 end

function [small,medium,large] = reorder(i,j,k,value)
%
% This funciton performs a "bubble sort" on the data. Since
%    there are only 3 items to be sorted, we'll write explicit
%    code rather than using for-loops.
%
large  = i; % We need to start somewhere. Simply make
medium = j; %    any assignments to initialize 'small',
small  = k; %    'medium', and 'large'.
if(value(small) > value(medium))
    temp = medium;  medium = small;     small = temp; end
if(value(medium) > value(large))
    temp = large;    large = medium;    medium = temp; end

% The largest value has now bubbled to the top. Check
%    that the next largest value is correct.

if(value(small) > value(medium))
    temp = medium;  medium = small;     small = temp; end
```

```
function [y] = invl(xa,ya,xb,yb,yyy)
%
% This function performs inverse linear interpolation
%  between the points (xa,ya) and (xb,yb) to find where
%  the function equals yyy.
%
y = xa + (yyy-ya) * (xb-xa) / (yb-ya);
```

Rather than following a contour through the data, each rectangular region of the data is examined to see if a contour line should be drawn. Then each region is examined sequentially.

Each rectangular region is divided into four triangles, and each triangle considered separately. It's interesting to note that any contour must cross the side of the triangle with both the largest and smallest vertex values, and one of the other sides.

The function relies upon two subfunctions, reorder, which identifies the indices of the smallest, middle, and largest vertices, and invl, which determines where the contour line crosses the edge of the triangle.

Hopefully, there are sufficient comments so that you can fully understand the operation of the function: what it does, and how it does it.

Help and Documentation

We've tried to give you a flavor for MATLAB, and a little push toward understanding the language and how to use it to write computer programs. Obviously, we've barely scratched the surface. To proceed further in this direction, teaching you MATLAB, is *not* our intention. Our ultimate interest is to teach computational physics—these notes (hopefully) have set you in the right direction. Clearly, you need to learn more, but where to go?

At the top of the MATLAB window is the MATLAB ToolBar. Under "Help," you'll find both "Product Help" and "Function Browser"—click on "Product Help." There you'll see a variety of topics, useful for everyone from true novices to experts. Since you're reading these notes, you'll probably be most interested in the Documentation Set. Start with "Getting started" to view a video, or perhaps click on "MATLAB Getting Started Guide." Either way, you see that there's a tremendous amount of information here, literally at your fingertips.

Earlier in these notes we mentioned that MATLAB has a full range of operations. On the left side of the Help window, under "Help Navigator," type "operators." You'll be presented with numerous search results—click on "Arithmetic Operators," for example, to learn more about the basic operations and the details of using them.

Imagine that you have a more specific question, such as "How do I calculate an arctangent?" This time, under "Help Navigator," type "arctangent." A search is performed, and a few possibilities are returned. Click on the first one (or perhaps it has already loaded), and on the right side of the window detailed information, often including a graph, is displayed. (This is the same information that would have been called up had you typed doc atan at the command prompt.) This is one of the very best sources of information on any topic in MATLAB. The only better resource is the MathWorks website.

Now, return to the "Product Help" page, and click on "Functions, By Category," then "Mathematics" and "Elementary Math." There you will find a list of all the functions, starting with the trigonometric ones. Down the list a bit, you'll see atan, atan2, and atand. And what's atanh? Click on it, and find that it's the inverse hyperbolic tangent function. Interesting. . . .

There's an old saying about giving a man a fish to eat, or teaching him how to fish. We suspect that you can infer where we stand.

MATLAB Clones

MATLAB clones are free open source software capable of running MATLAB code after minor changes, if any. The most popular of these are Octave and Scilab. These will run most of the code as long as no reference is made to other MATLAB toolboxes. They are very useful when all the functions needed by a given script or application are provided. Since Octave and Scilab are based on the GNU (http://www.gnu.org/copyleft/gpl.html) and the CeCILL (http://www.cecill.info/index.en.html) public licenses, they are freeware. Many scientists collaborate to develop such software with the ultimate goal to make them fast and reliable. Indeed, except for the lack of available toolboxes, the clones provide another avenue to carry out the computations discussed in this text. Finally, we note that Octave is convenient because it recognizes MATLAB's familiar M-file extension. In contrast, Scilab uses the ".sci" file extension, indicative of its differences with MATLAB. However, both applications benefit from large scientific community support.

MATLAB References and Other Tutorials

In addition to the help facility included within the MATLAB software, the Mathworks website contains excellent sources of information, help, and code examples.

1. http://www.mathworks.com/support/books/

2. http://www.mathworks.com/academia/student_center/tutorials/index.html?link=body

3. http://www.mathworks.com/access/helpdesk/help/techdoc/index.html?

Often the MATLAB clones' websites are excellent sources of code examples that could be ported into MATLAB after modifications.

1. http://www.octave.org/

2. http://www.scilab.org/

Index